NBC

EUROPE

and its

BORDERLANDS

EUROPE
and its
BORDERLANDS

ALAN G. OGILVIE

LATE PROFESSOR OF GEOGRAPHY
UNIVERSITY OF EDINBURGH

EDINBURGH LONDON

THOMAS NELSON AND SONS LTD

PARIS MELBOURNE JOHANNESBURG
TORONTO NEW YORK

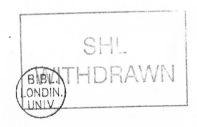

THOMAS NELSON AND SONS LTD
Parkside Works Edinburgh 9
36 Park Street London W1
312 Flinders Street Melbourne C1

302–304 Barclays Bank Building
Commissioner and Kruis Streets
Johannesburg

THOMAS NELSON AND SONS (CANADA) LTD
91–93 Wellington Street West   Toronto 1

THOMAS NELSON AND SONS
19 East 47th Street New York 17

SOCIÉTÉ FRANÇAISE D'EDITIONS NELSON
25 rue Henri Barbusse Paris Ve

———

First published 1957

EDITORIAL NOTE

PROFESSOR ALAN GRANT OGILVIE occupied the Chair of Geography in the University of Edinburgh from 1931 to 1954. From the period of his own early studies abroad he had maintained wide contacts with European geographers and their work, and the geography of Europe was the core of his teaching to the many students in the Faculty of Arts who chose geography as part of their course, and to the increasing number that eventually decided to specialise in geographical studies. The present work, however, was designed not only to meet the requirements of university students, but to interest a wider public in the complex interplay of physical and historical factors that have moulded the cultural landscape of Europe.

This was a work that lay very close to his heart, and he had almost completed it at the time of his tragically sudden death. Since I had been familiar with the work at every stage of its progress Professor Ogilvie had asked me to act as his literary executor should this prove necessary. This duty accordingly fell upon me. The arrangement of the work as now published is entirely as the author planned it, but I alone am responsible for the following sections, for which Professor Ogilvie had left no notes : Italy (pp. 279–81), the Atlas lands (pp. 281–4), France (pp. 317–21) and the British Isles (pp. 322–7). Few bibliographical references and no other acknowledgements have been found amongst the author's papers, and it is hoped that any persons consulted by him on particular points will accept a general appreciation of their help.

C. J. ROBERTSON

University of Edinburgh

CONTENTS

MAPS AND DIAGRAMS

INTRODUCTION

No fact about the Earth is more impressive than the concentration of its population on comparatively small parts of its surface, and none is fraught with greater consequences for the well-being of mankind in the future. Over three-fifths of the human race live in three great agglomerations, the Sino-Japanese, the Indian and the European, of which the first is the largest and the other two do not at present differ greatly in numbers. The western agglomeration, comprising the population of Europe and that of its fringes in southwestern Asia and northern Africa, is estimated (in 1955) at about one-fifth of the Race ; but its habitat amounts in area to only about one-twentieth part of the lands of the world. If the western part of the U.S.S.R. is included the population is nearer one-quarter of the world total. Moreover, the Europeans have carried their Western civilisation around the globe and by migration they have peopled the outlying continents in the west and the south. Yet the numerical importance of the homelands in Europe is a modern phenomenon which arose mainly because of the use of coal and the invention and development of machinery. Clearly, then, the presence of coal, a geographical fact, is of first importance in explaining some of the modern features of this type of civilisation. But most of the characteristics of the Western World existed long before these lands were densely populated by present standards ; they grew from the good ideas of a few men. They grew in certain places and spread to others, changing and developing as they were passed on. So the locations of the Greek city-states, of Israel or of Rome are facts of geography that bear upon the subject at least as much as do the position and content of the northern coal-basins.

The purpose of this book is to examine the geography of Europe and its borderlands as the theatre of Western civilisation, to study first the various natural phenomena which, by their action and reaction, compose the physical environment of the 'Western' peoples, then to recognise and record in a general way the results of human activity upon these natural features of the habitat. At the same time there is an attempt to assess the influence of environment on the modes of life and on some of the achievements of the Europeans, in their own lands. Where man is concerned this is manifestly no easy task, for the historical record is long and complex, while historical research upon the questions that interest the geographer most deeply has been comparatively slight. But it would seem that the task must not be shirked ; it is important that it be undertaken. About one-fifth of the human race living in the home-land of Western civilisation ! This surely calls for an attempt at systematic generalisation, however imperfect, of the facts, if only to give others the opportunity of improving upon the outline presented. But the purpose must not be misunderstood. Only certain facts are to be selected, described and coordinated. Attention is given throughout to the aspect and qualities of the land ; the human activities to be considered are mainly those which have made their mark on the landscape and are thus more obviously amenable to geographical treatment. And behind it all there is the attempt repeatedly to answer three questions. The first, ' What is it ? ' that is, what is the nature of this or that phenomenon that is deemed important and relevant. The second, ' Where is it ? ' that is, how is it distributed, is the essence of the geo-graphical approach, and it is answered so far as possible by the distributional maps that form an essential part of the discussion. To the third, ' Why is it there ? ' that is, why does it have this distribution and no other, there is often only a partial answer, and this especially where human affairs are involved. But in every such case the geographical distribution itself suggests the way in which the freedom of human action has been favoured or hampered in certain regions.

This volume is intended as an outline, but one that may give sufficient indication of causes, where this seems justified, while avoiding great detail as well as digression, unless this is essential to understanding the principal argument.

The traditional eastern limit of Europe, the Ural Mountains and the Caspian depression, is adopted as acceptable for the purpose of this study despite the fact that it is now quite unrealistic in view of the political and economic organisation of the U.S.S.R. ; the plain lying between the Urals and the Caspian Sea has always been the principal land-gate of Europe, and has been described as the ' pivot of history '. The fringe that is here named ' the Borderlands ' embraces the Caucasian region, the whole of Turkey and Iraq, with a strip of Iran, Syria, Lebanon, Jordan, Israel and Egypt, which together have merited the name ' Bridge-lands of Asia '. The settled northern parts of Libya, Tunisia, Algeria and Morocco are also in-cluded, so that the southern ' frame ' is the desert in Africa and Arabia. Interrupting the northern ' frame ' of ocean there are the islands surrounding the Barents Sea, and Iceland.

CHAPTER 1

LAND AND SEA

IN spite of all the windings of its coast, Europe may be regarded, like Arabia, India and Indochina, as a peninsula of Eurasia, the world's greatest land-mass. The main axis, which also coincides generally with the main divide of the rivers, extends south-westward to end at Cape St Vincent, and from this promontory the coasts diverge, roughly north-northeast to the North Cape and eastward along the Mediterranean Sea. From its position on the western margin of the largest continent, from its extent in latitude, subtropical to arctic, and from its triangular shape there follow all the leading facts about the climate of Europe.

The present coasts have existed only from a late stage in geological history, and many of the features of the land can be understood only by assuming a former extension of its area. This is true of both the southern and the north-western sides, and on the latter, for example, the British Isles are the remnants of a much larger tract that became slightly submerged during the Human Period to form the greater part of the Continental Shelf, of which an arm underlies the shallow Baltic Sea. The origin of the coasts may be stated broadly as the severe dislocations of the Earth's crust that formed in the Tertiary Period or later, and subsequent oscillation of sea-level, resulting in submergence. It is from these causes that the midland sea in the south is subdivided by peninsulas and islands, and on the Atlantic side that there are virtually two coasts in the northern part, an outer, in the British Isles and Norway, and an inner, from the English Channel to the White Sea. The partial submergence of the inner lowland has brought oceanic mildness to the continent, while in human affairs maritime influences have played a great part in Scandinavia, the Netherlands, Britain and several countries of the Mediterranean. From the time of the earliest southern explorers of boreal coasts, the breadth of the land between the two seas has been a matter of importance, the more so as the people had goods to offer which made it worth while to develop overland commerce. Thus the narrower crossings of Europe have tended at many epochs to be followed by some of the chief trade-routes ; the comparative direct distances should therefore be noted. The narrowest neck, across southwestern France, measures 250 miles, or 400 km. ; between the mouths of the Rhône and Seine the distance is twice as great ; from the Adriatic to the Rhine mouth or to the Baltic, two-and-a-half times ; and from the Black Sea to the Baltic, over three times. Eastward of this the peninsula widens rapidly, to merge into Asia. The opposite coast of Africa offers access to no comparable land-route save the valley of the Nile; but the arrangement of land and sea in the Bridgelands of Asia undoubtedly contributed to the precocious civilisation of these lands.

Among the oscillations of sea-level above mentioned, those most clearly recognisable occurred as the result of the successive glaciations during the Quaternary Period. During each of these ice-ages a large volume of the ocean was locked up in the ice-sheets; at the maximum this would have been enough to lower the ocean by 345 feet or 105 metres everywhere, on the assumption that all the ice-sheets reached their greatest volume at the same time and that deformation of the earth's crust was not taking place. While it is unlikely that this assumption is justified, nevertheless it is certain that changes in the distribution of land and sea, like the changes in climate that caused them, affected the wanderings of early man in Europe. On the other hand backward and forward movements of the shoreline have been of small extent within the historical period, except on the edges of very low coastal plains.

When we come to consider the seaward edge of the Continental Shelf, whether taken as 100 fathoms or as 200 metres in depth, and the slope into deeper water, we cannot but be impressed by the straightness and abruptness in many parts of this, the real limit of the continental mass. It is therefore reasonable to expect that its form is the result of the same geological processes that have affected the relief and the underlying structure of the land.

RELIEF

The heights attained by the land above sea-level depend first, upon the Earth's internal forces acting on the crust, which is mobile, though not equally so everywhere or at all times; and secondly, upon the processes of denudation. The kind of relief, or the land-form, depends largely upon the degree of equilibrium reached between these generally opposing forces.

About six-tenths of Europe is lowland, with its upper level conventionally chosen as 200 metres or c. 650 ft. Most of this forms a continuous triangular tract with its eastern base from the Arctic to the Caspian, and its curving tip in Gascony. In the west this low altitude is of great advantage in relation to agriculture, but in the much broader east this is much reduced on account of the continental character of the climate. This European Plain, then, separates the lesser highlands toward the outer coast in Scandinavia and Britain from the greater highlands and the mountain systems of the south, which in turn are but a section of the complex zone of mountains reaching from the Atlantic to south-eastern Asia. Beyond the mountains there is again lowland in Africa and the Near East. It is the proximity of high mountains and sea in southern Europe coupled with the extent of the sea which makes this region unique as a human habitat. We may get the measure of one result of this by marking on a map those parts of the sea which are within sight of land in clear weather; except in the southeast on the African side, there are but small areas of the Mediterranean where it is invisible. Where lowland reappears as in Libya, Egypt and Iraq not only scenery, but also climate and life are different.

This fourfold division of Europe and its borderlands in regard to altitude applies also, in a general way, to the rock-structures beneath the surface. However complex this is, and no matter what be the age of the last great geological disturbance in any particular region, it is more or less true that land is high because it is the surface of a part of the crust that has been raised at a late geological period. Given time and no further elevation it must inevitably be worn down. On the other hand a surface may be low either because the crust has sagged, or because denudation has proceeded for a very long time and upward movement has not kept pace with it. The Hungarian plain is an example of the first case, where a crustal block of unknown structure has been lowered and then deeply buried under the detritus of surrounding mountains. Finland and Karelia exemplify the second; they consist of a low plateau composed of the most ancient crystalline rocks which show by their structure that they were once part of a mountain system. This worn surface is overlapped on the south by undisturbed marine clays and other weak sediments of early Palaeozoic age, thus furnishing proof that for an immensely long period this part of the crust has been subject only to gentle vertical movements. The Fenno-Karelian rocks and the same peneplane surface extend into Scandinavia, and the relief of southern Sweden resembles that of Finland. But the peninsula as a whole furnishes the best example of the next type of land-form, one which prevails to the west coast, there to be broken as the structural trend is truncated by the deep furrow under the North Sea and Skagerrak. But both form and structure reappear in smaller outliers composing northern and western Britain and the fringes of Ireland. The dominant features are the massiveness of individual mountains and hills, which show general accordance of height over wide areas, and the great depth of the valleys. Since these are the most heavily glaciated parts of Europe, the final trimming has been the work of ice and later weathering by frost. But the forms are essentially derived from long-worn and smooth surfaces that have been raised and then dissected by rivers working before the glacial periods along all the lines of weakness. The different rocks lie in strips created by powerful folding during the so-called, ' Caledonian ' movements (pre-Devonian) ; these run parallel to the axis of Scandinavia and oblique to that of Britain. Partial submergence of the many deep valleys gives to these lands the most minutely indented shorelines in Europe.

The kind of highland just described, but lacking the touch of ice, recurs

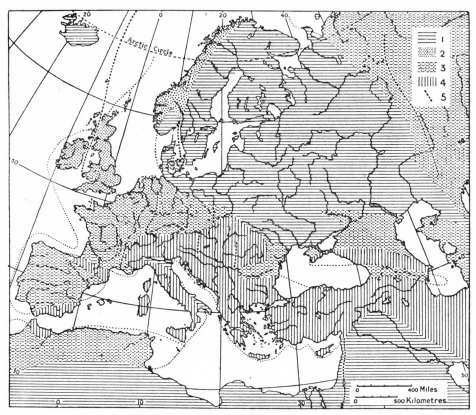

FIG. 1

Structural Regions of Europe and Borderlands

1 Primeval Shields, largely concealed by rock   3 Additions by Hercynian folding
  scarcely folded   4 Additions by Alpine folding
2 Additions by Caledonian folding (concealed   5 North-south lines of prolonged structural
  in south-east)   significance

in numerous parts of central and southern Europe, and beyond the Mediterranean as well. Again the rocks are partly crystalline or they are of hardened sediments, and they crop out in strips owing to the close folding of another mountain-building episode in geological history, the so-called ' Hercynian ' movements that began at the end of the Carboniferous Period. But these
(1,784)

highlands represent merely the entrails of the widely extended chains of mountains that became completely denuded during the Secondary Era of geological time. They are thus the remnants of a continent of low relief that was shattered, without being again seriously compressed, by the thrusts and tensions that accompanied the last of the great ' earth-storms ' or paroxysms of crustal compression during the Tertiary and even the Quaternary Periods. In northwestern Europe, far from the main regions of disturbance, the effects were largely the formation of fractures or the renewal of old ones, and the movement up or down—or laterally—of individual slabs against one another, and a great outburst of volcanism along some of the greater fractures as in western Scotland and in Iceland ; and it is likely that such movements defined the edges of the continent and the Atlantic deeps. In central Europe, too, the results of vertical displacements that took place may be likened to a pavement badly laid or in disrepair. Consequently the visible remnants of the older structure and surface stand more or less isolated from the greater mountains of the south. They comprise the Central Massif of France and the lower, Armorican Massif that is the larger counterpart of southwestern Britain, the Vosges and Black Forest, the plateau standing athwart the lower Rhine and Meuse, the blocks enclosing the Bohemian basin, the Łysa Gora in Poland, and the smaller massifs of central Germany. All these have smooth tops which, despite the deep trenching later on by winding valleys, betray their origins as a once widely extended plane ; and in the valleys the intensely folded rocks can be seen, folds that allow the trend of the ' Hercynian ' mountains, far older of course than the plane which truncates them, to be pieced together right across Europe from Portugal to the Ural. Other slabs of this older crust, similar in age and structure but larger in many cases, have persisted amid the southern mountains still to be described, and indeed beyond those, across Africa to the Guinea coast. But first, the existence of the great intervening lowland, the European Plain, calls for explanation.

We have seen that in northwestern Russia very old sediments lie undisturbed and not even greatly hardened since they formed. But almost the entire lowland is occupied by sedimentary strata, mostly younger than those mentioned, having been deposited under water chiefly throughout the Secondary era and, while they have been disturbed in places by slight folding, they have not been greatly changed or even toughened. The reason for this is not far to seek, the prolonged rigidity of the underlying crust of older rock. The varying depth to which it is buried under the younger strata is known in many parts owing to the numerous bores that have been made in search of minerals or water, and more recently by geophysical sounding for the same purpose. The underlying crust is thus shown to have been displaced by fracturing and vertical movements, but not to have yielded seriously to

(1,784)

2

lateral compression.   Moreover the whole tract is almost free of earthquakes (Fig. 2).

The lowland, while known as the European Plain, contains much hilly country.   The smoothest land is that of the flood-plains of rivers and the beds of lakes and seas from which the water has receded at very late periods ; the

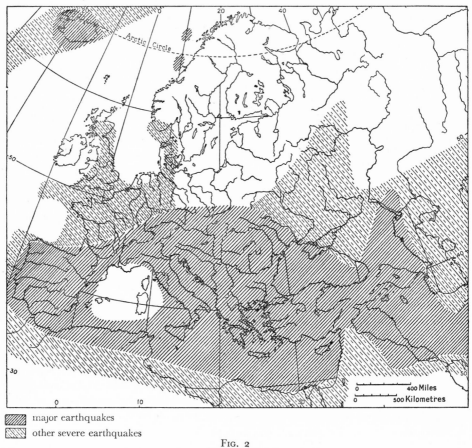

major earthquakes

other severe earthquakes

FIG. 2
Earthquake Zones

largest of these border the Caspian and the Barents Seas, while the broad coastal plain north of the Black Sea is smooth except where the rivers, following almost parallel courses, have cut into the surface as the sea-level declined. Very large areas in the north owe their slight relief to the deposits of ice-sheets. Apart from these tracts, however, it is the nature and the attitude of the exposed sedimentary rocks which are mainly responsible for the relief of the land.   It is the gently tilted sandstones, limestones and the like which impart characteristic form to the hills of the lowland with long escarpments marking the edges of the stronger rocks and overlooking vales worn out by rivers working on the weaker beds. This country of scarped plateaus and vales is most obvious in western Europe, typifying the triangular lowland of eastern England, north-eastern France, Germany between the Danube and the Main, the Crimea, and the area between the Vistula and the White Sea. Yet this leaves the greater part of Russia where the formations of all ages and types are scarcely recognis-able in the relief. There the vast system of rivers has dissected in part a surface that still retains its smoothness over great expanses irrespective of the structure of the rocks. This contrast of land-form in the western and eastern parts of the lowland may well have had some influence upon the course of human history. However that may be, the relative smoothness of the Russian lands is traceable to the long-continued rigidity of the slab of the earth's crust which is visible in Finland and extends to the foot of the Carpathians but for one interruption. This is the zone, with the River Donets along a part of its axis, which was folded by the Hercynian movements, and preserves in its folds the rich coalfield of ' Donbas '. The huge plains of western Siberia and Turkestan would seem to have a similar origin, rigidity and prolonged erosion ; but in this case the lapse of geological time is less. The Hercynian paroxysm is believed to have caused the crust almost throughout to be compressed into mountain folds with a north-south trend, and the Ural Mountains mark the western edge of these structures. This remarkable and important zone thus bears the record of its early geological history in the parallel banding of its rocks over very great distances. But the Ural as a range has a much later origin. The narrow zone revealed its crustal weakness again in Tertiary time and then yielded by uplift. Fortunately for the Russian state this raised no insuperable barrier ; moreover, the movement led to the injection of a great variety of valuable minerals. Hence from this posthumous movement of uplift along the sixtieth meridian there comes, on the one hand the conventional eastern limit of Europe ; but on account of the mineral wealth that it engendered the Ural has become a central pillar in the economy of modern Russia instead of the distant frontier it formed in the Middle Ages. But the Ural is unique ; elsewhere throughout the lowland the Earth's crust for the most part withstood the thrusts which compressed, crumpled and elevated the floors of former seas during the last (Tertiary) earth-storm, the so-called ' Alpine ' movements. The hidden edge of this bastion, then, can never be far from the present mountain-foot, and this feature presents an impressive course on the map. From the border of Afghanistan and Iran it runs straight, being an arc of a great circle, for 2,770 miles or 4,460 km., broken only by the Black Sea, to the Moravian Gate, whence it is prolonged by the hill foot in central Europe. With this northern edge the southern limit of the high mountains must be compared.

From their structure and geological antiquity, Africa, Arabia and Peninsular India resemble the rigid continental block just described. They have been immune from severe folding during a very long period and have undergone vast denudation, while, just as in Europe, portions of the crust that became rigid only after the Carboniferous Period had been added to the oldest masses. Hence these are lands of low relief except where uplifted subsequently. Here again, as in the far north, we find unfolded sediments resting upon parts of the most ancient structures. The remnants of such sandstones and limestones appear as tablelands ending in winding escarpments, as throughout the Sahara and from eastern Arabia to Syria and Iraq ; and since the climate is arid such features are much more rugged than their counterparts in Europe. And again among these rocks there are some which despite their age still lack toughness, e.g. clay of Carboniferous age in southern Algeria, and are preserved only by the stronger armour of the tablelands. But marking the junction of Asia and Africa there is an exception to the monotonous relief of these southern regions. Cataclysmic tensions and stresses that are still at work intermittently here found a zone of weakness in the old continent ; they cracked it like a pane of glass all along a belt reaching from its most northerly edge in Syria southward to Nyasaland, a direct distance of 3,900 miles or 6,300 km., but actually longer owing to deviations. Hence the rift-valleys of which the greatest holds the Red Sea, with a narrow northern branch extending to the foot of the Taurus Mountains ; hence also the great uplift of the land on both sides of the rift, in Nubia, Sinai and Arabia, and the subsequent uncovering of the crystalline bedrock there to leave extremely rugged hills ; hence the Isthmus of Suez, a keypoint in history—on a branching fracture, which is probably continued through the Aegean Sea and the Balkan Peninsula, and doubtless, too, the straight Levant coast parallel to the northern rift. To the same uplift is due the eastward tilt of Arabia and so probably the turning of the Euphrates away from the Mediterranean to the Persian Gulf. The rim of this generally monotonous southern borderland extends from the coast of the Atlantic opposite the Canary Islands to the head of the Persian Gulf, with a length of about 3,700 miles or 5,950 km., and divided into three segments. Those in Africa, south of the Atlas Mountains, and in Asia, south of the Taurus and Zagros Mountains, both bulge to the north ; the intervening segment, 1,400 miles or 2,250 km. in length, is now concealed by the eastern Mediterranean Sea. According to one view, the otherwise simple limits of the two great rigid continental blocks flanking the zone of the high mountains are interrupted by two narrow projections whose form would account partly for the trends of the rock-folds between them ; these are not included in the lengths given above. The one, projecting from the north, underlies the plain of the lower Danube, the other reaches from Africa northwestward under eastern Italy and the

Adriatic Sea to the foot of the Alps. The abrupt contrast in structure and relief at both edges of the mountainous Mediterranean zone and the simple outline of the edges must be stressed as of fundamental importance, since the foothill strips have ever been lines of human movement and settlement. It may be noted too that parts of both rims are climatic boundaries with deserts, the southern with the Sahara and the northern, in the east, with the Kara Kum.

The Mediterranean region owes its diversity of form primarily to the vast orogenic and other crustal movements of the Tertiary and Quaternary Eras. These were for a long period essentially movements of compression between the jaws of the two major crustal blocks already described, exerted upon a variety of sediments that had long been accumulating on the sea-bottom. These were therefore folded, often overfolded and, when less plastic, broken and thrust horizontally over one another as large slabs of rock ; in such manner were the original mountain chains elevated, but only after much compression had been accomplished under water. The rocks, because of the nature of the sea in which they were formed, include singularly pure limestone in a pro-portion greater than elsewhere in Europe ; hence the light colour of so many of the southern mountains today, as well as their permeability by water, and so its scarcity at the surface which constitutes one of the chief physical defects of the region. This general statement of disturbance and upheaval, however, is obviously insufficient to explain the complicated design of the relief as seen on the map, or even the design of the various rocks as they lie exposed on the land. To do this it is necessary to realise that in many parts of the region older earth-structures were involved, whether at first underneath the soft sediments of the sea-bed or, perhaps in some cases, as continental fragments that had survived as islands. In any case these blocks are comparable with the slabs mentioned above as now forming the plateaus north of the high mountains and regarded as unyielding remnants of the Hercynian system. Therefore, instead of simple earth-folds parallel to the edges of the enclosing ancient continental masses there are many bundles of folds which diverge, twist and rejoin, separated by chunks of the crust that are marked by much older structures. Some of these resistant slabs are held to exist although hidden beneath the sea or covered by more recent deposits on land. Thus the folds of the once plastic rocks are now found to lap around the blocks which largely resisted compression, e.g. the Andalusian folds against the Iberian Meseta or, as in the Algerian plateau, they are seen to be folded less closely because a somewhat compressed fragment lies beneath. Again, as in the Alps, the Pyrenees and the western High Atlas, smaller fragments are shown to have become incorporated in newer and more complex structures.

All this occupied long periods and the folding was effected not progressively but in phases between which the mountains upraised were greatly denuded—

in the case of Anatolia almost completely—before the renewed deformation
began.   The products of the denudation remain as the vast deposits of sandstones and shales found on the outer parts of many mountain chains.   Moreover
the orogenic forces were not equally active all along the front at the same time ;
thus for instance in the Alps the pressure came later than it did in the
Pyrenees and Carpathians, but earlier than in the Appennines and Dinaric
systems.

While the presence and the general plan of the high mountains of southern
Europe and its margins are due in origin to great compression, it may yet be
misleading to call them ' young fold-mountains ' or even ' fold-mountains ',
as is often done, because their present height is certainly not due to the original
folding.   Since these episodes immense masses of rock have been removed by
denudation, and this would have left the mountains much lower but for the
final outburst of the earth-storm, which took a quite different form.   Its physical
nature is still much debated, but of the result there is no question.   At the end
of the Tertiary Era and during the Quaternary as well, the whole system, by
then much more rigid, was subjected to forces which some regard as mainly
tensional, but in part the reverse.   Deep fractures formed in many directions,
and dislocations resulted in the massive elevation of the blocks that now form
the high mountains, or in places this took place by warping without severe
fracture.   Hence the mountains coincide largely with the belts of original
folding.

Equally important and probably mainly contemporaneous, is the formation of the hollows separating the mountain-systems, and now existing as
the deep basins of the Mediterranean and Black Seas or the depressions such
as those now drained by the Guadalquivir and the middle Danube.   Their
origin is controversial because geological evidence is concealed by the sea or
by alluvium.   Either huge masses of the crust foundered from lack of support,
or some of the cracks widened under tension to form yawning gulfs ;   perhaps
both processes were combined.   Certainly many areas of former land that have
vanished seem to represent the rigid slabs against which the earlier folds were
compressed, since the folds often lie along a coast or the edge of an alluvial plain,
while these places are often marked by igneous rocks of recent origin, and in
Italy by active volcanoes.   It is not surprising that such a series of cataclysms
was accompanied by volcanic activity in many parts of the region ;   lava-flows,
with or without craters, and innumerable hot springs betray the lines of latent
weakness throughout the zone.   Few volcanoes are still active, but the crust
still shudders on many deep fractures, showing that these have not yet healed ;
earthquakes remain one of the great defects of this region for man (Fig. 2).
Thus throughout Europe south of an arc enclosing the Iberian Peninsula, the
Bohemian highlands and the Caucasus, only one area gave no records of major

earthquakes during the period 1899–1933 ; this lies in the western basin of the Mediterranean Sea, and the reason for its immunity is still a matter for speculation.

Within the zone of high mountains it is not only the geologist who may detect the contrast between the ranges of Tertiary folding from the large fragments of more ancient slabs. The latter stand with the old rocks visible as even-topped plateaus, representing surfaces that were worn to smoothness before the final upheaval, and similar to those, for example, of central France or Bohemia. Much of the Iberian Peninsula has this type of relief ; so have Sardinia, western Morocco and parts of the Balkan Peninsula and Anatolia. The mountain ranges on the other hand are usually rugged, and the limestones and sandstones which compose so many reveal their folded structure to any eye. Yet however rugged in detail, they bear at high altitudes traces of the smoother form they once possessed before the posthumous elevation to present heights ; even in the Alps this is seen in the accordant heights of many adjacent ridges. But both types of land are affected by the latest dislocations and the movements, up or down, of blocks thus separated. Consequently fault-scarps, the torn edges of recent fractures, are widespread and characteristic features of Mediterranean landscapes : very many of the steep and straight mountainsides have this origin, some of them offering the most spectacular coastal scenery in the world. The distribution of depth in the Mediterranean and Black Seas is the key to their origin—a number of enclosed basins which at one stage would seem to have contained separate lakes with their own interior drainage. The western basin, however, was earliest connected with the ocean, by former straits, successively south of the Riff and north of the Andalusian Mountains, before the Strait of Gibraltar was formed. In the north-east, long before the formation of the deep Black Sea and the hollows that now form the Aegean Sea, a vast but shallow ' Sarmatic ' lake covered most of these areas and also parts of the Balkan peninsula, south Russia, Anatolia and Turkestan : the Caspian and Aral lakes are separate remnants of this. As a result weak Sarmatic deposits now occupy similar lowlands in all these tracts. The Hellespont derives from the later and lower stages in the history of this progressively declining inland sea. The Pontic lake (in a region now occupied by the Black Sea) was drained for a time by short rivers, over an isthmus to the Marmara lake, and thence through another isthmus to the Aegean lake. These river valleys by subsequent drowning have become the straits respectively of Bosporus and Dardanelles.

The full story of the vertical oscillations of the shores around the various Mediterranean basins awaits more comprehensive research ; but it is certain that, since the Pliocene period, they have been very great and widespread.

While, on the one hand, intricate coastlines like those of the Aegean Sea are the result of a very late depression of the land, smooth shores such as that of eastern Italy result from progressive emergence. But again there is evidence of raised sea-beaches at almost the same heights in many parts of the region both on the north and south of the Mediterranean shores. In view of the manner in which this sea is beset by high and steep mountains, it has been of the greatest importance to the human inhabitants that coastal lowland was to be found at short intervals, in strips and patches, since these form the main areas of easily cultivated land; and it is to the emergence of gently shelving sea-bottom since Pliocene times that such land owes its existence. It must be noted, however, that this, from the unconsolidated character of the rock, such as sand, marl or clay, is subject to rapid erosion by stream and wave.

Just as the present rock-structure has been evolved gradually throughout all the geological ages, so the drainage system of Europe has developed gradually; but in this case mainly in the latest phases of the Tertiary and in the Quaternary Eras. The basins of some rivers have been progressively enlarged by capture at the expense of others, while there are many instances of rivers maintaining their directions despite the slow elevation of the crust beneath them. The pattern of the rivers is therefore intricate, especially in the mountains and highlands of the south, but also in the greatest tract of otherwise smooth relief, the Russian Plain. Moreover, a feature characteristic of central and southern Europe is the plethora of gaps, narrow or wide, opened or maintained by the rivers during the later disturbances, thus providing means for the freer movement of air, plants, animals and men in regions which otherwise would be greater barriers. It is obvious too that, since the present limits of land and sea are still young, the rivers must have been greatly affected by the changes which produced the present coasts. Many rivers lost their lower portions by submergence of land to a small depth, which permitted the invasion of the North Sea. The submergence of land to a much greater depth occurred in the Atlantic basin off the Iberian Peninsula, and in the Mediterranean and Black Seas when the several basins of these were formed and rapidly deepened.

As a consequence of the later evolution of the land surface and the formation of marginal basins the main watershed extends from Cape St Vincent to the Ural Mountains in latitude 62° N. with only two sharp kinks, to enclose the Ebro and the Rhine, and in few parts does it follow the highest mountains.

Of the total area 58 per cent is drained south and east from this line, and 42 per cent north and west. Of the former large tract 35 per cent belongs to the inland drainage of the Caspian, and the other really large basins are tributary to the Black Sea ; this fact has placed the peoples of south-eastern Europe at a great disadvantage in modern times. The lower courses of these rivers flow over the dried bed of the former Sarmatic lakes and represent a very recent pattern of parallel streams, in strong contrast to the complexity farther north, referred to above. Again, on the Atlantic side the greater tracts are drained to the Barents and Baltic Seas which are frozen for much of the year. Hence the importance of the rivers as routes is not necessarily proportionate to their length or to the size of their basins. Moreover, navigation depends greatly upon gradients as well as upon volume, which in turn is related to the climate (pp. 69-70).

CHAPTER 2

ECONOMIC MINERALS

THE riches of the rocks have been appreciated progressively throughout human history, at first very, very slowly and with attention to but few substances ; latterly—in the last century—at great speed, which has been subject to special acceleration unfortunately due to the wasteful needs of two wars. The present great volume of the minerals extracted is matched by their ever-increasing variety, as industrial uses multiply and gain in complexity. The ' pitch ' that covered Noah's ark ' within and without ' was probably bitumen, which, gathered from seepages, has been used upon the river craft of Mesopotamia through the ages. Yet the mineral fuels, coal and petroleum were allowed to remain in the rocks, save for minute quantities, until two centuries ago. The same is generally true of the salts and the metallic ores. While common salt was one of the earliest articles of trade, the heavy chemical industry which depends greatly on this and the rarer salts is a modern development. The mining of metals on the other hand has a long history, but methods remained primitive throughout the Middle Ages, and only the shallower ores could be reached. This theme will be developed in a later chapter, but it is appropriate here to examine the distribution of mineral wealth, as it is now known, in relation to the broader features of geological structure. It will be convenient to consider the minerals contained in sedimentary rocks that have been little disturbed separately from those of the crystalline rocks and the more disordered sediments, which include most of the metallic ores, but with some notable exceptions.

The stratified rocks yield, as their principal products, coal, mostly Carboniferous in age ; the salts, chiefly Permian and Triassic ; and petroleum, as well as more salt, from the Tertiary. The formation of each of these is evidence of climates and other physical conditions differing completely from those now prevailing in this part of the world ; indeed, those of the three periods are strongly contrasted among themselves. While such matters need not concern us, it must be noted that the coal was formed before the Hercynian earth-storm, and while small pockets of it remain exposed within the folds of this great central system of Europe—as in Spain and southern France—the main coalfields lie in a zone on the northern edge of the Hercynian structural unit, and extending from South Wales to the Caspian Sea (Fig. 3). Within this zone, however, the coal has been preserved only where subsequent dis-

14

locations have allowed it to remain deeper in the crust than in the adjacent sections from which it has been removed. Thus the great coalfields lie widely separated—the 'Donbas' (along the River Donets), Silesia, Saxony to Westphalia, and thence with less interruption to the British fields, where the zone widens to include the many basins between South Wales and Fife.

The red rocks which were formed in deserts during the Permian and

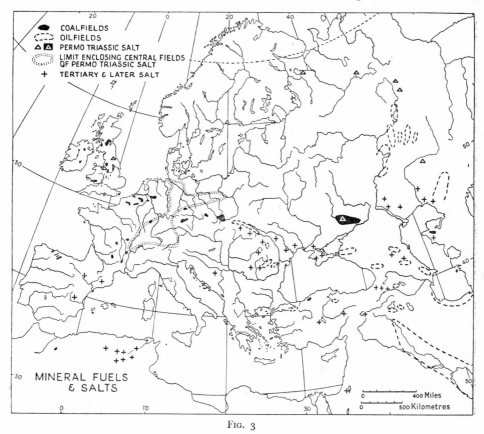

FIG. 3

Triassic Periods now occupy large areas in England and in central Europe, where they adjoin and overlap the zone containing the coal ; while the older formation that was named from the town of Perm follows the western foot of the Ural Mountains throughout their entire length. Thus the deposits of common salt, and more rarely the salts of potash and other elements evaporated in the former deserts, are found preserved in basins lying around the Pennines in England ; in central Europe between the upper Rhone and the lower Vistula ; and in an eastern arc in Russia, from the Donets to the upper Kama..

Salt of the same age also appears in the Atlas Mountains, sometimes at the surface, while there are salt-bearing rocks of similar character, but belonging to the Tertiary Era in eastern Spain, and those of Catalonia yield potash as well.

Mineral oil has been associated in its origin with strata containing salt and gypsum, while the latter sometimes has been the source of free sulphur —as in Sicily, the chief European source of this. The geological history and structure in the Tertiary Era have favoured the formation and the preservation of petroleum and of salt throughout a large tract that corresponds, in the west, to the basin of the Danube, and broadens out eastward to embrace the plain north of the Caspian Sea on the one hand and the coasts of the Persian Gulf on the other. Within this area the oil pools lie trapped in the gentler and unbroken anticlines and domes that mark the lower fringes of the Carpathians, the Caucasus, the Zagros and other major mountain systems ; in addition, similar folds lie buried beneath plains far from the mountains, as north of the Caspian Sea or on the coast of Arabia.

The distribution of other non-metallic minerals of the sedimentary rocks does not lend itself to useful generalisation ; but perhaps that of phosphate rock may be mentioned, on account of its great importance in modern agriculture, first in three districts of the Atlas lands and secondly at widely dispersed localities in European Russia.

The metals which are derived in part from ores that occur as relatively undisturbed sediments are iron, manganese and aluminium. The outstanding iron deposits of this type are those of the Jurassic rocks of Lorraine, Luxembourg and England, and those of Krivoi Rog in southern Ukraine, Kerch in the Crimea, Tula and Kursk in central Russia.

Large deposits of manganese ore are known at only two places in Europe, at the southern foot of the Caucasus and near the lower Don ; both are undisturbed sediments.

Bauxite, the chief ore of aluminium, is a residual material from which other compounds have been dissolved. It resembles the lateritic soils of the hot wet lands, and many of the occurrences are doubtless buried remnants of such soils formed in Tertiary or earlier times. It is found chiefly in southern Europe but also in the Urals and near Leningrad, and usually at small depth. It is of geographical and geological significance that the German word for a mine is *Bergwerk* (literally mountain work), a school of mines being a *Bergakademie*. By far the greater number of mineral workings until the last century were in the mountains, because it is there that denudation has revealed the valuable minerals sufficiently concentrated to be worth mining. This could take place only when the elements normally found in the deeper layers of the earth's crust could be brought upwards as hot solutions or gases in fissures, and be deposited by crystallisation either in veins, or by replacing other matter (whether by molecular replacement or by filling cavities due to solution). Such processes normally take place far below the surface, and the ores are found only where the surface has been brought down to them by prolonged denudation. Still greater masses of rock must have been removed to reveal minerals formed by the cooling of a huge molten mass, as of gabbro or even of the much lighter granite ; and it is with the intrusion of granite, for example, that the formation of gold and tin ore are generally associated. This somewhat incomplete statement must suffice to indicate the relation of valuable minerals to the disturbed and originally deeper-seated rocks of Europe. Such rocks are exposed throughout most of the mountains, but their surface may also be found at quite low heights where denudation has been still more prolonged, as in part of Scandinavia and in Finland ; so the mineral deposits thus produced directly by the internal agencies are found among the tougher rocks which are commonly, though not always, the older. In general then the two maps (Figs. 1 and 3) are complementary ; the sedimentary minerals are distributed mainly with the younger strata and at the lower altitudes ; the others lie among the older rocks or where these are not deeply covered, and so mostly in the higher lands.

Since disturbances in the earth's crust give rise to mineralisation from beneath, it may be suggested that the parts most likely to contain economic minerals are those where the rocks have been disturbed most frequently, as especially during the various periods of folding. This might account for the widespread mineralisation of central, and in parts also, southern Europe (Fig. 3). It might explain the paucity of minerals in Finland and a part of Sweden from prolonged quiescence. But it fails to account for their virtual absence, for instance, in the highlands of Scotland and Northern Ireland. The dots on Fig. 4 show localities that have yielded, in recent times, important amounts of minerals—chiefly metallic—from deposits due to the internal agencies ; the technical classification of these is given with the title. Since there is no attempt to show the relative importance of these mining regions, or indeed the nature of the minerals, some further generalisation may be attempted.

Iron mines are the most widely distributed, followed by those of lead and zinc or lead alone, and the lead ore commonly yields also a proportion of silver. Copper ore, too, in Europe is often associated with these. Tin ore is much more restricted, though found in widely separated regions, and the same may be said of mercury. Gold is, or has been, present in small amounts in a great many veins of other metals, but most of it has in the past been obtained from river sands eroded from the lodes. The ores of chromium and magnesium are commonest in the Balkan Peninsula, with the former also across the Aegean Sea in Anatolia, and the latter in the eastern Alps and Bohemia. Both platinum and nickel ore are specially associated with intrusions of basic igneous rock, the first only in the Urals and the latter in largest amounts there. The uranium of Bohemia is found, with other minerals, in veins occurring in metamorphic rocks. Mica in the large crystals most valuable in manufacture is significant in the Archaean rocks of Soviet Karelia, where the maximum denudation

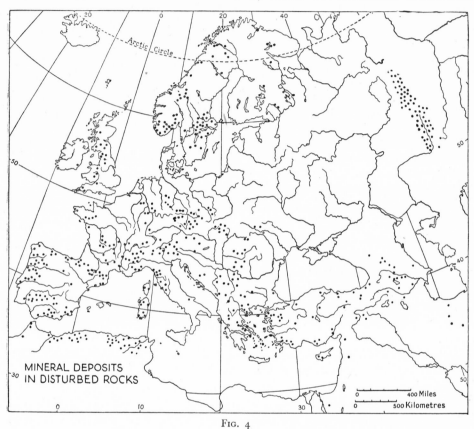

FIG. 4

Localities of mineral deposits other than sedimentary : metasomatic deposits, contact metamorphic deposits, magmatic segregations as at 1927 (Prussian Geological Survey)

has taken place since its formation deep in the earth's crust. The largest region that has been strongly mineralised throughout is the Ural Mountains between about 52° and 62° N.; for variety of minerals and total reserves of many, it may well be unequalled by any region of similar area in the world. The presence of such great mineral wealth in the Urals is in itself a substantial reason for rejecting these mountains as the eastern limit of Europe ; but the justification for adherence to this conventional boundary has been stated earlier. The region that extends from the Harz Mountains to the Ore Mountains of

Slovakia, which was the nursery of medieval mining, must contain still more mines than the Urals, many being still productive but many more deserted. Other long-worked regions are central Sweden, Cornwall and Transilvania ; but the districts that have yielded metals continuously for the longest periods must surely be those near the Mediterranean Sea. Good examples are the silver-lead district of Lavrion in Greece, the iron mines of Elba, and the Rio Tinto district of the Sierra Morena in Spain. The last contributed gold and copper to the wealth of ancient Tarshish, and it is now one of the world's chief sources of sulphur derived from the huge reserves of pyrite, the sulphides of iron and copper.

Thus the great and varied mineral wealth of Europe and its borderlands is on the whole very well distributed. The basic reason for this lies in the fact that, for the size of this tract of the Earth, there is a quite remarkable assemblage of geological formations which have been subjected at long intervals to crustal disturbances, each affecting the subcontinent in a different way and part. Hence geological history has led to complexity not only in the relief and in the coastlines, but also in the minerals that have proved specially valuable to mankind.

CHAPTER 3

THE OCEAN AND THE SEAS

ALTHOUGH the floor of the ocean is hidden, its relief exerts a powerful but indirect influence upon all terrestrial life. Europe is flanked by a series of deep basins, the inland Caspian Basin, the Pontic or Black Sea Basin, three forming the Mediterranean Sea, two of the Atlantic basins and one of the North Polar basins. These vary greatly in shape and size as well as in depth. Water is hampered in flowing from one to another since the floor rises to form partial barriers, while the Caspian is the world's largest inland lake and is shallower than the others (about 1,100 metres). The Mediterranean basins, though the smaller, are yet important features of the Earth. The Pontic and the Western Basins are comparable in depth, over 2,000 metres, and in their subtriangular form. The Tyrrhenian, also three-sided, resembles the eastern part of the large Southern Basin, which exceeds 3,000 metres, and between them the Ionian Sea is over 4,000 metres. There are but five considerable shallow tracts, to 200 metres ; one off Spain and France, the northern Adriatic, that between Sicily and Africa, the submerged delta of the Nile, and one flanking the Crimea on both sides. The rims of the basins are marked by slopes that are unusually steep for the sea-floor in many places ; and more obvious and important is the narrowness of the straits especially at the Hellespont and Gibraltar.

Facing the ocean the continental slope, whether starting at 200 metres or somewhat deeper, suggests by its nature an origin similar to that of the sub-marine escarpments of the Mediterranean. The North Canary Basin and the Spanish Basin, both reaching depths over 5,000 metres are limited by steep slopes which lie close to the coasts of Morocco and Iberia and the adjoining part of France. But the continental edge then recedes to 230 miles west of Kerry, leaving the British Isles and most of the North Sea on a broad continental shelf. The North European Basin, between Norway and Greenland, exceeds 3,000 metres in depth and presents a steep slope to Europe only off the Lofoten Islands ; farther east the Barents Sea is relatively shallow.

The North European Basin communicates with the greater North Polar Basin by a gap, about lat. 81° and nearly 1,000 metres deep. From the Atlantic Ocean it is separated by a swelling barrier extending from central Greenland to the continental shelf north of Scotland, and culminating in Iceland and the Faeroe Islands, both built of volcanic rocks. This submarine plateau approaches 600 m. in depth in two places—Denmark Strait and the Faeroe-Shetland

Channel ; this latter, lying in the section of the barrier named the Wyville-Thomson Ridge, is a water-gate of first importance to the climate and life of north-western Europe. Similar in width but less deep is the Norwegian Trough, a branch of the North European Basin close to south-western Norway, leading to the shallow Kattegat and Baltic Sea.

The ocean and the seas must be thought of in relation to the climate of the land, to the marine fauna and flora as a source of food and raw materials, to the salt it makes available, and finally to seafaring for all purposes. Climatically the ocean is the conservative element affecting air-temperature, and it provides the water in the air : hence the importance of landward winds. The chain of marine life, from the plankton to the whales, seals and birds, hangs

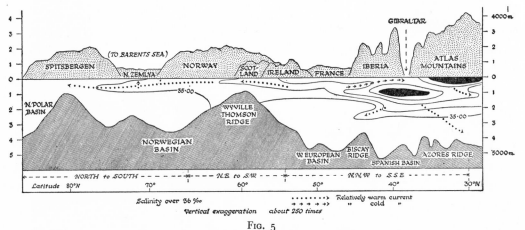

FIG. 5

Cross-section of the land surface and the ocean floor from Spitsbergen to the Atlas Mountains

upon the delicate relationships between temperature, salinity and aeration in the sea water, but it is also affected by the nature of the sea bottom. For the procurement of salt it is the character of the shore and the amount of evaporation, a climatic factor, that matter. As for seafaring, apart from the questions of human incentive and accessibility, there are those relating to wind and storm, current, fog and floating ice.

Europe derives tremendous climatic benefit from the circulation of waters and the prevailing drift of air from this ocean. The powerful mechanism of the oceanic circulation comprises two regions of main activity, both far from Europe but affecting it vitally—the Caribbean Sea and the North Polar Basin. The steady outflow of ice-bearing water from the latter passes southward on both sides of Greenland and so, again, far from Europe ; while the powerful mass movement of warm water from the Gulf of Mexico sweeps around the continental edge from Portugal to the North Cape, sending branches north-west to Iceland and east to the Barents Sea. The main body continues past Svalbard (Spitsbergen) to the Polar Basin. It has been estimated that each year pack-ice in volume about 20,000 cubic kilometres, floats out of the Polar Basin, and it follows that at least this amount of Atlantic water, warm and relatively saline and dense, passes into the Basin. It starts as the Gulf Stream,

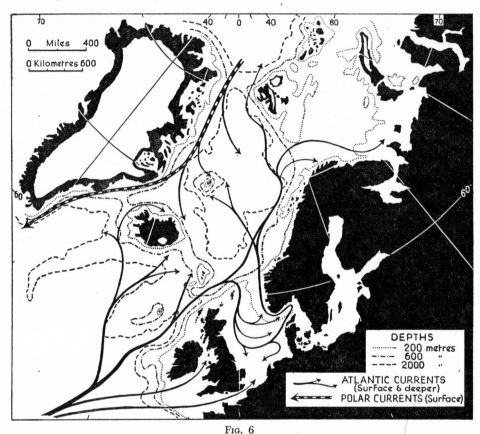

FIG. 6
North Atlantic currents

a highly concentrated ocean current; it spreads north-eastward, becomes somewhat cooler and, despite help given to the surface layers by the prevailing winds, loses velocity. But so powerful is this current known as the Gulf Stream Drift, that its water fills the north-eastern Atlantic almost constantly to the bottom. The warmth and the salinity of this water again are increased by the contribution which comes from the Mediterranean Sea; most of this warm discharge from the Strait of Gibraltar passes westward, but its presence is also traced northward.

The above statement refers to the Atlantic as bounded by the continental slope between Iceland and Portugal. Beyond this the effect of the ocean upon life on land and in the sea depends greatly upon the submarine relief. The 'forecourt' of the North Polar Basin is the lozenge-shaped North European Basin, in which Polar and Atlantic waters mingle to produce a deep mass of cold water of intermediate salinity.

This is hemmed in on the south-west by the broad Iceland-Faeroe Ridge, at the end of which is the narrow 'Wyville-Thomson Ridge' marking a 'pass' leading to the long Faeroe-Shetland Channel. Through this the Atlantic water flows, hugging the continental slope as the Norwegian current; but a part of this water turns southward from Shetland to sweep round the North Sea and Skager Rak with branches and eddies, finally receiving the very fresh water from the shallow Baltic as a surface layer. While this is the normal condition, it is possible that occasionally and for short periods the entire current makes this extended passage around the North Sea. Because of the dissection of the Barents Shelf by submarine valleys lying from west to east, a branch is able to pass eastward towards the Kara Strait south of Novaya Zemlya, to give to Russia a stretch of open coast, while the main current does the same to the west coast of Svalbard. All this, then, has been well named the 'gulf of warmth'; 'Atlantic' water in these northern seas does not form ice at its surface, and moreover being in great volume, the heat which it radiates has an important influence on the climate of the adjoining lands. This is, of course, largely an indirect influence, since it affects the formation and the movement of atmospheric depressions. The 'gulf of warmth' finds expression then in the average surface temperatures of the Norwegian Sea and northern and North Seas, which are from 4° to 5° C. (7° to 9° F.) higher than the normal temperatures for the latitudes, and also in the small amount of seasonal variation of temperature—only 5° C. (9° F.) between Shetland and Svalbard, but increasing quickly southward in the North Sea. South of about latitude 40° the general eastward movement of Atlantic water begins to change, since the shape of the bottom and of the coast make the right-handed rotational deflection more effective. Moreover, both the prevailing wind and the thermal conditions favour a southward movement off the coast of north Africa. It is the North-east Trade Wind, however, which produces the most characteristic feature here by driving the surface waters onwards in this direction, and so causing their replacement by upwelling of deeper and colder water. Thus at the Strait of Gibraltar the surface temperature begins to be lower than that proper to the latitude. Thus, too, the conditions which favour marine life in the European seas, and consequently the modern European fisheries, are extended along the coast of Morocco.

The Mediterranean Sea, having a single effective link with the ocean, differs in many respects from the other fringing seas of the Atlantic. The Strait of Gibraltar is less than 400 metres deep and only 14 km. wide, yet it provides inlet for seven-tenths of the water needed to maintain a volume of some 3¾ million cu. km. in the Mediterranean, by compensating for loss from intense evaporation ; the other three-tenths come from rain and rivers—including excess flow from the Black Sea. Beneath this inflow of Atlantic water in the Strait there is a westward current of the very salt water which fills all the basins of the Mediterranean. This deeper flow starts at the eastern end and passes from basin to basin. The narrow Bosporus carries similar compensating currents into the Black Sea (beneath) and out of it (above). While the surface water of the Mediterranean in winter differs little in temperature from that of the Atlantic beyond the Strait, in summer it is as warm as a tropical sea. The deeper water in all the Mediterranean basins is much warmer and saltier than that of the eastern Atlantic Ocean ; so this sea is a great storehouse of solar heat.

The Mediterranean water is unusually clear, since it bears little matter in suspension ; there are neither widespread mineral particles from rivers nor the abundance of the small living organisms—plankton—to be found in ocean water. This poverty of life is due to the various physical qualities of the sea, among them the uniformity of temperature in depth. This feature is due to vertical movements which, though slight, yet carry oxygen right to the bottom in amounts sufficient to sustain a certain amount of animal life there. In the Black Sea, on the other hand, there is complete separation between a thin surface layer of fresher water fed by rivers and by rain, and the remainder, derived from deep layers of the Mediterranean, which is virtually without dissolved oxygen, and so is devoid of life. In the Caspian Sea evaporation is balanced by supply, but, since there is no outlet, the water is brackish ; otherwise the conditions resemble those of the Black Sea.

The contrast between the Mediterranean and the Atlantic is seen to be further increased when the tides and the frequency of storm-waves are considered. The tides in the Mediterranean, Black and Baltic Seas are so slight as to be scarcely observable on the coasts, which means the virtual absence of foreshores, so productive of the varied flora and fauna of tidal coasts—life that is always interesting and often of economic importance. But even small tidal range, occurring in adjoining basins at different times, does produce notable currents in the connecting straits : those of the channels of Messina and Evrippos, for instance, have been famous since ancient times. In contrast, the British Isles and the Atlantic coasts to the south have a great average range of tides, which is further amplified in the numerous estuaries and inlets of these lands ; the range becomes less in Norway and less still beyond. Upon the broad continental shelf around the British Isles tidal currents play their part in moulding the bottom and the beaches, and no doubt, too, in determining or guiding the movements of marine organisms.

Since the part of the North Atlantic that is traversed by the greatest number of deep atmospheric depressions, and so is most often swept by gales, includes the area of widest continental shelf, it is evident that sea waves must affect the bottom greatly, just as they continually alter the shore. Moreover, storm-waves mix the different layers of water, and in breaking they increase the aeration. It follows that for many reasons these northern waters are unusually favourable to life. The water is rich in oxygen and in mineral solutions that are constantly renewed at the surface by the rivers, and more intermittently by influx of deeper Atlantic water. The continental slope is washed by bodies of water differing widely in origin and so notably in temperature and salinity. On the shelf the conditions in regard to light, aeration, nourishing solutions and mud are ideal for plants, including the teeming phyto-plankton which gives the water its greenish colour.

While a vast amount of research has been devoted to the marine life of these seas, knowledge is still very partial, for the complexity is great. Thus every kind of fish is adapted to the habitat suited to the organisms upon which it feeds, and this in turn means certain limits of temperature, salinity, light, bacterial content and so on. Again, adult fish live on small animals which consume smaller animals ; these as well as the small larvae of the fishes them-selves depend upon floating microscopic plants found wherever light penetrates. Such plants abound in temperate seas, especially where nutrition is favoured by new matter brought by rivers and made available by the chemical action of bacteria. All the requisite conditions vary, too, with the age of the fish, from hatching onwards, and each species has its own preference in the type of sea bottom ; thus cod prefer rocky ground and haddock a sandy floor. There-fore, to find what they need throughout the year the fishes migrate, generally over great distances ; and this applies also to the mammals, the seals and some of the whales, that prey upon the fish. Sea birds, again, are migrant, but their movements depend upon climate as well as on their food supply at sea. It is clear that the delicate balance of these relations may be upset both by fluctuations in any of the natural factors or by the excessive inroads of men upon any one species or in a particular area ; a fact which makes international agreement indispensable in regard to fisheries.

It would seem that the Scoto-Icelandic plateau formerly separated the marine faunas, as it still does in the case of deep-water animals. Among the important food-fishes those belonging to the northern and southern types now overlap in their distributions ; but the two groups are dominant respect-ively north and south of a zone which coincides roughly with the annual surface isotherm of 50° F. (10° C.), a line which curves northward to enclose the Rockall and Dogger Banks. Of the northern group the principal demersal fishes, i.e. those which feed mainly at the bottom, are cod, haddock, halibut, with plaice, coalfish or saith (resembling cod), lemon sole and ling less common. The pelagic fishes are herring and sprat. The typical demersals of the southern group are hake, skate, turbot, sole, brill, bream and gurnard ; the pelagics are represented by mackerel, anchovy, pilchard (or true sardine), tunny, bonito and the mullets. It is these pelagic species which are the chief object of fisheries in the Mediterranean. Since the Caspian Sea was formerly linked with the ocean, marine animals mingle with fresh-water species, and the fauna is in some respects vestigial. The deeper water is lifeless, but the upper layers with varying salinity teem with fish, the most valuable of which is the sturgeon.

CHAPTER 4

FISHERIES

THROUGHOUT Europe the coasts over long stretches are studded with fishing villages or small towns whose function has imparted to them a distinguishing stamp. The centre of life is the harbour rather than a market-place, houses tend to be huddled along narrow lanes leading from the quays, dwellings mingle with workshops for the making of nets, ropes, barrels, and for salting or smoking fish. Near by space is found for drying nets, and sometimes fish as well, and for the boat-builders' yards ; the smell of fish mingles with that of tar and its products. The small craft in the harbour betray by their hulls or rigging a distinctly regional variation that results from long evolution of design to suit the character of specific coasts and fisheries. But in some parts boats may still be built almost exactly as they were a thousand years ago or more ; for example, descendants of Viking vessels in Norway or of Carthaginian craft in Portugal. The fisherfolk on all coasts are themselves distinctive, with their own traditions, social character and a tendency to exclusiveness. Knowledge of the sea and the habits of fish, gained empirically through many generations, has enabled these highly individual communities to meet the vicissitudes of weather, sea and fish, with success sufficient for their own livelihood and the feeding of considerable landward populations. But certain specific inventions from time to time have greatly added to the success of their efforts as knowledge of these spread. Thus the Dutch procedure of gutting herring before salting while at sea, adopted at the end of the fourteenth century, is comparable with the modern invention of the packing tin, the acquisition of manufactured ice, or the still later provision of refrigeration plant in the vessels ; and all these have marked important extensions in the fisheries. The invention of the beam-trawl made it possible to fish systematically on the sea bottom, while that of the seine, as used in Denmark, gave a new method of surface fishing, and the introduction of the lighter cotton to replace hempen nets, coupled with machinery for making these, greatly enlarged the scope of operations at sea. Above all there was the application of steam and then of the oil-motor to fishing vessels. In recent years, too, the aeroplane, the echo-sounders and other instruments have placed new tools in the fishermen's hands for the location of shoals. Furthermore, the development of the sciences of oceanography and marine biology has proved of inestimable benefit to the industry. If fishermen have seen some of their traditional beliefs about

27

the habits of fish disproved, much of their previous half-knowledge now rests on fuller scientific understanding, and the scientists have been able to carry conviction by directing them to areas where mature fish congregate.

Because of reasons that have been stated in the opening chapters the opportunity for sea fishery is offered most unequally round the coasts. In the first place shorelines of unbroken beach are unapproachable from the sea, and harbours, even for small boats, are absent from long stretches of the Mediterranean coasts, particularly the eastern part and the Black and the Caspian Seas, as well as from certain Atlantic coasts on the Iberian Peninsula and France, and along the southern North Sea and the Baltic. But in many cases this disadvantage is lessened by the presence of sandy islands off-shore giving shelter for artificial harbours, and of lagoons which, though they may not be open to vessels from the sea, are commonly valuable sources of fish or shellfish that are easily taken. Secondly, the peoples of the coasts have not been equally inspired with the desire to put to sea or at least to make fishing their main occupation, notably in Bulgaria and Romania, as in Turkey where no doubt the Islamic ban on fish diet was powerful; and this reluctance is notable also on the western coasts of the British Isles, with the exceptions of the Cornish, Manx and Lewismen. The Russians again took to sea-faring only as a late development, although this inland people had long depended for food largely upon the fishing of rivers and lakes. Nevertheless the principal difference in the degree of inducement undoubtedly depends upon the unequal distribution of fish, which was suggested though not described in Chapter 3.

MEDITERRANEAN FISHERIES

The Mediterranean Sea is more than half as large as the part of the eastern Atlantic Ocean that is regularly visited by fishing vessels, yet the weight of fish taken from it amounts only to some six per cent of the total fish landed, apart from the unknown Russian catch which, however, comes from both the sub-Arctic and the Black Sea. This disparity is due mainly to the paucity of life in the enclosed seas, to the relatively slight extent of shallow water and to the generally small size of the fish landed, except the tunny. But it comes also from the relatively primitive methods used in the south; indeed the small amount of fish available does not encourage the large investment of capital in ships and gear that has marked the Atlantic fisheries in modern times. Thus, by far the largest purely Mediterranean catch is that of Italy, unless that of Russia in the Black Sea now exceeds it; the men employed number at least as many as the fishermen of the British Isles, who land from eight to ten times the quantity brought in by the Italians. But it must be noted that many of these probably are fishermen for only part of the year. Or, again, on the coast of Yugoslavia in 1933 there were 2,600 regular and 16,400 seasonal fishermen, but the total landing was only 7,000 tons.

Mediterranean peoples still derive much of their fish from the lagoons, estuaries and shallow bay-heads, as their remote ancestors did. Those who are thus engaged are essentially landsmen : watchers sitting constantly on pylons waiting to raise a scarcely submerged net—characteristic of eastern shores— visitors of reed-traps at inlets to lagoons ; or even the nocturnal wielders of tridents by lantern light in shallow-draft boats on the lagoons. They are all concerned chiefly with the seasonal movements of fishes—whether truly migratory like the pilchard, anchovy and eel, or sedentary like the mullets and various flat fishes—to and from the lagoons as they are affected by physical factors and nutrition. The business, however, has reached a scientific level in some of the lagoons of northern Italy, where the factors of temperature and salinity are controlled, and this is appropriate to the neighbourhood of Chioggia, the greatest fishing port of Italy, a unique town on its sandspit and one of the little medieval fishing republics which set up Venice as leader of their confederation.

Mediterranean sea-fisheries, which probably developed from those just described, take place generally at short distances from land where sailing is favoured all summer by the regular land and sea breezes, although powered vessels are now less limited on this account. Various seines and drift-nets are used, but there is little trawling. The normal catch includes many species of fish—there are at least 450 in the Mediterranean—and it is not confined to these, since such different animals as the sea-urchin, sea-spider and octopus find a ready market. But there are virtually only four shoaling fishes, the pilchard (or sardine), the anchovy, the mackerel and the tunny, all of them migrant species. For various reasons the fishing industry is much more important in the western than in the eastern basin, except for the Adriatic, and this applies especially to the tunny and the sardine. The causes and the course of the changing migrations are still somewhat mysterious, but the disappearance of the tunny in winter seems now to be explained by retreat to deeper water having more equable temperature. This great fish, larger than its Atlantic relation, has always been the chief prize which has evoked the greatest co-operation, courage and skill among fishers. The shoals appear near the coasts in the early summer, notably those of France, west Sardinia, north and east Sicily, and Tunisia ; they are taken in very strong nets of two main classes : either fixed stake-nets extending from shore, sometimes a couple of miles, to water of about twenty fathoms, where complex net ' chambers ' lead the tunny into the ' death chamber '—and there they are killed by spearing from the boats ; otherwise the system of nets is skilfully laid from the boats, with a similar aim. Tunny are now almost entirely disposed of by cutting up and packing in tins. The more placid occupation of sardine fishing takes place in similar waters and culminates about the same period, the shoals being caught in fine drift-nets or in seines.

These and all other ' fruits of the sea ' fall far short of supplying the demand for fish in southern Europe, where the fasts imposed by both the Roman and the Orthodox churches call for this food in large quantities ; hence the great importation of cured fish, especially cod, from northern waters, but the Iberian Peninsula is in a favoured position in this respect.

In certain patches of the Mediterranean sponges suited to the bathing needs of modern man grow in sufficient numbers at accessible depth ; and the specialised industry of gathering these occupies several remarkable communities, notably that of the Greek island, Kalymnos. The grounds lie at some six fathoms off the coasts of Dalmatia, Syria, Egypt, Tripolitania and Tunisia, and the sponges are obtained partly by dredging, but more selectively by diving, formerly without apparatus and to the ultimate detriment of the swimmer. This specialised industry is matched by the gathering of red coral, chiefly by Neapolitans in Tunisian, Sicilian and Aegean waters. The steady, though formerly much greater, markets for this luxury lie in India and Arabia, where it is an effective adornment of dark-skinned beauty ; but the profit was never easily won.

The upper film of the Black Sea and the brackish waters of the Sea of Azov and the Caspian form habitats that differ from most of other southern seas and offer special opportunities for fishing. The Hellespont is, of course, an avenue to fish migration, including formerly that of the tunny, which by its shimmer is said to have accounted for the name ' Golden Horn '. Yet these eastern fisheries until recent Russian exploitation have been highly localised in a few shallow localities, the deltas of the Volga and Danube and their vicinity, together with the Sea of Azov, although the steep western coast of the Caspian is a source of herring, and one-quarter of the total landings of this fish in the U.S.S.R. lately came from the Caspian. Coastal submergence and wave-work on the northern and western coasts of the Black Sea have produced great lagoons—the limans— which vary in salinity and fostered local fishing ; this was started in some places by ancient Greek colonists, then resumed by the different European settlers in the eighteenth century, and is no doubt now under active promotion. In all these cases the prime object is the capture of the typical migrant fauna, for which the Russians earlier depended on the rivers, above all the large sturgeons (*Acipensa sturis* and *stellatus*), but also their small relative, the sterlet, and the cat-fish of eastern Europe. The inland run of sturgeon in the spring results in huge catches, and the conserved product including the black caviar is most valuable; the latter is a monopoly of the Russians since it is they who developed the fisheries in the delta of the Danube. In recent years, too, they have modernised methods of all fisheries, for instance by placing trawlers on the Caspian and building preserving factories, while the whole industry is organised collectively in *kolkhozy*. This applies to the Atlantic and the inland fisheries as well ; the former of these awaited the greatest development, since those of the lower Volga and Caspian till recently provided some 40 per cent of the total landings of the U.S.S.R.

From the foregoing it is evident that the resources of the southern seas are found in only a small part of their area and that there has been no great extension of fishing grounds in modern times. In consequence the small fishing community continues to be characteristic of these coasts, and fishing remains a part-time occupation to a much greater extent than is now the case on the coasts of the Atlantic.

ATLANTIC FISHERIES

The peoples of the Atlantic fringe have always been accustomed to sea fish as an essential part of their diet, although those who could eat it fresh were limited in the past to a narrow coastal belt ; on the other hand salted or cured fish was carried far inland by routes that are partly now deserted but still marked by names such as ' herring road '. Thus with a long tradition at least of inshore fishing some of these peoples have been pioneers of other seafaring, and they have led in colonisation overseas. Perhaps the chief nursery of sailors has been the North Sea with its vast supplies of herring and other species, while pursuit of the cod to Iceland and Newfoundland greatly developed navigation of the high seas. The Atlantic fishing grounds lie almost exclusively upon the continental shelf and the upper parts of the continental slope. Throughout the shallower and nearer tracts of the shelf the hidden relief was well known long before the existence of systematic surveys, for cod and other demersal fishes were caught by the long many-hooked line that reached bottom ; so the rich nomenclature of the sea-bed, in several languages, is a by-product of historic fisheries.

Herring and cod are by far the leading species in the Atlantic fisheries, amounting together to about two-thirds of the total weight taken as well as that of the catch landed in each of the countries from France northward ; the reasons for this are their relative abundance and their suitability for preservation, chiefly by salting but also by curing. The modern increase in the catch of herring in the North Sea and in the taking of white fish from much wider areas should be regarded as stages in a long evolution due mainly to the Dutch, English, French, Norwegians, Portuguese and Scots ; the part played by the other nations was either more local or much later. It is not without reason, too, that large numbers of English words relating to ships and sailing are derived from Dutch, since Holland by the seventeenth century had probably evolved more types of small vessel and rigging than any other country. The herring fishery of the western North Sea was developed mainly by the Dutch, English, Scots and French, and the rivalry between the first two in the narrow sea between them led to war. But the Norwegians had ample shoals off their own coasts, and their fishery is still distinct ; these two areas remain the chief sources of herring.

The search for cod, pursued along with that for whales, led the explorers from the British, French and Iberian coasts northward to the most prolific seas near Iceland, and so to the Grand Banks off Newfoundland ; but the first experience of rich harvests of cod was gained on the Dogger Bank of the North Sea, still a great source of white fish. Voyages extended thence by the Shetlands and Faeroes to the Icelandic grounds in the fifteenth century. Meanwhile the Portuguese had sampled the Newfoundland Banks before 1500, and during the next century these attracted cod-fishers from England, France and the Basque Provinces ; and so began a new form of life, called ' the great fishery ' by the French, that has persisted in these two regions. Each spring fleets of schooners have sailed from European ports, carrying small boats from which lines are laid throughout the season, to return with their preserved catch in the autumn. But the system has now declined in importance ; with transatlantic colonisation British sailings ceased, and even those from France are much reduced, although in 1939 there were still some fifty Portuguese schooners on the Grand Banks, and with them were trawlers from France and Spain. However, it is more convenient to fish these grounds from America, with fresh cod as the product, and Newfoundland probably will soon cease to figure as an outlier of Europe in this respect. None the less, the yearly international assemblage on the Banks will remain an interesting historical fact, and the social effects of this systematic migration can be traced in many seaports from Dunkirk to Lisbon. Although the French ' great fishery ' has declined similarly in Icelandic waters, these provide for a very different story, which belongs to the revolution in European fisheries brought about by technical progress. Up to this period deep-sea fishery was mainly directed to herring, caught with nets in the western North Sea, and to cod taken with the long-line in the northern part of this sea and along the Scoto-Icelandic Ridge to Iceland, while similar netting of mackerel and line-fishing for hake and other demersals was practised to west and south of the English Channel. Coastal fishing, too, was widespread, worked from small open boats ; and this was the case even in Norway, for despite the very large proportion of the population engaged, fishing was a part-time occupation, as indeed is still the case to a large extent ; neither the shoals of herrings and sprats nor the migrating cod have to be followed far by the Norwegians, since the fish make seasonal entries to coastal waters. Thus the Atlantic stage was set for a revolutionary change that was to provide the rapidly growing population of Britain and industrial Europe with the palatable protein-food needed to supplement the produce of agriculture. The means were forthcoming by the inventions mentioned earlier in this chapter, and Britain was the natural leader in the campaign for the mass production of fresh fish. Variants of the beam-trawl, which had long been used in Devon, were the new instruments, and the steam trawler was quickly evolved and its range gradually extended ; so the continental shelf came to be known in all its variety. Britain led also in the commercial organisation of the fish traffic at a reduced number of favoured ports, and with the change from line-fishing to steam-trawling small enterprise had to give place to large. In the herring industry there was also a reduction in the number of ports, but, since the steam-drifter is a small vessel and the auxiliary motor came to the aid of still smaller craft, the fishermen were able to benefit more directly from their own investments of capital. In all these developments the British lead was followed by the other nations around the North Sea, and more recently by Iceland.

The North Sea remains the principal source of fish for the countries around it, and will doubtless continue so if the nations can agree to proper restraint ; it yields the demersal fishes throughout the year, and herring mainly in summer. Great Britain has a great advantage in regard to the herring, since the main shoals are near enough to allow vessels to bring their catch to port daily. The fish are at their best before spawning, and various ' races ' appear successively in this condition from May near the Hebrides, through June around the Northern Isles, and then southwards to reach the vicinity of East Anglia early in October. The herring are caught in drift-nets by night when swimming near the surface ; by day, when they have retired to the bottom, they are taken by trawling, so practised as to avoid catching the ground-living demersals, a method used more by foreign than by British crews. When the steam-drifters of several nationalities are assembled in these western waters ten thousand miles of drift-nets may well be in action at once ; these are suspended from groups of ships at the bows so as to form a vertical wall several miles long across the course of the shoals, and the herring are enmeshed by the gills. The catch is often enormous, so the British ports are gradually being equipped to avoid the risk of waste following a glut by the immediate reduction of the surplus into products such as oil and animal fodder. Only in Britain and Norway do fresh herrings have a great market. The main purpose of the fishery is to provide for later consumption of salted herring in barrels throughout the continent. The British herring ports are therefore very active during short periods, and a notable feature is the migration of the Hebridean girls, skilled gutters and packers, who travel to various ports after the early season at Stornoway is over, and end their labours at Yarmouth and Lowestoft.

The industry in the Irish Sea is most active in September, and in the English Channel, which is now the chief source of herring for France, during the following three months. But neither these seas nor the Baltic Sea are to be compared with the coastal waters of Norway and those of Iceland. In Norway there are three distinct seasons: first, the winter fishing outside the skerries from Cape Stat northward to latitude 65°; next, the spring season on the west coast south of this cape, when the herring come inshore to spawn; finally, the advent of fresher water from the Baltic causes the adult herring to disappear, while the young, called 'fat-herring', move north and provide for the autumn fishing inshore, all the way from Aalesund to beyond Tromsø. In Iceland there are two herring seasons, the greater in summer along the northern coast, and the lesser, during spring in the western gulf, the Faxa Bay, and this reflects the seasons of the white-fishing that are still to be mentioned.

The proportions of herring in the landings of fish by the Atlantic countries, less the U.S.S.R., from the chief areas in 1938 and in 1946 were as follows: North Sea, 64 per cent and 59 per cent; Norwegian Sea, 13 per cent and 13 per cent; Iceland, 9 per cent and 12 per cent. The place taken by the herring in the total catch of the Atlantic countries in these two years was 39 per cent and 32 per cent respectively. Mention should be made here of the special Scandinavian interest in the sprat or brisling. This small pelagic fish is taken by seine in summer, when it abounds in the southern fiords, and is used for canning in oil; thus it competes with the sardine of southern waters, but the canned output of the latter is from four to eight times larger.

Turning now to the demersal fisheries, we find that the 'great fishery' of Iceland and Newfoundland has a Scandinavian counterpart in northern Norway. Migrant cod begin to appear off the Norwegian coast in winter, and from Stavanger numbers increase with latitude until the water about the Lofoten Islands seethes with fish, and so onwards around the North Cape. Hence in the Arctic darkness vast numbers of craft come to the snow-clad Lofotens, from large schooners with their dories to half-decked boats, and, ashore, multitudes of huts have their tenants, who come from a long range of coastal settlements, together with others such as Lapps and even Finns travelling overland. The fishermen number from 12,000 to over 30,000, and the cod landed from ten to over forty millions in the season, which lasts from January to April. Less spectacular but equally important is the migration to the farther Finnmark, which indeed owes its colonisation in the nineteenth century mainly to the cod; the season here is from February to June.

These fisheries have been described separately because of their seasonal character; but the Norwegian Sea is fished continuously by large trawlers from other countries, since the demand for fresh fish persists throughout the year and is still increasing, especially in Britain where it is oldest and most general. The British trawling activities are therefore organised so that the smaller ships fish in the nearer seas and the larger in distant waters. The other nations have followed this lead, and the German fisheries, fostered energetically by the state, were served in a similar way, with the larger trawlers eventually reaching the farthest grounds; by 1938 Germany took third place for the amount of fish landed, including herring. The Second Reich inherited no maritime tradition, so not only had the industry to be virtually created but also the taste for sea fish, except near the coast. Thus by 1913 the annual consumption per head had reached 5 kg. or 11 lb., and by 1938, 12 kg. or 26·4 lb., but this amount was exceeded in Britain and Norway; and all the time the latter countries were exporting large amounts of salt herring to Germany as well as to Russia. In catching herring the Germans use separate fleets for drift-netting and for trawling, and as in Britain the demersal trawling is quite distinct. But Holland, Belgium and France, being farther from the grounds, found it economic to build vessels suited to all purposes and taking both herring and white-fish according to the season. Distance from the source of fish again is reflected in the composition of the catch; French, Belgian, Dutch, Danish and Swedish boats bring the varied produce of the North Sea, including the valuable plaice from the southern part, and this applies also to the smaller English and German vessels. Cod and haddock are landed in greater quantity by those fishing the northern part, and these species along with whiting mark the Scottish landings. Then throughout the Norwegian Sea it is cod, haddock and saith (or coalfish) which dominate, while halibut in this sea and plaice in the Barents Sea are additional attractions in the far north-east. Beyond the Shetlands to the Faeroes and Iceland the tale is similar, and modern takings near the latter are so important as to require renewed mention of this island. During the period of line-fishing from foreign schooners the Icelanders had confined their efforts to small boats; but it was inevitable that a people having such small resources on land should develop the new methods on their own account. Hence, as a result of commercial enterprise they now lead in these fisheries, and Iceland took fourth place in the total Atlantic catch in 1938, and again in 1948. No country in the world is now so dependent upon fishing, and this is evident in the recent movement of settlement from the interior to the coast, whereas in Britain activity becomes concentrated in fewer seaports. The weight of fish landed in 1938 per head of the population was nearly four tons compared with about one-half ton in the case of Norway, where fisheries play the next largest part in the national economy. In addition to this Icelandic vessels make landings in British ports. It will be recalled that there is a strong contrast between the marine conditions to south and north of Iceland (cf. Chapter 3), and the currents and drifts play a large part in the life of the fishes. The majority spawn in the warmer water of the west and south-west ; then the fry along with rich plankton drift around the island clockwise, and mature fish follow the same course later. Consequently the spring fishing, including that for herring, takes place off the west and south-west coasts and extends along the south coast in May and June ; and three-fifths of the cod are taken between January and June. Then, following the drift mentioned, the fishing for herring and demersals alike moves to the north of Iceland, where white-fish are caught until December. As in other northern waters cod, saith and haddock predominate, with plaice and halibut among the valuable species ; the livers of halibut and redfish are a source of medicinal oil, which, however, is far exceeded by that of cod liver. The market for these oils is of course shared by Norway.

It will now be clear that an essential element in the modern fishery is the specialised commercial seaport provided with ample space for ships, with means of supplying these and dealing fully with their catch, and with adequate railway connection. In each country a few such fishing ports now predominate greatly. In Britain by far the greatest are Grimsby and Hull on the Humber, both trawler ports and with the former devoted almost entirely to fish. Before the second war these were matched by two on the Weser, Wesermunde and Bremerhaven, and two on the Elbe, Hamburg-Altona and Cuxhaven. Ports of the second rank in respect of their landings comprise, in Britain, the great herring ports, Yarmouth and Lowestoft, and the third and fourth white-fish ports, Aberdeen and Fleetwood, as well as the leading port of France, Boulogne, and of the Netherlands, IJmuiden. In the third class Britain has six ports on the east and two on the west coast.

The prosperity of various ports however is subject to rather rapid change, and so their order in importance. But apart from those of Iceland and Norway the railway services form an element in maintaining economic position ; in Britain the trade in fresh fish is aided by special fish-trains throughout the year from Aberdeen and Fleetwood southwards ; in France similarly from Boulogne and several western ports to Paris, with traffic facilities for southern towns also, while daily trains from the main German ports reach Switzerland and Austria.

SOUTHERN ATLANTIC FISHERIES

The fisheries of Spain and Portugal and those of France not already mentioned take place nearer to the coast, since the continental shelf is relatively narrow. They depend too upon different species ; herring, only in the northern part, pilchard (or sardine), mackerel and tunny are the chief pelagic fishes ;

among the demersals hake replaces cod in importance, while brill, with the flat-fishes sole and turbot are common. The pelagic fisheries are seasonal, whereas the white-fishing, which deals mainly with sedentary species, goes on throughout the year and is organised as in Britain according to distance from port. Thus, for example, the French fishermen are most devoted to the Channel, the tract between Brittany and Ireland and the Bay of Biscay, but the large trawlers visit the coasts of Morocco and Mauritania as well. Among the pelagics most of the pilchards of France and Portugal are destined for canning, and likewise the large tunny when chopped up ; this fish is caught by the French on long-lines throughout the summer. The presence of herring in the Channel allows the same boats to follow them from October to February and then turn to mackerel and certain white-fish as well ; but the French sardine fishery is distinct and goes on from May to November along the entire coast between Ouessant (Ushant) and the Spanish frontier.

A small part of the fish landed in Spain comes, mainly to San Sebastian, from trawling and line-fishing on far northern banks ; so the high-seas tradition of the old Basque whalers is continued. In Portugal, too, schooners still bring enough cod from Newfoundland to constitute an important fraction of the national food, and Lisbon trawlers range along the African seaboard. But most of the fish taken by the Spaniards and Portuguese are caught within sight of land. Spain derives at least four-fifths of her fish from the Atlantic ; sardines take the lead by weight, but value depends more upon the large and the small hake and the tunny. The latter is taken both in the Bay of Biscay and in the south, mainly in fixed nets, from Cape St Vincent to Cadiz, where it is absent only from November to January and most plentiful during a double migration, to and from the Mediterranean, between May and August. The Iberian sardine fisheries are widely known from the Portuguese canned product which dates only from 1880, and was developed to take advantage of the failure, for eight years, of the French fishery. But the Spanish, and especially Galician, landings are about as great. Consequently large numbers of people around the north-western corner of the Peninsula are engaged in canning as well as drying sardines. The various types of lagoon fishing already described in regard to the Mediterranean are practised in south-western France, Portugal and Andalusia. Indeed the Ria de Aveiro, south of the Douro, has been described as ' the chief nursery of fishermen and sailors ', surely a notable distinction in view of the Portuguese contribution to exploration.

Never in history has the harvest of sea-fish possessed greater importance for Europe, since it is unlikely that the other protein-foods can be made to meet the needs of the population. It is, therefore, disquieting to find evidence of decline in the supply of fish. During the two world wars the North Sea was largely immune from fishing so, as was expected, the weight of the catches in the years immediately following each war was abnormally great, only to decline in each case to a level lower than that taken before the war. Thus it is clear that the fish do not now have time to mature fully and so further diminishing returns are in prospect. It is necessary therefore to reduce the intensity of fishing, and especially to prevent the taking of immature fish. But this can be done only with the fullest co-operation of governments and more thorough supervision of fishing by their own nationals; and this can surely be attained in time, even if selfishness that can do great harm may not be completely eliminated. More immediately it would be possible to get more food from the sea if a taste could be developed for some of the many species that are so far unknown on the table, and in particular for those which are abundant, such as the redfish of the northern seas. Meanwhile the fisheries owe much to international collaboration on the scientific side, although not all the nations concerned are participants. Unfortunately agreement has been less obvious in respect of territorial waters, and this has led to the frequent arrest of foreign vessels held to be trespassing in waters forbidden to them.

The shores of the Atlantic yield various products other than fish, especially ' shellfish ', a term covering both molluscs and crustacea, and the seaweeds. Before the development of trawling vast quantities of molluscs, especially mussels, were needed for baiting the long-lines, and gathering them between the tide-marks took up much of the fisher-folk's time. The mussel is still of local importance for bait; moreover in France and elsewhere it is cultivated for food. The other mollusc of commerce is the oyster from which a great revenue is obtained. Unlike the mussel it is now rarely taken from natural grounds, except in Portugal, since most of these have been destroyed by fishing or other human activities. So while many of the sites of oyster culture have been natural beds in the past, usually inlets with salinity slightly lower than the average, the process of rearing the oyster may perhaps be compared in its specialisation with the growing of orchids. This industry flourishes in the Thames estuary and neighbourhood, but it has its greatest development in France which has by far the largest output, with centres along the Channel west of the Seine and again on the Biscayan coast to the Gironde. This is the limit of the northern species (*Ostrea edulis*), but the lagoon of Arcachon has also been a great producer since the Portuguese species (*Ostrea angulata*) was introduced. This oyster is still taken from its natural haunts which cover a large part of the Tagus estuary and other inlets.

The larger crustacea, the lobsters and crabs, resemble the oyster from the commercial point of view; they are valuable delicacies which have to be eaten fresh, and must therefore reach the market alive. They are not cultivated, however, but are caught upon rocky shores in submerged traps and creels. Unfortunately many of the coasts most suitable for the lobster are not well served by railways, so transport requires organisation. The industry, however, is often a subsidiary occupation either of fishermen or small farmers.

From ancient times the greater seaweeds have been gathered and spread upon neighbouring fields as manure, a source of enrichment especially in potash. They have also been dried and burned to produce this substance for other purposes from the ash or kelp ; this kelp, too, was for long the only source of iodine. These uses have never greatly depleted the supply of the plants, much of which is served naturally to the farmer when thrown up by storm-waves. The kelp industry in general has declined with the opening of the great deposits of potassium salts and the production of iodine from Chile saltpetre. It had been known for over sixty years that seaweeds contain alginic acid before this was put to industrial use in Britain for a variety of purposes, including the making of fibres for textiles. But the industry is in its infancy and it remains to be seen to what extent the vegetation may be removed without harm to the associated animal life.

INLAND FISHERIES

The fishing of rivers and lakes is almost universal, but in few parts of Europe is the yield adequately recorded, and it is thus impossible to assess the nutritional value of the fresh-water fishes throughout the continent. But there are records for Germany before War World II to show that inland fisheries, including the yield from systematic culture in ponds, equalled the sea fisheries in value, although producing less than half the weight of fish. It is certain, too, that all over the eastern plain the inland waters have provided a principal source of food ; thus it was estimated in Russia at the beginning of this century that there were some half-million fishermen on rivers and lakes, while several million peasants were thus engaged in their spare time. Certainly the produce was, and still is, an indispensable part of the Russian diet. In regard to western and central Europe there is unfortunately a factor with all too general application, the decline of fishery owing to pollution of the rivers by the discharge of untreated sewage and the still more poisonous effluents of many factories. Thus the incidence of pollution and elimination of the more edible fishes may be said to vary broadly with the density of urban population.

While it will not profit to pursue this subject from the economic standpoint, allusion should be made to angling as a pursuit. Here the use of the artificial fly upon tumbling waters comes to mind, but this sport is for the few. On the other hand a geographical fact of considerable social significance is the prevalence of the patient angler on the banks of sluggish rivers, canals and ditches throughout the plains of western Europe. The numbers of this legion are unknown, likewise the part it plays in national or regional economy ; but these leisurely fishermen are as typical of the landscape as the willows and poplars of the river banks.

Chapter 5

CLIMATE

THE main characteristics of climate in our region are determined by its extent in latitude and by the distribution of land and sea. From the first comes the length of daylight throughout the year and likewise the changing angle at which the sun's rays strike the Earth. If there were no surrounding seas latitude alone would also determine the temperature of the air and its movements. We need not pursue this speculation, but certainly Europe would have a much less favourable climate, with very great seasonal contrasts. Thus its position on the western margin is of prime importance, as is its virtual severance from Africa and southern Asia by arms of the ocean. This is important, first because of the different capacities of land and sea to gain and to lose heat, and secondly because in these latitudes the drift of the atmosphere is, in general, from west to east, thus allowing the maritime air to penetrate the lands at least during most of the year, with the exception of the southern deserts. We have seen that the annual variation in the temperature of the sea is small. The specific heat of water is nearly twice that of land, which means that it takes nearly twice as long for a water surface to be heated to a given temperature as it does for a surface of bare soil ; and the same is true in regard to loss of heat by radiation. Moreover the sea, and especially deep sea, is even move conservative of heat than this on account of its mobility by which surface layers are constantly being replaced from below. It follows then that the mean temperature and other qualities of the air vary both from south to north with latitude, and also with distance from the sea, that is chiefly from west to east, in which direction the 'continentality' is said to increase. It may be stated broadly that during the summer half-year the latitudinal influence prevails, while in winter the maritime continental contrast has the greater effect, at least in the west.

The unequal distribution of land and sea is responsible for distortion at all seasons of the parallel belts of temperature, pressure and so on that are to be expected on a uniform globe, and which are in fact a feature of the Pacific Ocean. Our northern mid-latitudes, from about 35° to 65°, form the theatre of a perpetual contest between gigantic masses of the air, that are to be described as ovals rather than belts, each having a distinct physical character and dominant movement. The contest, however, is not equally displayed over the whole region we are reviewing ; its effects are more continuously apparent over the ocean than the land ; they are apt to be most violent along the oceanic border, and especially during the winter half-year when the contrast of air temperature over sea and land is greatest. During this period part of northern Asia shows the lowest temperatures known, while those over the Norwegian Sea are only some 5° lower than they are in summer. Here, therefore, is the best example of opposition between the very cold, dense and almost stagnant air-mass in the east and the much warmer and mobile air-masses of the Atlantic. The steep gradients of temperature and pressure near the margin create great turbulence, and the battle of the air-fronts is at its height; the winds are strongest and most variable in their direction and source, and their upward movements bring much rain or snow. These fronts mark the moving boundaries or discontinuities of the different tongues of air meeting in the cyclonic depressions or ' lows ' that are the signs of turbulence. The tongues themselves emanate mainly as winds from air-masses whose main bodies lie afar, coming from varying directions across the ocean, and less frequently as continental air from the land; and they differ widely in temperature and humidity. Even the maritime air currents show considerable differences. At one time it is Arctic air coming directly from the Arctic Sea, at another Polar Maritime air from Greenland or farther west, and this will be modified in its quality according to the curving course of its passage over cooler or warmer ocean; or again, finally, Tropical Maritime air from the wide area around the Azores, the main bearer of warmth and moisture to the higher latitudes. The depressions in which pairs of these streams may meet and override one another, the warmer and lighter over the colder and denser, are associated with the main discontinuities or fronts along which their centres move in a general easterly or north-easterly direction. Thus the Arctic Front lies north of the Circle, and far north of it in winter except near Iceland. In winter the North Atlantic is divided between the Atlantic *Polar Front*, extending from Florida to Iceland and approximating to the zone of the Gulf Stream and Atlantic Drift, and the *Mediterranean Front*, along the line of the main axis of the Mediterranean Sea.

These then mark the normal courses of the winter storm-centres. But the fronts are not stationary, for just as the shape of individual depressions changes from day, to day, so the fronts of which they form parts move their position; but the major air-masses continue separate. Two of these through-out the year are nourished from above and while relatively stagnant send out air towards the various fronts, both being high-pressure areas west of Europe. The one is the vast source of Tropical air, the ' Azores High ' which is all-powerful in summer but reduced in winter; the other over Greenland and the Canadian Archipelago is the source of Polar air. In winter a third and much larger area of high pressure lies over northern Asia, the source, as already stated, of Polar Continental air which extends then as a wedge covering most of Europe. In summer the Intertropical air circulation exerts its influence upon southern Europe and the Asian bridge-lands. At this season there is a steady gradient of pressure towards the Intertropical Front then lying in about 10° N. on the Atlantic, ' the Doldrums', and across the broadest part of Africa. In the western part of the Mediterranean lands and the Sahara rotational deflection to the right produces the North-east Trade Winds ; but in the east the gradient is much more powerful and is directed toward the area of very low pressure lying between N.W. India and the outer Persian Gulf. Hence there is a widespread and steady movement of air, called Tropical Continental, following a south-eastward course, counter-clockwise, to take part in the great influx of the Indian Monsoon.

These vast movements of the atmosphere have been stressed because we are too apt to think of climate as something static, since it is described in terms of average value of temperature, rainfall and so on. But these averages really reflect the proportion of a period during which the different air-masses have held sway in a locality, and since the periods of their influence do not coincide with those of the calendar, our conventional reckonings lack some of the reality that is desirable. The fact that on the western seaboard few weeks elapse without the influence of a depression has led to the saying that ' Britain has no climate, but only weather '. This condition is certainly very different from that of the Azores, which lie permanently under Tropical Maritime air, or of Crete, where for at least three summer months hot dry weather with a northerly wind may be expected. So averages vary in the degree of their realism. In the present state of meteorology we cannot discard the traditional data of climate, but their use should be supplemented by recognition of the sequences of weather which are characteristic of a district or a season.

It is unfortunate that hitherto students of climate and biology have shown little co-operation, with the result that many of the elements of climate which must affect the life of plants and animals have not been studied adequately, and very few data that are likely to be significant have been worked out for Europe as a whole. It is therefore possible to note only in an all too general way the kind of controls which climate exerts upon life ; precision must await knowledge of the atmospheric conditions supported by many kinds of plant during each phase of the vegetative cycle, and similarly in the case of the life of insects and other short-lived animals. It may well be doubted whether plants can be expected to respond to the averages of the various climatic elements. Yet vegetation has been well described as the mirror of climatic complexities. In default of full climatic data of this kind which would serve in a sound classification of climates in relation to life it is reasonable to begin by studying the distributions of types of plant and of the associations of plants, and by correlating these with such atmospheric characteristics as are well known ; and this in fact has been done by Köppen, by Wissmann and others in recognising climatic regions throughout the world. But in acting in this way it is necessary to bear in mind that the vegetation has not only been

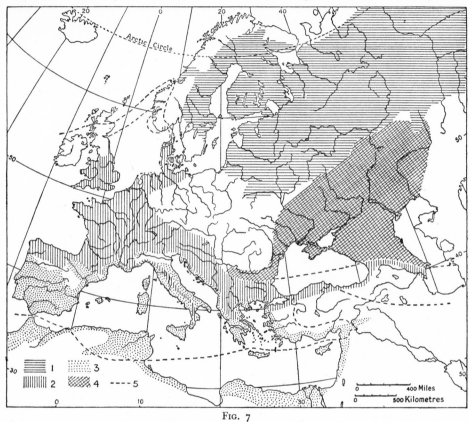

FIG. 7

Distribution of five groups of trees

1 Spruce without beech or Tatar maple   4 Tatar maple without 1, 2 or 3
2 Beech and holly without olive   5 Limit of holy where not otherwise shown
3 Olive without spruce and beech

For clarity, the westward extension of spruce, to the Alps, and the eastward extension of beech (without holly) to Poland, have been omitted

altered by man, but it has undergone progressive natural change in the past, ever since the end of the last Glacial Period.

During the last 120 centuries the northern ice-sheet has not extended beyond Scandinavia, and the more or less progressive peopling of Europe has gone on for perhaps sixty centuries. But it was at about 4000 B.C. that a revolutionary advance of civilisation took place in the Nearer East, and in Europe some fifteen centuries later. Now throughout the last 6,000 years

the margins of sea and land have changed materially and repeatedly, and
the climatic belts have shifted more than once, a fact that is best explained
by swing of the normal courses followed by atmospheric depressions.   The
vital consequences of such oscillations for all forms of life are being gradually
discerned by the botanist and the archaeologist, and some of their conclusions

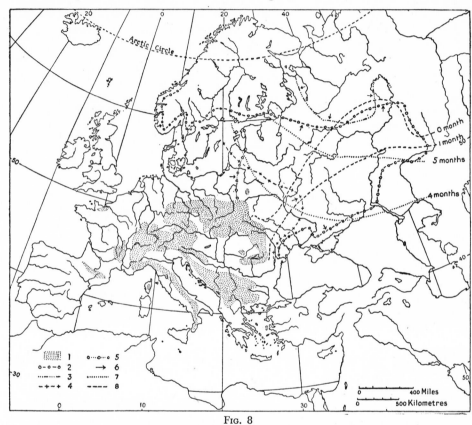

FIG. 8

Limits of certain trees ; data of temperature

1 Distribution of silver fir (*Abies alba*)
2 Partial limit of pedunculate oak
3 Partial limit of Siberian larch
4 Partial limit of hornbeam
5 Partial limit of yew
6 Direction of advance of species
7 Limits of area where mean temperature is 32° F. or 0° C. for 4 or 5 months
8 Limits of area where mean temperature attains 68° F. or 20° C. for less than one month.

will be referred to in due course.   But it is clear that, as the present types
of climate became established, the land was reoccupied progressively by
plants and animals adapted to them.   This implies a general advance of many
species from their Ice-Age refuges remote from the glaciers ; hence, the
character of the flora and its distribution must be regarded as still subject to
alteration, quite apart from the interference of man and his domestic animals.

Yet, while making due allowance for this, we may regard the present distribution of individual species of plants as a valuable index to the prevalence
of the various types of climate. This is even more true of the associations of
plants, the main types of vegetation (Chapter 8), since the present extension
of individual species is partly the result of the opportunities each species has
had to spread in particular directions. Nevertheless the extension of plant
species can tell us much about the climate and especially about temperature,
if the species be suitably selected. Fig. 7 shows limits of range, and certain
combinations in distribution of five kinds of tree, viz : spruce, a narrow-
leafed evergreen ; holly and olive, broadleaved evergreens ; beech and Tatar
maple, broadleaved deciduous trees. The olive is shown as cultivated, the
others in their natural habitats ; e.g. the beech has been introduced into
Ireland and Scotland. Three of the trees are clearly favoured by climates
prevailing respectively in the north-east (spruce), the east (Tatar maple), the
south (olive), while beech and holly are suited to a climate that seems to
extend from the Atlantic in a wedge to the Black and Caspian Seas. Fig. 8
shows that the Siberian larch has a more limited distribution than the spruce,
and this deciduous conifer is evidently adapted to the more extreme form
of the boreal type of climate. From the same map it will be seen that Leningrad
lies just within the limit of the oak, which has a wedge-shaped distribution
in Russia, avoiding the extremes of the two types of continental climate. We
may now examine the climatic environments of these trees by considering
two of the obviously important elements, temperature and rainfall, and see
whether they may be taken as good indexes of four contrasted climates which
interlock over Europe. Fig. 9 shows the mean monthly temperature and
precipitation for places within the regions of the several trees. These graphs
give a general idea of the length of the growing season, and the probable
amounts of heat and water available during that period. Most plants are
inactive where the temperature is below 43° (F.), below 50° indeed they grow
little, and the rate of growth depends upon the excess of temperature above
this, to be measured from these graphs in month-degrees. Adequate water
also must of course be available for the plant to permit growth.

At Leningrad the growing season lasts only five months, during which the
excess temperature accumulated up to September is 66° ; the graph, of course,
fails to record the advantage of long days in the warm season, nearly nineteen
hours at midsummer. Moisture is adequate, since the water hoarded as snow
melts just as growth starts, and this is followed by a rainfall of 9.4 inches in
four months. These conditions are tolerable for coniferous, but barely so for
most of the broadleaved trees. At Saratov the growing season is slightly
longer, and with the excess of temperature at 109° growth is so rapid as to allow
a deciduous tree to complete its life-cycle in an abnormally short period. The

limiting factor is aridity, for even with water hoarded as snow the amount is insufficient to support unbroken woodland, and trees such as Tatar maple are helped by ground-water in valleys and hollows. At Paris the excess temperature is similar, but the growing season is over seven months in length ; rainfall is less concentrated in summer and in the prolonged autumn ; and

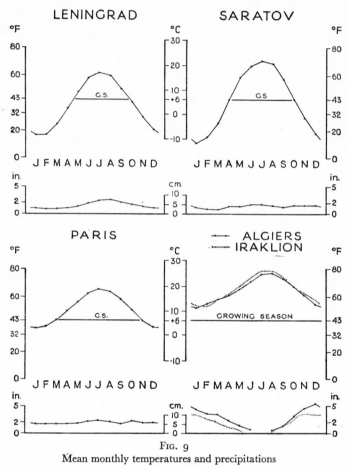

FIG. 9
Mean monthly temperatures and precipitations

these conditions become more moderate westwards to the coast. At the two Mediterranean stations there is abundant heat throughout the year, but lack of water virtually prevents growth during some three months at Algiers and five in Crete, and these are the months of highest temperature.

Thus in relation to plant life there are continental climates of two types, both with winter too cold : in the northern region, with a cool summer and moderate rainfall, growth is sufficient for narrow-leaved trees and a small number of deciduous species ; the southern, with a hot summer and little rain, just permits of deciduous broadleaved species, but it is more favourable to grasses and other herbaceous plants. The west-maritime climate is marked, on the Atlantic fringe, by even and moderate conditions to which a wide range of plants is adapted and some are limited ; this climate shows its influence in varying degrees right across southern Europe to the Caspian shores, because of the near presence of warm seas. The Mediterranean type on the other hand is characterised by aridity in the hot season, and to this all the plants are adapted.

The graphs, of course, tell nothing of the variations due to ordinary changes of weather. Still less do they tell of abnormal fluctuations, and an example of this kind will serve to emphasise the adaptation of plants to average conditions. During February 1947 there was a quite unusual outflow of Polar continental air, and the British Isles were subject to strong east wind bringing heavy snow, and then to a calm spell with remarkably dry and cold air. Many plants were killed, and the damage was most widespread among such evergreen shrubs as broom, gorse and holly, all of which belong to the maritime Atlantic fringe, and are presumably least fitted to resist prolonged boreal influences.

The mountains of south-central Europe form the only continuous habitat of the silver fir (*Abies alba*) and the distribution (Fig. 8) of this tree serves to remind us that in this area, owing to relief, the main climatic influences corresponding to the facets of Europe do not merge gradually as is the case on the plain. It may be said either that there is a distinct mountain climate there, or that ' mountain ' varieties of the three main types meet in this high region. The continental climate, as we have seen, appears in two main variants. The other types are less easily divisible when only mean temperature and rainfall are considered.

The southern mountains of Europe form very real climatic boundaries that are strongly reflected in the distributions of various forms of life. On the other hand both north and south of the mountains there is marked uniformity over great distances. In the south the sea is the unifying influence ; in the north from the Atlantic to the Ural Mountains there is no serious obstruction to movement of air or life. But with the widening of the lowland and growing distance from oceanic influence, the climate becomes more continental. Yet although gradual transition is the main feature, there are two transverse zones at which the change becomes somewhat more abrupt. The first of these marks the heights extending from the Central Plateau of France by the Jura to the Ardennes ; the second coincides nearly with the basin of the Vistula, and the cause of its existence may be traced to the increased breadth of the lowland beyond it as the Baltic Sea and the Carpathian Mountains diverge, northward and southward respectively. The significance of this zone may be shown, first by reference to the freezing of the Vistula. It is frozen over at Warsaw, for sixty days per annum, but this average has little meaning, since the period varies widely as compared with the mean periods of freezing for the rivers farther east. Again the zone stands out as marking the eastward limit of the beech, while those of the yew and the hornbeam lie not far beyond this (Fig. 8) : so three important trees with oceanic affinities disappear. On the much broader lowland in Russia the contrast between the two types of continental climate becomes more and more real towards the east. This is evident from the crossing of the isothermal lines, such as those drawn here to show

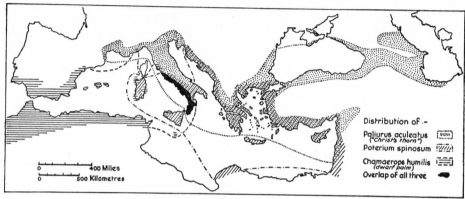

FIG. 10
Distribution of three perennials

periods of heat in summer and cold in winter. The tendency for plant limits to run parallel to seasonal isotherms is thus sufficiently illustrated, but it does not follow that the temperatures chosen, as having general climatic significance, are necessarily the critical ones for plant life. Indeed it is likely that the length of growing season is more important, and this will be discussed later.

Turning now to the Mediterranean Basin, we find remarkably uniform temperature prevailing ; on the other hand there are notable differences in the amount and the monthly incidence of rainfall. This is probably one of the reasons for the restriction of many plants to the eastern and western basins respectively, as seen, for example, in the distribution (Fig. 10) of three common perennials all adapted to resist the aridity of summer ; comparison may be made with the climatic map of aridity (Fig. 11), which, however, is based on averages for the whole year. In the east two very thorny shrubs are shown : *Paliurus* or ' Christ's Thorn ' is the more widely spread and extends to the Caspian Sea (cf. beech and holly) in a more rainy and humid climate than the other shrub, the stividha *Poterium Spinosum*, seems able to tolerate. In the west the dwarf palm—the only European palm—extends into the territory of the other two only in southern Italy. Along with such suggestions of climatic control it is well to bear in mind the possibility that the distributions have been determined by former land connections rather than by present climatic conditions.

With the increase and spread of mankind the natural vegetation has been

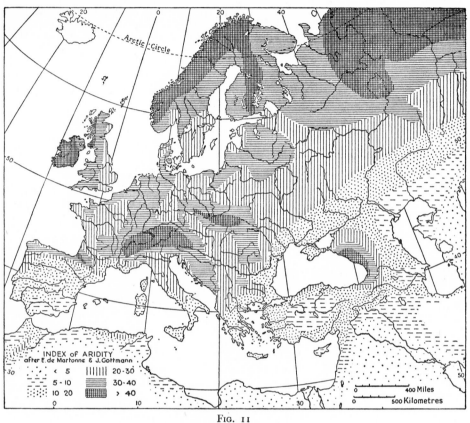

Fig. 11
Climatic map of aridity
The figures give the average annual rainfall in inches

altered and largely replaced. The growth of selected indigenous plants has been encouraged at the expense of others : e.g. succulent grasses for fodder in place of natural forest ; and other plants have been carried, in cultivation, far from their ancestral homes. The outstanding example of this is the cereals, which, derived from grasses native in the semi-arid south-east, have been so modified by man that they are now grown mainly under quite different types of climate. For every species of plant, however, there are climatic limits, and those of the cultivated crops will be examined later in some detail. But the governing fact of most general application is the length of the season during which temperature is high enough, and available water sufficient for growth and reproduction. Thus the temperature, of soil and air, and the amount of rainfall or melted snow in the growing season are the most important elements of climate ; and happily they are the best known. But the amount of evaporation, the relative humidity of the air, direct sunshine, strength of wind, incidence of frost during the growing season, all have their effect. Furthermore, climate is usually measured by averages, but the farmer is concerned with individual seasons ; hence, in assessing the worth of a region for agriculture, reliability must be borne in mind.

At this point it is necessary to examine some of the results of prolonged observation of the various climatic elements and the chief consequences of their interaction. We may begin by referring again to the blanket of dense air that forms over northern Asia in winter, when the loss of heat by radiation is greatest, with very long nights and a low sun by day. These conditions exist in Europe also, although the area is much less and the somewhat inert blanket extends, as already mentioned, in wedge-shaped form along the continental axis to central France, while a small separate mass covers the Iberian tableland. But the wedge narrows, the air becomes less cold and less dense and its boundaries more subject to change as they are involved in the disturbed maritime circulation. The European winter, then, is hard and continuous where, and so long as, this stable air-mass is in control. A fair measure of its effectiveness may be gained from the map showing the average period in which the ground is covered by snow (Fig. 12). But it is necessary to bear in mind that mountains, from their height and exposure, hold their snow longer—permanently in parts of the Alps, Caucasus and west Norway—and also that the total snowfall differs greatly throughout Europe ; so this figure should be compared with a map of the annual precipitation. However, the trends and the relative closeness of these lines on the central and eastern plain are significant, especially perhaps the zone of rapid increase from 80 to 140 days. The distribution of mean temperature for January should also be noted here. In southern Europe and the Borderlands the isotherms lie from west to east ; in north-western Europe, from south to north ; and over Russia in curves concentric on Siberia. The isotherm 32° (F.) if there were no mountains would run south from the west coast of Norway and Sweden to bend eastward at about the Venetian plain : actually it thrusts westward to embrace the Central Plateau of France, and seems to be related to the limits of certain ' Atlantic ' plants such as the holly, mentioned above. Thus in winter the contrast between the inner and the outer climates is very great, for beyond the axial wedges the atmosphere is more turbulent than at any other season. Depressions come from the Atlantic in quick succession ; the largest and deepest tend to follow the north-eastward paths just beyond the continent, but smaller though still powerful disturbances on the fringes of the primaries push farther inland, in the west frequently but less so in northern Russia ; some centres enter the Mediterranean, passing either north or south of the Iberian Peninsula, to continue their progress eastward, and more of them form over one or other of the sea-basins. These southern depressions by their frequent presence account for the existence of the

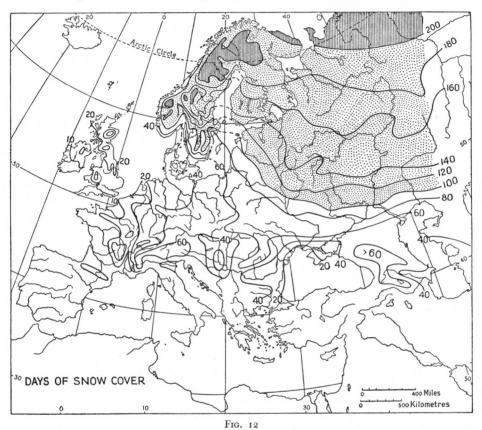

FIG. 12

trough of low pressure that then separates the European axial zone from the subtropical 'high' zone which, in winter, lies over the northern Sahara. It is scarcely comparable in size with the trough over Ireland and the Norwegian Sea, but the depressions themselves are vital as bringing the great bulk of the annual rain to the Mediterranean lands ; and this applies also to the Barbary Lands as well as to the Asian Bridgelands where, however, the storms are fewer and less effective.

It will be seen, then, that in winter the eastern core of Europe has steady

cold weather interrupted only occasionally by sharp oscillations of temperature
and strong winds when a depression passes to north or to south. The two
maritime fringes, in contrast, are marked by constant changes of weather.
These are most rapid on the Atlantic coasts, where also gales are most frequent
and the rainfall reaches its seasonal maximum between December and February.
Despite the periodic thrusts of Polar air the oscillations of temperature are
relatively slight and snow lies long only on the hills. Nevertheless when an
anticyclone forms and remains stationary the west margin gets a taste of continental conditions—an exceptionally severe case was mentioned above—and
such periods become more prolonged in the central part of the European Plain.
This region has therefore been said to have a number of ' little winters ' of the
Russian type, often with clear calm weather, when radiation leads to very hard
frost ; other calm spells bring fog, and their appearance is more common in the
northern part of the plain and in the basin of the Elbe than anywhere else.
But the hard spells are separated by mild windy weather when thaw and rainfall ensue, an event which often brings about floods in the valleys.

In the Mediterranean Lands intricate coastlines and high relief lead to
great contrasts within small distance, especially in the amount of rainfall.
But all the coastal lowlands share in the mildness of the average winter temperature, for while cold air from the north forms the rear of each depression,
it is very quickly replaced by a warmer current. Throughout half the year such
disturbances follow the seas and the lands to the east, and their tracks avoid
the peninsulas where the air-pressure remains higher. The Iberian Peninsula,
at least from December to February, is crossed by an air-divide from south-west
to north-east from which the winds blow outwards. Similarly the Appennines,
Balkan highlands and northern Anatolia form similar, if less constant, reservoirs
of cold dry air ; a vigorous thrust of this from the Balkans may bring a ' cold
wave ' far up the Nile valley. Other supplies come from farther north, as by
the Rhone valley with its ' mistral ' wind, or over the Istrian saddle with its
' bora ', or again as an almost permanent north-west wind over the lower plains
of Romania to the Black Sea. Very different air-masses reach some of the
Mediterranean depressions as hot southerly winds from the Sahara, commonly
known as ' scirocco ' ; these initially very dry winds may become humid over
the sea.

In the Mediterranean regions the prevailing direction of wind in the winter
half-year is westerly, so there is ample opportunity for air, whatever its origin,
to acquire the moisture that is later partly precipitated in the depressions.
Rainfall is extremely heavy but usually much less prolonged than in the northern
regions, so a given amount is received on a very much smaller number of days.
The western basins see many more depressions than the eastern and, except in
the Black Sea, the northern coasts are affected more than the southern. The

western side of each of the peninsulas is the rain side. It is important to appreciate the manner of onset and recession of these southern rains, since the agricultural year depends upon them, and the accompanying map (Fig. 13), in its lower part, illustrates the advance by showing where average rainfall first attains 2 inches (50 mm.) in the months named. From this are seen the effects of Atlantic cyclones entering from the north-west in September or forming in

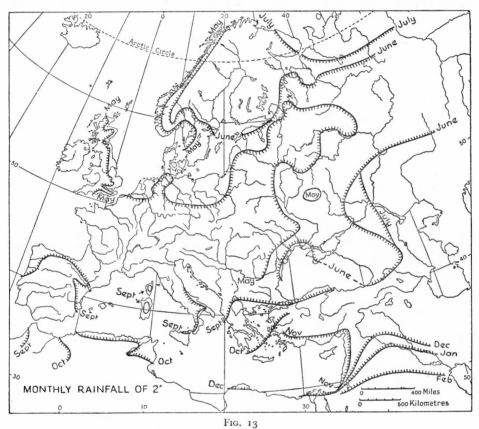

Fig. 13

Spread of rainfall in summer (north) ; in winter (south). The lines show mean isohyets of 2 in. (5 cm.) for the months named

the north and passing to the Black Sea. Then in October Tunisia and Greece are involved ; in November the Levant coasts ; in December the Egyptian coast and most of the Bridgelands ; but lower Iraq only in February. It may be stated generally that the rains recede in much the same way as they advance, and that vigorous cyclones appear in the spring only on the northern fringe. It is the southern edge and the eastern lands which receive the principal rainfall from December to February, the remainder having a more prolonged rainy season.

Let us turn now to the conditions governing the climate in the height of summer. All the lowlands on the African side and in Asia south of about 45° N. have mean temperatures exceeding 80° (F.). In Europe there is then the least difference in temperature between south and north, and the July mean for 50° lies near the Arctic coast ; the isotherms diverge slightly from the latitudes, the gradient perpendicular to them being generally from S.S.E. to N.N.W.

The atmospheric circulation, as already stated, is controlled by two vast systems of low pressure, the Icelandic and the Indo-Persian, upon which air must converge, together with the subtropical high-pressure area in the Atlantic centred near the Azores and then very pronounced between latitudes 35° and 40°. It may be noted that by joining these three centres by great circle arcs a narrow triangle is formed whose sides are as 3:8:9, the last representing *c.* 4,500 geographical miles. From the ' Azores high ' a wedge of high pressure extends through the Bay of Biscay, northern France and central Germany, and finally reaches central Russia in August. This zone of divergent air feeds a steady circulation to the south, and to the north it enters the Atlantic depressions which continue to arrive between Iceland and Britain, although weaker than those of winter. By May some of these can pass by a great circle track over Scandinavia to the Caspian and beyond, but as the ' high ' axis, just described, extends into Russia they follow more easterly paths into Siberia during July and August. Hence it comes about that throughout central and most of eastern Europe the most copious seasonal rainfall is that of the summer months, June to August ; hence, too, the fact that the changeable weather of the ' variable westerlies ' prevails over Europe north of the Mediterranean Lands. The presence of the dividing axis of high pressure does not mean the exclusion of moist oceanic air from central Europe, for the *prevailing* winds are westerly throughout the whole year and, as temperature rises, local turbulence increases and the ensuing thunderstorms greatly increase the precipitation due to other depressions. In north-western Europe, including the Baltic, spring is relatively dry ; in view of this and of the above account of cyclonic activity, it is interesting to note the manner in which the summer rains spread month by month towards the North and Baltic Seas as well as over Russia (Fig. 13, upper part).

The southern and south-eastern lands have high temperatures throughout the summer, accompanied by generally clear skies apart from dust and haze due to vertical movements over land in the afternoon. Severe thunderstorms however occur locally, and especially in the vicinity of mountains. Dryness of the air mitigates the effect of its heat for human beings, and it causes the high evaporation to which native plants are adapted, reducing their transpiration. On all coasts there is a sea breeze by day and a land breeze by night which reduce the discomfort of the inhabitants. All these features are related to the general air circulation which is marked by great regularity, in contrast to conditions prevailing in winter. The entire eastern basin and the Bridgelands beyond are under the influence of the summer monsoon directed to the south-east. These dominant northerly winds, the Etesians of the ancient Greeks and now with various names, vary little in direction but considerably in force ; there is a regular rhythm, weaker by night and stronger by day, while, on occasion, they rise to gale force causing high seas, but under a cloudless sky. The western Mediterranean is scarcely affected by this huge air system, for relative coolness over the sea creates a fairly constant anticyclone there from which the surrounding lands receive more or less on-shore winds : north or north-east in Algeria, east or south-east in Spain, west or south-west in Italy. Thus the Iberian Peninsula is seen to behave like a little continent with monsoonal inflow and outflow of air for periods of about three months, summer and winter respectively. These winds blowing on to land around the Mediterranean produce very little rain because, owing to the high temperatures on land, the air is ready to take up additional moisture. A separate wind system is found in the northern Adriatic from which a stream passes up the valley of the Po to cause the summer rainfall there which helps to distinguish the climate of this plain. Still more distinctive is the unique ' Pontic climate ' of the mountainous strip around the eastern part of the Black Sea. It is marked by its mild winters and hot humid summers and by rainfall throughout the year. The prevailing onshore winds are derived from depressions in winter, and these bring most of the rainfall ; but in summer the general monsoonal stream is strengthened and diverted at intervals by the presence of specially low pressures in eastern Transcaucasia.

Autumn and spring as transitional between the hottest and coldest seasons are naturally subject to considerable variations in character from year to year ; but it is always true that during autumn the contrast between ocean and continent is assuming preponderance over latitudinal influence ; and also that during spring the opposite applies. Furthermore, since temperature falls and rises much more slowly over sea than land, the onset of winter lags behind on the western margin, and so does the onset of summer. The isotherms for September, when reduced to sea-level, approximate closely to lines of latitude, and the actual average temperatures for London, Berlin, Warsaw and Saratov —similar in latitude—are all within a degree of 57° F. or 14° C. Yet by November the lines covering Germany, France and the British Isles already have a north-westerly trend, marking the increased contrast between margin and interior, with fine quiet conditions affecting the first of these and great turbulence the latter. The Atlantic depressions become larger and deeper and they bring heavy rains; around the North and Baltic Seas autumn is the season of greatest precipitation. It is also a period of great cyclonic activity in the north-western Mediterranean. Then, as in spring, rainy depressions traverse the Iberian Peninsula, while in the basin of the Po rain is particularly copious. It is notable, however, that inland from the western areas of relative warmth and great turbulence there is an area where autumn is a relatively cold and calm season; this embraces the central plateau of France and extends north-eastwards nearly to the south Baltic coast; the mean frost line for January lies in this zone. Again, high pressure and very clear weather mark the Danubian lands and most of the Balkan Peninsula.

The outstanding event of spring over most of Europe is the thaw, and this, of course, absorbs much of the solar energy before the soil and overlying air can be warmed; again the rivers, by bearing the cold melt-water to the ocean or seas, serve to keep down the surface temperature there. On the whole the land warms more quickly despite many recurrences of frost, and it does so owing to local heating rather than to the influx of maritime air; for, except on the southern margin, cyclonic activity is at its lowest. Along the northern side of the Mediterranean from Iberia to Anatolia depressions continue to form or pass, bringing their rain largely along with thunderstorms. Spring is the wettest season on the plateau of Iberia, in Bulgaria and inner Anatolia. On the other hand, throughout north-western Europe it is the driest season, especially around the North and Baltic Seas, where there is much calm weather with easterly winds; the fundamental cause of this is the relatively slight difference between the temperatures over sea and land.

At this point we should note how the average temperatures differ in the extreme months, for this mean annual range of temperature is the best measure of relative continentality in climate. On such a map the small range on the western seaboard is striking, with only 10° (18° F.) along the coast of Britain and at Cape St Vincent. On the shores of the western Mediterranean it is greater, 14° to 16° (25° to 29° F.). From northern France eastward on the plain the range increases rapidly at first, then steadily to about the longitude of Leningrad, where it is 24° (43° F.). There the gradient steepens and then evens out, but near the Urals the value exceeds 33° (60° F.). While this degree of continentality is not matched in the south the range is considerable in certain areas: in Iberia and Anatolia over 20° (36° F.); in northern Italy 24° (43° F.); in the Danubian lands as in Armenia over 26° (47° F.).

In the light of these descriptions of the seasons and the air-circulation, distributions for the whole year may be considered. The first is that of the total rainfall (not reproduced here), and the following are the more out-standing features of it. The increase of precipitation with altitude is most pronounced where mountains are near to regular tracks of depressions, and especially where they lie perpendicular to maritime winds; such mountains are the wettest areas, above all in Norway, western Britain and Ireland, the Dinaric mountains and western Caucasus, the Alps and Spanish Galicia. Next, apart from a few small areas in the Baltic lands and between the Elbe and the Vistula, western and central Europe receive more than 20 inches (50 cm.); but only the north-western part of Russia has this amount, the limiting isohyet running from central Finland and the central Carpathians to converge upon the Urals in the basin of the Oka. South-eastward rainfall decreases to under 5 inches in Transcaspia, but the Asian Bridgelands justify this name in respect of rainfall, as a wetter wedge inserted between two deserts. Their rainfall exceeds 20 inches on the steep coastal faces, and it is under 10 inches in only a few areas. About one-half of the Iberian Peninsula receives less than 20 inches, including the driest spot in Europe, Cape Gata, with about 4 inches. Across the Adriatic from the driest part of Italy where Foggia receives under 19 inches, the Dinaric summits record the highest rainfall of Europe, up to 180 inches (457 cm.). These exceptions serve to accentuate the great variety of the Mediterranean lands.

The other map showing average conditions for the year represents one of the attempts that have been made to integrate temperature with rainfall, and so to discover the relative effectiveness of the latter. It may seem odd that by this method, based on an index of aridity (Fig. 11), the low figures on the scale denote the most arid land, but this is unimportant.[1] The utility of the map may be questioned more seriously because it represents average yearly conditions and not those of the season of plant-growth. But since this period differs widely throughout the lands it would be difficult to con-struct a uniformly useful map on this basis. This map certainly has real significance in the south, from the degree in which it corresponds with the classification of land as fitted for agriculture without irrigation. In regard to the rest of Europe, the map is suggestive in several ways and, while the matter is too complex for discussion here, the aridity index may be borne in mind in relation to the length of the growing-season in northern Europe, as based on temperature alone (Fig. 14). This map represents an attempt

---

[1] The following formulae were used by E. de Martonne and J. Gottmann. The index of aridity is obtained from the ratio P : (T+10), where P is the precipitation in mm., and T the temperature in degrees C., 10 being added merely to avoid negative values. From this both the yearly index (A) and the index for the driest month (a) were obtained separately. These were then combined, by the formula $Y = \dfrac{Aa}{2}$, the purpose being to take account of the unequal distribution of rainfall.

to show two related distributions together. The lines and the figures written on the areas between them indicate the number of months during which the mean temperature exceeds 6° C. (43° F.), already mentioned as just allowing plants to grow. No doubt it differs slightly with the species, and a somewhat lower figure is sometimes adopted. The shadings indicate the amounts of temperature accumulated (in degrees C.) above this critical one, during the season, i.e. the period ending when the monthly temperature is again below 6°. This

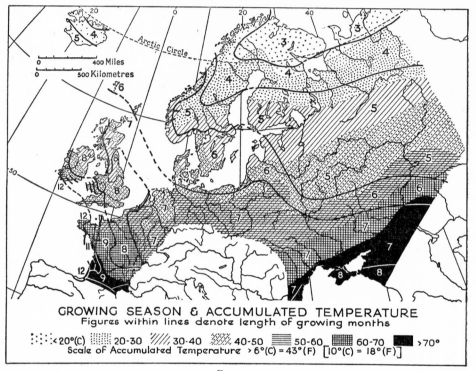

GROWING SEASON & ACCUMULATED TEMPERATURE
Figures within lines denote length of growing months
⋮⋮⋮ <20°(C) ▦ 20-30 ⟋⟋ 30-40 ▨ 40-50 ▤ 50-60 ▦ 60-70 ▉ >70°
Scale of Accumulated Temperature > 6°(C) = 43°(F) [10°(C) = 18°(F)]

Fig. 14

is, of course, rather a crude method, and for less general purposes a map based on daily averages would be required ; also on this scale it is impossible to show such distributions where relief is intricate, hence the blank area on the map.

The advantage of the Atlantic seaboard in the length of season stands out ; in this respect it resembles the lowlands of the Mediterranean. But the period shortens rapidly in the British Isles and France, from twelve to eight months. Most of central Europe has seven months, and on the eastern plain there is a decline northward to five months—in the same zone that showed a lengthening of the snowy period (Fig. 12). North of the great lakes the season drops to four, and then to three, months.

The zones of equal accumulated temperature are differently arranged—in arcs concentric on northern Scandinavia. Thus in the British Isles only the extreme tips have over 50° despite an unbroken period of growth, while on the central and eastern plain this figure is surpassed with a growing season that declines from seven to five months in length. In the course taken by this line 50° in central Europe, the maritime influence of the North and Baltic Seas may be detected.

We have now accumulated a considerable array of data with which to examine the suggestion made that there are at least four strongly marked types of climate in Europe, namely, two kinds of continental climate in the east, a West Maritime and a Mediterranean ; the existence of a central mountain type was also suggested. The first three, with the latter, must belong to the so-called ' Temperate Zone ', although the name is scarcely applicable to the continental climates, and the Mediterranean to the Subtropical Zone. However, the systematic classification of climates need not concern us ; its main purpose is to achieve a real basis for comparing climate the world over, and it is beyond the aim of this book to discusss the various climatic divisions that have been made. The fact is that the main climates generally merge into one another and the identification and the naming of several transitional kinds will not help our theme very much. All the authorities agree upon the suggested four-fold division, at least by implication, and they agree substantially about the sub-division of the southern regions, as well as the extreme north. But instead of following the climatologists farther let us return to the plants, this time as they have been grown in good seasons and bad by a long succession of peasant-farmers who have acquired and inherited between them a vast practical know-ledge of climate. Attention has often been drawn to the relationship of climate to predominant crops, and the subject was comprehensively treated at the end of the last century by T. H. Engelbrecht. In discussing his work much later, C. Troll argued, with much reason, that where a staple crop for food or fodder comes, after long trial, to prevail over another, this prevalence in the main rests on a climatic basis, even when allowance is made for human preference and the nature of the soil. Hence the special value of Engelbrecht's statistical mapping of crop-areas at a period which precedes the substantial changes effected during the present century ; for these are due largely to the breeding of new varieties fitted to withstand certain climatic excesses, such as cold or dryness or rainfall. Most of the facts displayed on Fig. 15, which is mainly after Troll, thus refer strictly to dates prior to 1900, but for convenience the present tense will be used in discussing them. Europe is divided into zones according to the dominance of the two bread-cereals, wheat and rye, and the three grains that are used chiefly as fodder, oats, barley and maize.   Thus, for example, oats are grown throughout most of Fennoscandia, but north of the ' oats zone ' this crop has a smaller area than barley ; and so throughout, the main divisions are lines along which two adjoining plants are in equilibrium. Barley matures during a shorter season than the other cereals and so succeeds

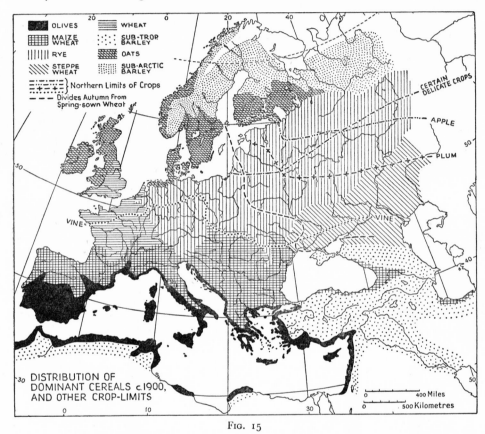

FIG. 15

both farther north, from cold, and farther south, from drought.   The subarctic zone, where the ' six-row ' variety is grown, includes the largest remnants of the European forest and is of little agricultural importance.   This barley must not be confused with the ' two-row ' variety of the main agricultural regions farther south.   The subarctic zone is succeeded by the ' oats zone ', occupying the most northerly tracts with considerable agricultural land ; here the area of oats exceeds that of barley in the north, and that of wheat and rye together in the south.   The zone of the bread-grains, wheat and rye, is divided by the line, from Holland to the Lake of Constance, separating predominant wheat from predominant rye. This, of course, corresponds nearly to the ethnic division between the French, traditional eaters of white bread, and Germans, devoted to ' black ', but there are other grounds for expecting a climatic change here. Both the wheat and rye areas are bounded on the south by a zone among the mountains and basins where the bread-grain is wheat and the chief cereal for fodder is almost everywhere maize ; and this grain in certain areas replaces wheat as a food, just as oats and barley also do, or did, in the northern zones. To the east of this ' maize-wheat zone ' lies the ' steppe-wheat zone ', in which the chief fodder-cereal is the subtropical variety of barley. To the south the boundary shown is the northern *limit* of olive-cultivation, already stressed as a valuable climatic index. It thus differs in nature from the other lines, but in the ' olive-zone ' the leading food and fodder-grains are wheat and subtropical barley.

Now in reviewing these distributions we may trace broadly the influences of the four climates with which we began. In the first place it is clear that the rigours of the boreal continental climate vary greatly in degree. Leningrad, taken previously as a sample, is seen to stand on the boundary between the ' oats ' and ' rye ' zones, and the tapering shape of the former reflects the influence of the Baltic Sea and great lakes upon temperature, rainfall and other elements. Saratov, again, chosen as a sample of the semi-arid continental type, lies in fact near the northern limit of the ' steppe-wheat zone ' with its rainfall, largely in the early summer, decreasing eastwards from about 20 to 8 inches, and also becoming less dependable. This zone narrows westward, to end in Bessarabia where rainfall is higher and more prolonged. Between these two wedges lies the huge tract of Russia in the ' rye zone ' ; within this the climatic differences are largely those of growing-season and risk of early and late frosts, and they vary both northward and westward. To bring this out three lines have been inserted on the map, viz the northern limits of plum-orchards and apple-orchards, together with a generalised limit of the more delicate crops such as sugar-beet, tobacco and hemp. In previous sections various evidence has been given to indicate a *relatively* sharp change of climate in the belt joining the southern Baltic with the western Black Sea. This is here amplified by the line separating the regions where more of the wheat grown is sown in spring (to north-east) and in autumn (to south-west respectively) ; and this may be compared with the northern limit of vineyards in Europe, which may be taken also to enclose those parts of the bread-grain zones that produce a great variety of the more sensitive fruits, such as have come originally from the Mediterranean region.

Because of the distribution of land and sea west of the land-mass of Asia there is clearly an inter-fingering of climates in the east ; the semiarid wedge is succeeded by that of the ' maize-wheat zone ' in the domain of the ' Pontic ' climate which has an outlying area on the Persian side of the Caspian Sea. The southern flank of the steppe, moreover, has a milder winter, so that the vine is cultivated north of the Black Sea and wheat is sown in autumn north of the Caucasus.

The ' maize-wheat zone ' for the most part coincides with the southern mountains of Europe. Here, generally, there is abundant water from rain or melting snow throughout a growing season of at least eight months, the maximum rainfall occurring in summer in the north and in autumn or spring in the south. Crops are grown, of course, chiefly on plains or basins among the mountains; but cultivation at relatively very high altitudes is a feature of the mountain climate in these latitudes. All forms of life are arranged in narrow altitudinal zones, above which summits are under frost almost continuously and snowfields still nourish glaciers where precipitation is adequate. The very high relief produces many local differences in climate, but there are certain prevailing characteristics. Calm weather in winter promotes downward creep of cold air and so, inversion of temperature; irregular heating in summer causes rapid up-draughts and so, thunder-storms; at the higher levels evaporation is great and there are various results from the strong insolation in the pure air of low density, among which the effectiveness of ultra-violet rays may perhaps be mentioned.

CHAPTER 6

MANTLE ROCK AND SOILS

THE products of rock weathering during the later geological times, whether remaining in place or moved and redeposited elsewhere by rivers, glaciers. wind or sea form the subsoils, and so the basis of all life. Where erosion has lagged behind weathering the mantle may be considerable, but in Europe alluvial deposits in lowlands are generally much thicker than such residual sheets on the uplands. Moreover, this statement applies only to the mid-latitudes of Europe. In the north, the regolith—or mantle rock—of preglacial periods has been entirely removed, and redeposited often far from the source. In the Mediterranean lands it remains here and there, but since the former protection of a closed vegetation was broken by man, most of it has been carried away from even moderate slopes. Such is the power of torrential erosion in winter, following vigorous mechanical weathering in the dry summer. Thus in two areas almost bare rock predominates in the highlands. First in Fennoscandia, Iceland, and the higher hills of the British Isles, all of which were centres of ice-dispersion under the glaciation : in these, as well as in the glaciated ranges of southern Europe ice-scoured rock is the characteristic acquired just prior to the advent of man ; but since then, there has been little change. Again, on all the highlands surrounding the Mediterranean Basin the strong skeleton stands revealed in every view ; but here, in contrast to the northern lands, changes may be noticed from year to year. Once the scars were begun by the early inhabitants, weathering and erosion could act at a rate unknown elsewhere ; so the dominance of rocky slopes may almost be taken as a signature of the Mediterranean climate ; another is the bright yellow or red colour of the soil. Continuous soil, however, is found there chiefly where slopes are gentle, either as the residual mantle of smoother plateaus, especially in Iberia and Anatolia, or developed on the sediments of coastal plains and aprons, and interior basins of all kinds. These lower surfaces include the tracts that were under the sea in the Pliocene Period and are therefore covered largely by rocks so soft as to be scarcely distinguishable from other mantle rock, but they are commonly of much greater thickness. Around the coasts of the Mediterranean they constitute, together with later alluvial patches, the major part of the cultivable land, and so have been of tremendous historical importance. But much greater areas of such land are found north of the Black Sea and throughout the Danubian Basin as far west as the Alps and again in

Lower Mesopotamia, while large interior expanses of Iberia, the Atlas Lands and Anatolia may be classified along with these.

The Pleistocene glaciers not only scoured from northern Europe all the residual mantle, but also eroded the solid rock deeply in many parts. Much of this glacial waste now lies under the North Sea : the rest covers the low-

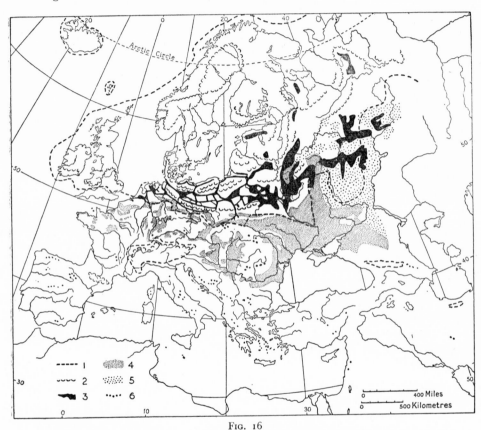

FIG. 16

Mantle Rock

1 Probable limit of maximum glaciation   4 Loess and similar deposits
2 End and recessional moraines of last glaciation   5 Deposits similar to 4
3 Marshes, outwash sands and meltwater valleys   6 Glaciated summits in southern Europe.

lands of the British Isles and a belt extending across Europe which spreads fanwise from the North Sea to the Ural Mountains. This complex of the various kinds of mantle rock due to glaciation remains arranged in character-istic parallel zones (Fig. 16) curving around the great centre of dispersion, Fennoscandia ; while a similar but much smaller arc of the same type laid by the Alpine glaciers extends from the northern foot of these mountains. The zones consist of till (or boulder-clay) and stony end-moraine, both left by the glaciers on recession ; sheets of gravel and sand carried by rivers from the ice-laid debris and redeposited after sorting, and with them are strings of kames and eskers of these materials ; finally there is the silt and clay, often covered by fen-peat, which accumulated in lakes that lay in front of the ice, or later on filled hollows in the till or kettle-holes in the sands and gravels. South of all these but partly covering the older till is the loess, a product of the fine dust blown from the other deposits by the winds that swirled clockwise from the high-pressure system covering the ice-sheets ; some of it was re-sorted by water to form similar material of loamy character. The chief complication lies in the fact that of the various glaciations the most severe was not the last. Hence there are tracts of older till and other glacial deposits extending beyond the farthest of the raw stoney end-moraines, i.e. southward and, in the case of the Alps, northward, but this is covered to a large extent by sands and the loess derived from the newer moraines.

Special mention should be made of the channels of the great rivers by which the immense quantities of melt-water were carried to the ocean from the receding ice-sheets. These must have varied in volume and direction from stage to stage with changes in the ice-front and in the position of the coast. The latter was, of course, approaching the present position as the water forming the ice of the last glacial period was progressively given back to the ocean, as it melted away. Many of the melt-water channels are now followed by rivers or canals, but the vaster volume of the former rivers is recorded by the swamps—drainage ditches—which flank the present water courses.

It will be seen, then, that the character and arrangement of these deposits of mantle rock have had a profound effect upon the human occupation of a very large area of Europe. From a very early period to the present day the physical qualities of the ground have guided human settlement, throughout the great plain. In general, the raw end-moraines have proved too stony to cultivate, the valleys of the old melt-water rivers and their smaller successors too boggy until modern times, many of the sheets of gravel and sand too dry or too wet—in accord with low or high ground-water. These three types of land, therefore, have tended to repel human beings, or at least to call for strenuous effort to make them habitable. But, to compensate, there was land that was easy to cultivate and has ever proved highly productive. First there is the loess, partly overlapping the glacial deposits, but mostly beyond them and reaching far to the south : apart from the Mediterranean coasts it attracted the first real agricultural settlers (see Chapter 14, page 155). The southern position of the fertile loess-lands, favoured in climate and accessible to the sources of civilisation, must be reckoned as a leading factor in European pre-history. In addition to the loess, there is the till or boulder-clay—the bottom-moraine of earlier or later glaciations, where this is not concealed by other deposits. This occupies the spaces between the stony moraines and the marshy or the sandy areas : no doubt hard to clear of forest at first, and often heavy to dig and plough, but good land, and the land on which both the Teutonic and the Slavonic peoples grew up. The intricate pattern of the map (Fig. 16) suggests how their habitat must have influenced their social development divided into many tribes. It also reminds us of the importance of boats for movement in such a region.

To say that the upper layer of the mantle rock constitutes soil is an incomplete statement, because soil is not an inert mineral substance but an association of inorganic and organic matter, and of air and water, in which living organisms, from bacteria upwards, play essential parts. Since the Ice-Age the soil has not had time to become fully adjusted to the climate ; but it is upon the tendencies to such adjustment that soils are classified in the broadest way ; and this relation between climate and soil established under natural vegetation has bearings also upon agriculture. The aspect of climate which matters is the ratio between the amounts of rainfall and evaporation ; and this may now be considered in regard to the examples given on page oo, beginning with Leningrad. It is clear that in this area the ground must be damp during most of the year, with snow lying for some five months, and with most of the rain in summer when the mean temperature exceeds 60° F. in only two months. Evaporation, therefore, is slight ; moreover, the soil is poorly aerated, so, as the water seeps through the thick layer of partly rotted pine needles and other superficial material, it becomes acid and so dissolves the alkaline minerals from the next layer, bleaching those that are left, and then precipitates lime, iron and others as a hard rusty crust, still farther down. Soil, then, has a zoned structure, called the profile ; the zones are called horizons, named A, B and C—C being the parent material or subsoil. In this case A_1 is dark grey, A_2 very pale grey, and B_1 rust-red. The pale powdery substance beneath the vegetable mould, called in Russian *podzol*, has given the name to this class of heavily leached soils found in a cool wet climate, and the process named ' podzolisation '. When such soils are cultivated it is necessary to dig or plough deeply, to bring up the nutritive matter to the plant roots ; and usually much manure is needed.

In the other type of continental climate, as at Saratov, snow or frost may last for five months ; but the total precipitation is under 15 inches, and in no month over 2 inches, while the July temperature is 72° F. The vegetation is grass ; with short heavy rains a part, but only part, of the soluble minerals is carried down ; but a portion of this is raised again somewhat by capillary action during the hot dry weather with strong evaporation. Hence there is a deep horizon specially rich in lime and other valuable salts. In this climate plant remains decompose very slowly, despite good aeration, so that the very thick 'A' horizon is heavily charged with humus. Thus it is a black or dark-brown soil, called *chernoziom* in Russian. It is not to be confused with dark soils found in northern Europe, in which the vegetable matter is largely raw and undecomposed as in acid peat; this has not reached the condition of humus. In contrast to these, the black earths prove most fertile over long periods on account of their composition and their depth. They are typically developed on loess and so are very thick soils; for the loess itself accumulated gradually as fine dust settling among grasses, and it derives its structure and porous quality from the vertical casts of former grass-stems into which the soil-nutrients filter from above.

It should be noted that Saratov, with 15 inches of rainfall, is at the drier edge of this soil-belt, and where the colour changes to chestnut-brown. On these soils the grass is shorter and opener. With less moisture the humus is less dark, and the lime accumulates nearer to the surface. On the wetter northern rim of the black earth, where rainfall is about 20 inches, there has been woodland in the past, and this marks the transition to forest soils.

Climatic conditions that favour deciduous broadleaved forest also, in time, produce a soil quite distinct from those of grassland, but less clearly separated from the podzols. The facts stated e.g. for Paris (p. oo) suggest that the amount of rain and evaporation do not differ greatly. Under the broadleaved woods the leaf-mould contains more lime and other alkalis than does the needle-carpet of coniferous forest, so the water while it partly leaches the soil, does not bleach it; worms and insects, too, are more active. Hence, the colour is grey to brown, and the humus is well mixed but decreases downward to the 'B' horizon which is more clayey. Under the trees, except beeches, herbs living upon the rich topsoil, and so a few crops and weeds, tend to use up its fertility; so the brown forest soils have to be ploughed deeply. Since they are partly leached they are akin to the podzols, especially where rainfall is high and evaporation reduced, as is the case nearer the ocean. But since the Ice-Age they have not had time to mature, and so they vary greatly with the character of the parent material, the mantle rock, and this in turn depends on the rock beneath. Therefore the soils can be identified to a large extent with sandstones, limestones, igneous rocks, acid and basic, and so on.

The soils of southern Europe and its fringes are the much more difficult to understand, because, as stated elsewhere, the relief is so great and erosion and deposition are so active. Hence it is only upon surfaces of little slope that unchanged profiles of mature soil are to be sought. Indeed soil is now virtually lacking on steep slopes. However, it must be due to the Mediterranean climate that the soils are characteristically light[1] in colour: red, yellow, chestnut-brown or grey; but wherever pure limestone is found there is the deep-red terra rossa remaining in patches. Most of these tints are acquired from the iron oxides which in this climate are not all carried down from the surface. It has been suggested that some of these soils represent the deeper parts of older soils formed in a more uniformly wet climate, and from which the topsoil has been eroded. On the other hand the chestnut-coloured soils of Iberia, believed to have been formed under a former canopy of xerophytic forest, seem to lack the lower ('B') horizon. Again it is certain that Mediterranean soils are poor in humus, and certain, too, is the fact that the mineral salts which are leached by the heavy winter rains tend to return to the surface by capillarity, in summer. Thus, while the deeper soil is rich enough and remains moist enough to nourish tree-roots throughout the year, the surface loses water quickly in summer and may also become encrusted by 'salts'. For this reason the cultivator of annual crops is concerned with the topsoil only, for here the fertility resides ; but he must till it often to reduce capillary action and keep weeds from using the precious water ; and this he does with the hoe or the shallow plough.

As the desert is approached the pale tints of the soil are found to correspond more closely to those of the underlying rock. But in addition to the rock-minerals there is much incrustation of alkalis, including common salt in parts. Again since the cover of plants is not continuous the amount of organic matter is small ; and where the plants disappear the surface ceases to merit the name of soil. The soils on the mountains cannot become mature ; they are composed of weathered rock particles that do not remain in place long enough for this to happen, and they are termed 'skeletal soils'.

CHAPTER 7

RIVERS

THE map by itself gives a very incomplete idea of the rivers ; it allows comparison of length, direction and drainage area, but tells nothing of the water carried, or of the rule of the flood. The average total flow should, of course, be studied in conjunction with the annual distribution of rainfall, when it becomes clear that the most voluminous rivers are those that are fed from the largest tract with high precipitation—over 40 inches (102 cm.)—extending from Switzerland to Albania. Thus, for example, the Rhine, Rhône and Po, which drain an area comparable with the combined basins of the Seine, Loire and Garonne, have an aggregate volume nearly three times that of the French rivers : the figures in cubic metres per second are, respectively : 2,330, 1,780, 1,720, 530, 860, 960. But the French rivers resemble the Elbe, Oder and Vistula, for which the mean volumes are 710, 570 and 960 m.³/sec. respectively. Again, the Danube makes an interesting contrast with the Dnepr and Don ; it drains an area smaller than these Russian rivers combined, but its flow (6,240) is over three times greater (1,700 plus 1,000). Finally, to take a northern example, the basin of the North Dvina is twice as large as that of the Rhine but the mean volume (2,200) is smaller.

The seasonal rate of flow, or regimen, follows generally the seasonal rainfall, but with a lag in time which varies with slope, vegetation and permeability of the rock. This applies to all lands not subject to important snowfall. In these, of course, the water is held up until the main melt comes, when the high flood takes place and continues as long as the snow persists. Rivers that are fed substantially by the melting of permanent snowfields and glaciers have their floods prolonged throughout the summer from this cause. So it will be seen that every river possesses, as it were, an individual pulse ; nevertheless some classification is permissible and useful.

Mediterranean rivers are the most obviously seasonal in their flow, and spate follows rainfall, immediately where impermeable rock forms the basin, more slowly where it is in limestone. All are roaring torrents at some period between October and March ; but throughout the summer most of them are either streamlets in wide beds of shingle or sand, or they dry up altogether, leaving their beds to serve as ' roads '. The valleys of some of the larger rivers, like the Guadiana, betray their Mediterranean regimen by their double bed—a narrow channel for summer, cut far below a broad rocky shelf that is the winter bed.

The flow of all the great rivers of Russia is dominated by the spring thaw, which swells them from low water to their maximum within a period of from three to six weeks ; in this spate, too, they carry away the broken ice. From its peak the flood declines more slowly on account of summer thunderstorms. All are comparatively low by August, but minimum flow is in February.

Throughout western Europe the snow is much reduced and with it the effect of the thaw, which is also much less regular ; eastward across the plain it becomes more marked and more regular. Low water occurs in summer because evaporation is then greatest and is sufficient to offset the effect of the rainfall which is higher in this half-year, except near the ocean. Such is the rule ; but uneven flow may follow from the succession of wet and dry spells of weather, and it is the former which bring serious floods to the lowlands of the region. The sequence which leads to the most serious inundations is associated with the passage of a large depression following prolonged frost, with snow lying on the hills. The warm air then causes rapid thaw, but the ground remains largely impermeable through frost ; the ensuing rain then leads to disaster. Moreover, the flood-plains of rivers near the Atlantic and North Sea coasts may suffer specially, because gales, coinciding with a spring tide, raise the sea-level and so impede outfall from the rivers. This raising of sea-level by westerly gales has been the main cause of the recurrent inundations of Leningrad by the Neva.

Thus the rivers of Europe may be classified into three main types according to the rule of their flow. But many do not correspond fully because of the varied sources of their tributaries, notable examples of composite rivers in this respect being the Rhine and the Danube.

On the desert fringes, again, the beginnings of civilisation were intimately related to the seasonal flow of rivers—stranger-rivers that exist there only because of their great volume, acquired in other regions. The rivers of Mesopotamia belong to the Mediterranean order, but are hybrids in a sense, for the spring thaw in the mountains of Armenia plays its part. Moreover, the Tigris is a long river, and the Euphrates still longer, so the flood from winter rains reaches the deltaic plain only in spring and persists well into the summer. The Nile is even more of a stranger in our region since its high flood, in Egypt reaching its peak in October, is produced by rains of the summer monsoon in Ethiopia, while its low water, persisting from January till June, is derived from the equatorial sources of the river.

The shape of a valley has much to do with the extent of inundation, and human settlements are usually placed in safety from the river in ordinary spate, but with scanty regard for the occasional catastrophe, such as is induced by the sequence of weather outlined above. True flood-plains where the river has built its banks higher than the more distant ground have therefore been occupied, in general, only after embanking in recent centuries. But fortunately most valleys enclose strips of terraced land safe from all inundation, these terraces being parts of former flood-plains which the river has trenched after some rejuvenation, such as follows upon uplift of the land. It is the presence of such features and their good soil which above all have led to progressive population of the valleys among the hills of Europe.

For mankind rivers have ever been obstacles, but at the same time lines of attraction, according to the character of the streams, and to human ability at the period, to cope with their natural powers and vagaries. Thus the course of settlement along a river has been guided by the accessibility of its banks ; and this was often restricted by marshes to widely separated places which commonly do not coincide on both banks. Such valleys easily served as frontier zones, from which international boundaries developed later on. With increased use, and measurement, of valleys containing such boundaries the position of the line ultimately had to be exactly known and defined. So the river boundary is now taken to be the *thalweg* or line formed by the lowest points of the riverbed, where water is deepest and the current usually strongest. Yet despite the precise nature of this delimitation these fluvial boundaries may be unsatisfactory, if only on account of the subsequent natural changes of the river itself. Nevertheless, international frontiers over hundreds of miles were so defined as lately as 1919.

With the growth of population and of technical skill bridges have multiplied, for roads and then for rails. Even so, the rivers still constitute a powerful network of obstacles in human affairs. The daily expenditure of time and effort upon journeys lengthened by unavoidable *detours* to bridges is quite incalculable—to say nothing of the desired journeys held to be ' not worth while ' by distance of the bridge. The closeness of bridges, ferries and fords is a feature of regional geography, and no generalisation need be attempted here. But it should be noted that special paucity of river crossings due to sheer difficulty occurs both in narrow valleys of the mountains and on plains with broad channels fringed with marsh. An extreme case of the latter is that of the lower Volga, which was first bridged, at Saratov, 600 miles (900 km.) from the mouth, only in 1935, 65 years after the railway reached the river.

Apart from the abundance of soil in the valleys, rivers possess a fourfold attraction for man—for fishing, water, transport and power.

River fisheries were once vastly more important than they are now ; fishing was formerly universal along all ' inhabited ' rivers except the streams of the Mediterranean lands ; and fishing rights have been jealously guarded. In addition to the various fresh-water fishes, and among the most valuable even now, are the salmon, shad and the sturgeon which come from the sea to spawn, and the eels which go down to the Atlantic Ocean for this purpose.

Decline of fisheries has been due partly to opportunities for getting other foods, but also in the past century to pollution of the rivers by sewage and factory waste. But it should be added that, in the same period, the north-western rivers famous for their salmon, as in Norway and the British Isles, have represented a new source of income based on fishing for sport. At the other extreme, the fisheries of the lower Volga and, in lesser degree, the rivers of the Black Sea have gained commercial importance with improved transport, and from the special value set upon two products of the sturgeon—caviar and isinglass.

While the geography of water supply is best treated regionally, it is as well to remember the differing degrees in which river water is essential to the population. Broadly, it is of greatest importance to townspeople to meet their ever-growing needs, and to rural communities where irrigation is practised. Urban supplies are taken to include those of factories which require vast quantities of water; without it, many of the other raw materials are unworkable, and for some industries water of special chemical quality is required.

The other great use of water is for irrigation. This began as the normal inundation of the flood-plain in Egypt, and it has continued to make life possible in that country—since 1908 as perennial irrigation. The rulers of ancient Sumeria and then of Babylonia were faced with greater difficulties than those of the Pharaohs, and, responding with remarkable inventiveness, they established earthen dams and derivation canals for irrigation—not, however, perennial. These are the great examples of irrigating flood-plains in the desert. Irrigation of the northern desert bordering the Caspian Sea, begun on the delta of the Volga, is now proceeding on a large scale. Throughout many centuries there have been extensions of this type of watering around the Mediterranean Sea, wherever there was a small perennial supply from springs in limestone or even lifted from wells, and a larger supplement in winter. Abundant water was available, however, only where rivers come from beyond the region; and this is the case in Macedonia, the south of France and north-eastern Spain, in all of which water is needed badly, as well as in the northern plains of Italy, where the extra supply is put to very good use. Thus rivers from the Alps and Pyrenees, voluminous in summer, confer great benefits, but modern engineering skill was required to make full use of them. Nevertheless, within the mountains remarkable systems of channels, made by peasants from the Middle Ages onwards, have enabled more hay and fruit to be grown. So the mountains, and especially the Alps, have supported in the past surprising numbers of domestic animals and people.

Throughout the remainder of Europe there is, clearly, no need for irrigation; yet it is very widely used near the banks of innumerable streams where the purpose is, as a rule, the maintenance of water meadow for the production of specially rich hay ; and in recent times for other vegetable produce for the market.

As waterways the rivers have a long history, which forms part of the record of commerce ; and much of this remains to be written. Boats on rivers have long been the principal means of transport for goods on all lowlands, except those of southern Europe, throughout the historic period. The roads of the Roman Empire were the sole competitors for goods traffic, and they ceased to be maintained in the Dark Ages. Water transport, then, was essential for merchandise, and it was much used by passengers, for example by bands of pilgrims. Most of the traffic probably went downstream only, in lightly-built craft for breaking up at the destination ; where it moved upstream also sail was used on favourable rivers—never those with many loops, but more craft were towed from the bank, by animals or by men ; so a towpath and regular repair of this were required. With the arrival of the steamer the rivers came to be used for much heavier barges ; and consequently the nineteenth century was marked by the widespread improvement of rivers to create and maintain suitable navigation channels. In many cases this entailed the making of an entirely new river-bed, but more generally the process of confining the stream to a narrower channel which it should keep clear by its own power. These were costly works, but in mature rivers, with stable sandbanks, heavy dredging may be avoided thereafter. In more youthful rivers, however, such as the Rhône, the detritus shifts with every flood, and operations have to be begun afresh from time to time. The removal of rocky obstructions also promoted the freer flow, and reduced congestion of floating ice at the barrier and the rise of dangerous floods farther upstream. Two notable examples are the deepening of the Rhine at the Bingerloch and the Danube at the Iron Gate.

The modern canal system of the European plain makes use of the great melt-water valleys of the Ice Age, which provide for transverse waterways linking the various rivers between the Rhine and the Neman. In Russia the sources of most of the great rivers lie in similar swampy hollows, which link the systems and so served earlier boatmen as portages across the ill-marked divides between the large drainage basins. Now, carrying canals, they complete the system of waterways without which the huge Russian state could hardly have developed. Elsewhere in Europe canals which cross watersheds are hampered not only by the necessity of having many locks, but also by the difficulty of finding enough water to keep the canals filled throughout the year.

Navigation on all waterways, then, is dependent to greater or less extent upon seasonal flow and the incidence of freezing temperatures ; low water and freezing being the limiting factors. In Russia these fortunately coincide, but on the lower Rhine, for example, low water comes in October. Again while boats are hindered by too slight depth, too strong a current is also a disadvantage, mainly, of course, to upstream traffic. Thus when the speed of the current is doubled, the weight moved by given horsepower is reduced to about one-quarter. It follows, too, that while many rivers are navigable in their lower courses the upper courses of the majority are fit at best only for the floating of lumber either as rafts or logs, for when the gradient exceeds $c.$ 1:1,000, normal navigation becomes impracticable. It is most fortunate that the rivers of Sweden and Finland, with many rapids, are well suited to this purpose; moreover, the lakes between the rapids serve for the grading of the lumber which is sent down indiscriminately.

Power from running water has been used to grind corn, at least since Roman times; and, because of the simplicity of building water-mills and the small head of water needed for them, such corn-mills appeared gradually after the sixth century in nearly every inhabited valley where grain was grown; the floating mill, too, with wheel astern of a moored craft, appeared on the Danube. From the later Middle Ages the water-wheel came to be used in a variety of manufactures, at first for local needs, and then in certain areas for wider markets. It was of special importance in the development of the mining and working of metals in central Europe. Finally, with the invention of new textile machinery in England, availability of water-power largely determined the placing of such manufactures along rapid reaches of rivers; water in large amount was needed for textile operations, apart from the power. Hence the foundation of these modern industries brings to notice the importance of interrupted profiles in rivers; and this in turn relates the uses of rivers to their former rejuvenation. It was, of course, the rapids near the lowlands that were sought as industrial sites; for many economic reasons factories could not be established among the mountains, where falls are most numerous. Thus the great modern textile industries were located in the lower valleys of the Pennines in England and at similar sites in Scotland, in the Vosges and the Black Forest, around the lakes of Zürich and Wallenstadt, along the edges of the Bohemian massif, and even on the small rivers of Normandy. The creation, too, of falls by damming led the manufacturers into conflict with those concerned with waterways. But soon the need for supplementary power when waters were low led to the introduction of steam engines. So, while the established industries of Britain, for example, could remain because coalfields were at hand, industries in other countries were enabled to do so owing to the cheap transport of coal on the waterways, as in Alsace.

With the advent of electric power and the means of generating it with the turbine, rivers came to have an enhanced value, and a geographical transformation was soon effected by the utilisation of the power of the mountain torrents. The full realisation of this became certain about 1900, when the ability to transmit current over long distances had been demonstrated ; and the rapid development of this ' white coal ' in Europe is, of course, the result of the demand for mechanical energy in a convenient form. The existence of the potential energy is determined fundamentally by the coincidence of high relief and abundant flow of water—from high rainfall. But the available water includes snow and ice, released during only part of the year. This is a defect of the high mountains, for which, however, there is compensation : the rivers of lower plateaux adjoining the high mountains yield less power in summer, so the power produced by the two systems may be smoothed out by pooling the current of both sources throughout a common system of transmission.

The Alps, the Pyrenees and the mountains of Norway are marked by the large number of high falls, which allow of comparatively economical installation. This is because of the special modelling of these mountains during former glaciation, which left abrupt steps in the main valleys and at the mouths of the ' hanging ' tributary glens. Behind the brink of many such declivities there are lakes, too, which may be enlarged by further damming. The Alps also provide lower but greater sources of power near their margin. These are comparable with the waterfalls on the great rivers of Sweden, and at lower levels those of Finland and northern Russia, or with that of the Shannon in Ireland, and again with many (much smaller) sources in Scotland.

The Central Plateau of France exemplifies the power that can be harnessed from rivers flowing in canyons. The profiles of these show natural breaks, marking stages in rejuvenation, which may be raised artificially to impound water. The Rhine and the Rhône call for special notice ; each emerges from the high Alps, passes through a large lake and plunges steeply through a gorge —the Rhône in the Pre-Alps, the Rhine through the Jura ; and both gorges are marked by great power-stations. Finally both rivers still flow swiftly in the first parts of their lowland courses, so there, too, vast amounts of current are to be generated at series of low-head stations, already partly established on the Rhine below Kembs, and the Rhône between Donzère and Mondragon. The Iron Gate on the Danube, already mentioned, offers a similar or even greater opportunity.

Among the great rivers of southern Russia only the Dnepr presented rapids indicating an obvious and great hydro-electric site, at Dnepropetrovsk at the sharp bend of the river, but other dams have now been built on the Volga and its tributary the Kama.

Estimates of potential waterpower—such as could actually be harnessed—

are of doubtful value for comparative purposes ; but such a comparison of economic hydro potential, made for 1950 by the Economic Commission for Europe, may be quoted. According to this, 32 per cent was in Fennoscandia, and 28 per cent in the Alps.

On the Mediterranean rivers, apart from those on the northern fringe, reservoirs have to be built to prolong the period of flow. Yet the potential energy inherent in some of them is very considerable. This is the case where the profile steepens in the lower part of the watercourse ; a characteristic of the western rivers in Iberia, and where the rapids also lie in canyons offering good sites for dams. The short rivers of central Italy have the advantage of sources in the limestone of the Abruzzi Mountains, and so an unusually regular flow.

Chapter 8

VEGETATION

HUMIDITY of the air has been mentioned although not discussed ; its significance to human comfort is well appreciated when in summer sultry weather gives place to dry heat, and in winter ' raw ' cold to dry cold. For plant life atmospheric humidity is vital because it controls the rate of transpiration from the leaves, and so affects the whole economy of the plant. The rainfall map, or better, that showing the index of aridity, indicates how far vegetation can depend upon a supply of water at the roots and so upon nourishment ; maps of temperature and that showing the length of the growing season undoubtedly help to explain the range of different species. But in addition information is needed about the relative humidity of the air, i.e. the nearness to saturation ; moreover, related to this is the prevalence of wind, since strong wind promotes rapid transpiration. Again, when plants seem to die from cold, death is really most often due to drought, a dry wind having caused transpiration at a time when frost prevented replenishment of water from the soil. Thus, unlike human beings, plants, in northern Europe at least, prefer a damp to a dry cold wind. On the other hand the olive, a tree adapted to reduce transpiration, has been known to resist 25 degrees (F.) of frost.

The climate as it has prevailed during the Christian Era is such that trees ought to dominate the vegetation over nearly all of Europe and parts of the borderlands ; the highest form of vegetation which the climate can sustain— the climax—is forest. If all the great cities were to be laid in ruin and deserted, it is highly probable that their sites would in time be covered by a mantle of trees. Yet forest is very far from dominating the landscape now, for man has been destroying it ever since he began to cultivate the soil and keep domestic animals. The map (Fig. 17) which is an attempt to generalise the relative density of woodland, is in great measure the obverse of a map of population-density, and this relationship will be discussed in a later chapter. But it may be noted that the forest of the Mediterranean is much more vulnerable, and that it has been under attack for the longest period. Furthermore, very few areas of forest, except in the sub-Arctic, still have their primeval character ; they have suffered degradation or else, in western countries, have been planted and often with trees not indigenous to the region.

There are three main types of forest : first, the evergreen forest of needle-leaved, resinous and cone-bearing species occupying the north and east, together with the higher mountains of the centre ; secondly, to the south of this the summer-green forest of broadleaved deciduous trees ; and, thirdly, the forest of the Mediterranean lowlands, of evergreen broadleaved species as well as conifers.   These types interpenetrate, especially the first two, giving a mixed vegetation as in western Russia and the hills and plateaux of central Europe.

Towards the south-east in Russia forest gives place gradually to grassland,

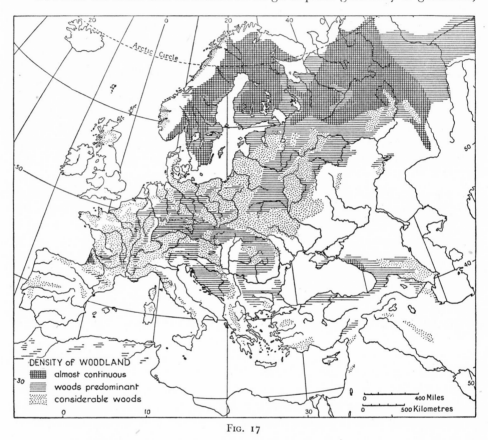

FIG. 17

which in turn passes to scrub, in both cases obviously owing to dryness.   In the far north is the tundra, and on the higher mountains elsewhere a similar treeless vegetation.   The absence of trees in both cases is commonly ascribed to low temperatures, but, as we have seen, wind has to be reckoned as a leading factor, so that drought may be said to delimit the forest except where the soil is so wet as to produce marsh or bog.   But excess, or lack, of water is only one of the natural features, besides climate, affecting vegetation.   These are mostly related to the rock and the soil (the edaphic factors), and they cause substantial variation within the main types—the 'associations' of plants as distinct from the great 'formations'. It should be mentioned again here that the structure of the soil is intimately bound up with the vegetation under which it evolved (Chapter 6), and with the climate.

The Northern Forest

Because of the short season of growth and the cold at other times the climate favours the conifer, which, with its narrow leaves, transpires slowly, except from the young shoots. The conical form and sloping branches prevent collapse under snow. Growth is slow, and this gives strong fine-grained timber, the best for construction. The forest is dense and dark, especially the spruce woods, with little growing in the carpet of dead leaves. As in all forests, dominance of a species results largely from success in the struggle for light, and seedlings remain as dwarfs until an old tree falls, when they can grow to fill the space. In its eastern part Siberian species predominate, fir, spruce, pine and larch ; in the west the trees are similar but the species are European. Exceptions to the dark monotony of the evergreens, apart from the deciduous light-green larch, are due mainly to edaphic causes, and notably to the poor drainage in many parts of this glaciated region, for this leads to the formation of marsh and peat bog. Both repel trees, but the latter when dried out is invaded by pines. Fires, too, provide open spaces, and for a period light-loving plants have their opportunity, only to be suppressed later on by the evergreens. For these and other reasons the dark northern forest—the taiga of Russia—is spattered with deciduous trees, especially the birch, which in places reaches farther into the northern tundra than any conifer ; others are the alder, aspen and rowan.

In its eastern part the forest is still primeval and hard to penetrate ; systematic felling has proceeded from the river banks, and as clearing extended scattered agricultural settlements have developed ; so far the North Dvina has been the chief artery in the extraction of lumber. Westward the presence of lakes and more widespread exploitation give greater variety : in Karelia and Finland most of the forests probably have been burned at some time, naturally or for agriculture, leaving birch, alder and aspen especially near the Baltic Sea. Yet here as throughout Scandinavia modern management gives a constant output of lumber, with rivers and lakes providing for transport. The northern forests constitute the one great reserve of soft-wood timber in Europe, and therefore also of wood-pulp, chiefly from spruce, for the making of paper and other things ; they have yielded, too, enormous quantities of wood-tar from the distillation of the stumps and roots of pine and larch. Timber and tar from the Baltic have played a notable part in sea-borne trade, and so in forging cultural links between Scandinavia and western Europe.

MIXED AND DECIDUOUS FOREST

Compared with the northern forest whose character is little affected by man, the natural vegetation of the other lands is to some extent an abstraction. Its nature can be learned by study of the altered remnants of the old forest, of the herbs that linger when the trees have disappeared, of the pollen from vanished trees that lies buried in neighbouring peat, and finally, of the soil itself. Historical evidence also may be available, including place-names referring to trees. The general conclusion is that Europe in its mid-latitudes has witnessed a prolonged struggle between the climatic influences of the ocean and of Asia, with advances and retreats of species and of vegetation favoured by one or other. Thus to consider only the lowland, the great plain shows a transitional zone in which conifers mingle with broadleaved trees, whereas western Europe is the domain of the deciduous forest. Mixed forest covers a huge tract that is quite narrow near the Ural, widens to its maximum east of the Baltic, and continues across it to southern Norway ; to the south also it is prolonged upon the late-Glacial deposits with pine indeed dominant on the sands as far as the River Elbe, but summer-green woods prevailing on the clays.

From the Atlantic to the Ural the aspect of the deciduous forest changes gradually in two ways. The first, which may be recorded precisely, is due to the varying dominance of the different species. Reducing this to the simplest terms by allusion only to the two commonest, the oak and the beech, it may be stated that the beech has prevailed wherever the air is sufficiently moist and the growing season long enough within a huge area of plain and mountain extending from northern France to the southern Baltic as well as south-eastward to the Balkan Peninsula and Anatolia. Oak forests predominate to west and to east and in the basins among the central mountains. Thus from the Iberian Peninsula through western France and again in all the lower parts of the British Isles oak woods of various kinds once covered the land. In the east they form the belt of deciduous forest lying across the Russian plain from the southern Ural to the Carpathians, and giving place gradually to the steppe. Among the central and southern mountains there is an oak zone about the basins and clothing the lower slopes, above which beech woods take its place. It may be noted that the sequence is reversed in northern latitudes, including the British Isles, where oak woods reach much farther north than those of beech.

The other difference of aspect, east to west in these forests, is more subtle, since it relates first to the *habit* of the trees and to other associated vegetation, and secondly, to the annual rhythm of the vegetation. In regard to the latter, the west is marked by comparatively slow progress at each stage in the annual cycle of plant life and by less regularity in the dates of their onset. As for the general habit, only one feature can be mentioned here : the effect of high humidity near the coasts in the luxuriance of moss, lichen and even fern growing on the trees and the wealth of ground-fungi in the autumn. Moreover, to return to the subject of species, it is only in the west that the deciduous woods are mixed with broadleaved evergreens. Along with holly, yew and juniper rise under the canopy, while ivy climbs the stems ; on the seaboard, too, from Ireland southward, the undergrowth includes shrubs like the arbutus that play a large part in Mediterranean vegetation. The oak forest everywhere, unlike the beech woods, contains many kinds of tree, generally subsidiary but locally dominant, that in England include all the native trees, and on the Continent many others as well. Of the primeval forest none remains unchanged ; trees of all ages intermingled, the younger growing among and upon the decaying remains of the dead and, save in beechwood, beset in a tangled undergrowth. But here and there along the valleys there are dense remnants of the swamp forest of willow and alder that once made the rivers so difficult to approach.

Owing to arrangement in altitudinal zones the vegetation on the mountains reproduces continental contrasts over small distances, with the general sequence already indicated—oak, then beech, then the various conifers to the treeline ; above this come shrubs, then meadows famed for their brilliant flowers, and finally the scattered cushion-like plants, adapted to resist drought, which we know, properly, as ' alpines '. These last three zones resemble in many ways the vegetation of the Arctic tundra beyond the northern treeline. This inter-locking of the zones on steep slopes has led mountain peoples to adopt highly specialised modes of life in order to exploit all the possibilities of each zone above or below their homes. Two general features of vegetation on the mountains should be noted. The first is the importance of exposure, which modifies greatly the climatic change with increasing height. Thus the angle at which the sun's rays meet the ground varies enormously, while the period of daily sunshine differs greatly from place to place on account of the relief. Hence the vegetation on slopes with southern exposure differs from that of the opposite slopes ; for example, larch or pine may clothe the former and spruce the latter. Moreover, for the same reason, plants belonging to more southerly regions have often established themselves on distant sunny slopes, Mediterranean flora, for instance, colonising places within and beyond the Alps. The other peculiarity applies especially to the Alps because of their great breadth, but in less degree to other mountains. The climate becomes more ' continental ' from the margins toward the interior of the system ; as a result of this some associations, like beechwood, are found on the outer parts only, while the limits of others, including the treeline, are higher towards the interior. We may note in passing that the beech further emphasises its preference for humid conditions by tending to stop at the upper limit of frequent mist.

All but the highest mountains surrounding the Mediterranean are suited climatically to support summer-green forest ; even where there is little rain for three months the subsoil is doubtless damp from the thaw. In the Balkan Peninsula and northern Anatolia forests are still considerable, but in the other tracts the remnants are small. These woods are, or were, mainly composed of oaks, of which there is a number of different kinds, along with the chestnut whose range was greatly extended for food in the Middle Ages, and species similar to those which accompany the oak in the north. But the beech zone was also important, and even now remnants are to be found throughout the Appennines and even overlooking the Gulf of Corinth in Greece, which serves to remind us of the narrowness of the belt of really summer-dry climate below these mountains. Above the summer-green forest coniferous woods again appear, at levels ever higher to the south, those of the Atlas and the Asian Bridgelands being marked by the very distinctive cedars.

Destruction and Degradation

The generalised map of density serves to show the great loss which the deciduous forests have suffered ; indeed they are greater than the map indicates since the principal modern plantations consist of evergreen trees. The greater part of the forest has been either rooted up or degraded. The process began with agriculture in Neolithic times, doubtless with little system at first, but as population increased the forest's edge was pushed back around each community, while the nearby woods began to be degraded by the encouragement of grass wherever cattle and sheep could find some sustenance. Once a close turf is established germination and growth of seedlings is hindered and such as become established are killed by these animals, or by rabbits when they appear upon the scene ; mice and voles, too, are responsible for destruction of buried seeds. Swine feeding on acorns and beechnuts, on the other hand, are not believed to have contributed seriously to degeneration. Systematic clearing of forest outside the Mediterranean basin probably proceeded in a general easterly direction, but also from distinct areas of early agricultural expansion such as those in the British Isles, Bohemia, the Vistula basin and the oak forest of central Russia. In western and central Europe a special wave of clearing for agriculture and pasture was begun by monastic effort, notably of the Cistercian Order. It is probable that felling for ordinary building purposes and for domestic fuel did not generally mean destruction of woodland, at least until modern times ; but in many parts severe depredations were caused by charcoal-burners making fuel for smelting and glass-works, the materials for which were brought to the sources of wood.

Continual grazing, of course, impoverishes the soil in most situations and increasing acidity brings about the dominance of plants that can support it. It is mainly for this reason that large areas of western Europe are under heath of various kinds, where the leading plants are heath (*Erica*), ling (*Calluna*) covering the greatest expanses, or gorse (*Ulex*) mingled with wiry grasses. Once formed, these heaths have been used continuously as pasture and regularly burned to produce young growth and in the case of gorse and broom (*Genista*) also cut for fodder. Such heaths are found from central Norway to northern Portugal, where they pass into the Mediterranean bush-wood, and they are widespread in western Germany, the British Isles and Brittany. Given protection from animals and fire most of them would support forest of birch, pine and juniper, and many now carry large pine plantations.

On the highlands bordering the ocean high wind is the enemy of trees ; moreover heavy and almost incessant rainfall promotes the formation of peat bog on all gentler slopes, owing chiefly to the growth of sphagnum and other specially adapted plants. The absence of forest, then, from the higher parts of Scandinavia, Britain and Ireland is due to a climatic cause. The drier parts of these mountains are covered with heath of various types passing, upward and northward, to dwarfed alpine associations. Along the maritime fringes the climate has led to the encroachment of bog upon other vegetation, but always where drainage is impeded in some way.

MEDITERRANEAN FOREST

The third type of forest is that adapted to the Mediterranean climate, with its hot dry summer, and so by its habit and particularly its foliage it is special-lised to reduce transpiration. While there can be little doubt that this water-saving formation once covered the lowland and lower slopes shown on Fig. oo, there is no certainty about its original aspect. Probably it was a rather open woodland in which one or other of a few species was dominant locally. These include six conifers : the maritime and the Corsican pines, the umbrella-shaped stone pine and the feathery Aleppo pine, together with the cypress in the east balanced in the west by the thuya, with similar form. Of the evergreen oaks, the holm-oak (*Quercus ilex*) is the most widespread, the cork-oak (*Q. Suber*) favours silicious soils in the west, while in the east are the Valona oak (*Q. Aegilops*) and the gall-bearing oak (*Q. infectoria*). Of all these none but the stone-pine casts deep shade even when standing close, so the next tier of

vegetation must always have been well developed ; today it is far more prominent than the tall forest. This brushwood, composed of bushes and small trees,
may form a complete and impenetrable thicket where rainfall and soil are most
favourable ; but it is more often seen variously degraded whether by fire or
the axe or by the browsing of goats, and all generally supplemented by torrential
erosion. There are many common names for it : in Greek *longos* (λόγγος), in
Spanish *monte bajo* (or ' low wood '), in Italian *macchia*, while we have adopted
the Corsican—and French—*maqui*('s). It is a mixed association of evergreen
plants, their wood tough and generally twisted, their flowers often brilliant and
scented, and above all their foliage distinctive. This is of many shades of green,
but mostly either dark and shiny or glaucous as in the olive. The leaves of
some are broad as in laurel, cistus or arbutus ; less so in others like the box,
lentisk, broom, myrtle and oleaster ; or, again, minute as in the heaths ; while
many species have spines. Whether the oleaster be the ancestor of the olive or
not, this cultivated tree introduced throughout the entire region now appears
not only in compact orchards but also scattered in the brushwood or forming
apparently natural woodland. Over considerable tracts one type of bush may
dominate ; this is characteristic of the Iberian plateau where it may be caused
by the pasturing sheep, and the association is then known by the name of the
plant—*jarales* from *jara*, cistus.

In the more arid regions or sites, or where degraded, the maquis ceases to
form a close canopy and rock appears as the soil is removed. Plants with roots
suited to this are fewer and they must be the better water-savers ; the evergreen
prickly oak (*Q. coccifera*), for example, is widely distributed in such places. This
type of more stunted and open vegetation, known in France as *garrigue* and in
Greece as *phrygana* often consists of low shrubs, among which still humbler plants
grow in patches ; typical of such shrubs in the east is the thorny *stividha*
(*Poterium spinosum*), or in Spain, lavender, rosemary and thyme each in their
districts ; the dwarf-palm again, covers large areas in the south-west (cf.
Fig. 10). Throughout the summer plants like these are in colour barely distinguishable from the rock or dry soil. Into this vegetation two alien succulents
have come, the ' prickly pear ' (*Opuntia*) and the larger agave, both introduced
from Mexico and allowed to spread all round the Mediterranean, and not only
in the garrigue.

These varieties of hard-leaved woody vegetation have evidently succeeded
one another, by deterioration, and it has been demonstrated that with encouragement garrigue may be restored to maquis. But the types in their broader
distribution also correspond to the zones of increasing aridity ; and so toward
south and east there comes another formation that has no connection with the
undergrowth of forest and is known as subtropical grassland—by some called
' steppe '. It covers the plateaux of the Atlas region and the northern fringe

of Arabia. In the former region it is composed mainly of the hard tussocky grasses, alfa (*Stipa tenacissima*) and esparto (*Lygeum spartum*), both of which have always been valued for their fibre and now possess great importance for paper-making.

Herbaceous plants so far have been disregarded ; in the Mediterranean vegetation they are prominent only in the cool moist season, since most of them are either annuals, which die before the summer drought, or bulbous plants which rest during this period. The cultivated annual crops of the region are adapted to the climate in the same way ; they must be harvested before the soil is too dry.

The banks of the southern rivers, even of those with little visible water in summer, are lined with broadleaved trees as well as some evergreens ; many are akin to northern species, but the most prominent shade-tree, the plane, is indigenous in the east. The two outstanding evergreens are the dark oleander with pink flowers and the feathery tamarisk, both confined to the lower valleys ; but the tall poplars, elms, ashes and others may be followed upwards to join the deciduous woods of the mountains. Many hillsides are clad in mixed brush-wood of evergreen and summer-green plants, giving place often to tall thickets of Christ's thorn (*Paliurus*). This feature has been discussed in the chapter on Climate. (See page 48, and Fig. 10.) The hard-leaved species have probably moved upward as the deciduous forest was cut down ; but the groves of sweet-chestnut have been spared, and indeed extended widely as a source of food, at the expense of oak wood ; and these mark the present southern limit of the summer-green forest.

The Mediterranean vegetation has an outlier in the little riviera of the Crimea, and on the southern shore of the Black Sea it pushes eastward in a form that betrays the effect of cold winds. Farther east, however, it merges with a very different formation, the Pontic forest. The climate prevailing around the eastern end of this sea and the southern rim of the Caspian with its heavy rain, relatively equable temperature and high humidity, gives a unique character to the vegetation. This is as remarkable for its luxuriance as for its variety of trees, shrubs, herbs and climbing plants. On the lower slopes evergreens like rhododendrons mingle with deciduous bushes and trees in such prolific growth as is seen nowhere else in this part of the world. From these forests many species have migrated westward, and not a few cultivated plants are derived from them.

From the foregoing summary it is clear that the space in which the Europeans have multiplied and developed their ways of life has been carved out of the forest. As a result, great changes have taken place first, in the processes of erosion, with acceleration of these in the south especially ; secondly, in the character of the soil ; and thirdly, in the drainage of the land.   Various aspects of these matters are discussed in other chapters, but the part played by the vegetation in the natural cycle of water must be mentioned here.   There is no need to consider the question so often asked, whether forests induce rainfall or not, but only their action upon the rain that has fallen.   Much of it, wetting the vegetation, never reaches the ground, since it is evaporated and so keeps the air within the forest relatively humid ;   again, the soaked carpet of leaves and moss allows water to percolate slowly into soil, roots and mantle rock.   This serves to maintain the table of ground water at a fairly constant level, and so in turn to feed springs and streams with regularity.   Hence in general there is much less direct flow from the surface where it is wooded than there is from ground of other kinds ;   forest serves to reduce the incidence of floods until the water-table reaches the surface throughout, which is exceptional.

Throughout most of Europe, apart from the Mediterranean lands, such forests as still existed a century ago had maintained themselves from their own stock, while yielding the timber that was needed.   Moreover, since then enlightened management has aimed at cutting trees only in so far as others grew to replace them, whether from seedlings or by plantation ;   and a system of regular rotation prevailed in western and central Europe.   But unfortunately the practice of clear-felling was adopted in Britain, with its comparatively small amount of woodland, during two long wars, and even in Germany, where scientific forestry had been unsurpassed, it became general from about 1935.   It is evident that the water economy is bound to suffer abrupt change when forest is cleared, the uncovered soil becoming more compact and less permeable ;   run-off is quickened, and unless a closed vegetation forms erosion must ensue.

Before this last phase of destruction set in, the European broadleaved forest was losing ground to the evergreen because the need was for softwood rather than hardwood, and also because the conifers grow to maturity in a much shorter time.   The radical effect of this change in the landscape is often deplored on account of the monotony of planted spruce or pine.   Certainly the conifer, either native or introduced from America or Japan, will grow better on many soils that would now need costly attention if they are to support the broadleaved trees that once grew upon them ;   but the new plantations have not been confined to such areas.

Before leaving the subject of forests certain products should be noted which do not involve felling, although some of them lead to systematic mutilation of trees.   The practices mostly belong to southern Europe, where they have led to the preservation of woods rather than to destruction.   The most widespread of these is the gathering of resin by ' bleeding ' the trunks of pines, especially the maritime pine in France and the western Mediterranean lands, and the Aleppo pine in the eastern. The source of cork is the bark of the oak *Quercus Suber*, which is stripped every decade to give southern Portugal one of its chief commercial resources, and is of value in lesser degree to the neighbouring countries. The acorns of this tree and of the holm-oak provide fodder for swine, while those of the Valona oak in the western Balkan Peninsula and Anatolia are gathered and exported for the tanning material they contain. The young leaves of almost any deciduous tree may be used to supplement the available pasturage for stock, so throughout the southern lands trees are pollarded or young branches cut for this purpose. Finally by the stress, given above, to the degradation of dry woodland, attention has perhaps been diverted from the swamps that have been a curse to many a coastal lowland in the south, chiefly on account of their becoming breeding grounds for malaria. The aspect of these has in many cases been changed for the better during the last century by the planting of the ' blue gum ', an Australian eucalyptus. Apart from its shade and other uses this quick-growing tree has proved most beneficial, since it acts like a pump and transpires the unwanted water.

THE TEMPERATE GRASSLAND

The ragged ' front ' between forest and heath or bog along the humid western margin may be compared with the zone of contest in the south-east, between the deciduous oak forest and the grassland or steppe. This ' front ' extends from the middle basin of the Danube eastward into Asia. The essential contrast of environment for the two formations lies in the fact that forest makes use of both rainfall and ground-water, whereas grass is dependent upon current rainfall alone, and this must fall frequently throughout the season of its activity.

Long before the systematic destruction of the southern woodland to make way for cultivation this forest, dominated by the oak, had advanced on to the loess which had accumulated among the grasses in a drier climate. Although most of these woods have been cut away, strips along the valley slopes and many clumps elsewhere remain to justify the name forest-steppe that is applied to a broad zone across Russia from the Ukraine to the southern foothills of the Ural. The oak still predominates, with pine where sands occur, but these gradually give place to trees and shrubs that tolerate greater dryness, including the Tatar maple mentioned in Chapter 5. The grassland which formerly prevailed among the woods was known as ' meadow-steppe ' because commonly mown. The vegetation, now restricted in area, is a tall herbaceous growth covering the black earth with a coherent sod, the feather-grasses intermingled with other herbs which flower brilliantly in the early summer. Southward and eastward, as the depth of the black soil becomes less, the grassy cover declines in height and density to form the opener growth of the true steppe. In this the grasses form separate tussocks, and other plants, whether annuals or perennial bulbs and tubers, virtually disappear after their brief activity, shrivelled in the aridity of the summer afternoon, which is often accentuated by a strong east wind. As the colour of the soil passes to ever paler brown and then to grey on the curving plain around the northern Caspian Sea, the vegetation, more and more sparse, consists of low-growing plants, which over large tracts are adapted not only to resist drought but also to live in soil that is impregnated with salt and gypsum. Such is the semi-desert.

CHAPTER 9

FAUNA

THE natural fauna of Europe must have been adapted in the past mainly to forest, and with the forest this earlier fauna has receded and partly disappeared. Woods have given place to farmland which, to wild animals, is essentially grassland; consequently, species have spread from the eastern steppes and have thriven at the expense of man's agricultural effort. But wild life is held in check, competing as it does for food with man and the domestic animals under his protection. In the Mediterranean lands the succession has differed, as in these lands forest is not easily replaced by an herbaceous flora, and therefore animals akin to those of the hot desert have multiplied.

Of the large mammals of the ancient forest the elk is still to be found in Scandinavia and northern Russia, and the (wild) bison remains only in the Caucasus. The brown bear is commoner than these, but only in the east and in a few mountain forests elsewhere. Red deer and roe deer and the wild pig, however, are still widespread, and in Scotland the first now flourishes on deforested mountains. The fallow deer belongs properly to the woods of southern Europe, but has been introduced to other parts. The wild-cat, too, persists in southern forests and also in Scotland, while its relative, the lynx, with two species, is more common in the south and especially the north-east. The beaver which once haunted European rivers is all but extinct. Few of these mammals now have much more than a sporting interest for man; and this applies also to the smaller animals of the forest such as the squirrel, the glutton, and the marten, although the last, especially the stoat (or ermine) are sought for their skins.

The high mountains of the south retain the distinctive chamois, and moufflon which graze in summer far above the forests. Both these animals differ somewhat according to locality owing to long isolation in particular mountain ranges; the mountain hare on the other hand is almost indistinguishable from the Arctic hare despite wide separation. This animal, like the birds breeding in the same region, the ptarmigan and snow bunting, changes to a white coat in winter. But where it lives near the ocean, as in Britain, the adaptation to the present climate seems to be incomplete, since the white fur persists, in most winters, after the snow has disappeared and renders the hare conspicuous.

Wild life on the northern fringe of Europe varies greatly with the season on account of migration, most obviously that of the birds, but also of other animals. Thus forest dwellers like the wolf range far out over the tundra in search of beast and bird, and the arctic fox of the tundra may almost join the polar bear as a coastal carnivore. The most typical mammal of the tundra, the reindeer, seeking suitable lichen or other forage, makes long journeys which in Europe are now guided by the Lapps, by whom it has been domesticated.

The southern fringe, beyond the Mediterranean, lies in a different faunal region, since the Sahara was formerly no barrier. Thus, Hannibal was able to capture and train his elephants in North Africa ; but the elephant became extinct in the first or second century A.D. Dwarfed crocodiles have been found, in the present century, living in pools on the desert's edge. To the early French colonists of Algeria the lion and panther were pests, and one species of ape is still fairly common in the Atlas Lands. More familiar now are the herds of antelope, mostly gazelles, inhabiting the semi-desert margins of our region in Africa and Asia, and with them hyenas and jackals. Most of these as well as the rodents, reptiles and insects have a protective light-brown colour.

In the Mediterranean region proper, as already mentioned, similar traits occur because of the restricted vegetable food in the summer. Hence it is the abundance of reptiles, especially lizards, tortoises and snakes which is so typical ; and this of course depends upon the insects—dealt with below. Nevertheless we must note that the western part of these lands forms the home of the rabbit, a subject to which we must return.

The animals of the open land where cultivation prevails have been left till last because they are of such direct importance to man. As already stated, the creation of this artificial ' grassland ' led to the great expansion of some elements of the eastern steppe-fauna, just as a post-glacial period of drier climate led to westward spread of plants representative of the steppe-flora. Above all, it is the small rodents that have seized the opportunity, some of them being burrowers, so having an easy protection against marauders. These latter include many carnivorous birds as well as the weasel and the fox. The latter, like the wolf, belongs also to the forest and even the tundra ; but both have proved highly adaptable and bold even in the face of man. It may be stated generally that the rodents multiply in proportion to the intensity of cultivation, and so require corresponding opposition from the farmer and stock-keeper. Moreover, it is not merely in the open land that this anti-rodent war must be waged, for the mouse and more recently the rat have adapted themselves to townlife and a varied diet. The rats, too, by invading ships unfortunately have spread widely overseas. Of the grass-eaters, the hare and the rabbit, the former continues to flourish on account of its speed and its habit of feeding at night ; it is probably quite typical of the progressive westward spread from the steppe. The rabbit on the other hand seems to hail from the open lands of central Spain and the Atlas Lands in which its burrowing habit would no doubt help it to resist the rigours of the summer climate. From these parts expansion northwards would be less natural, and this has most probably been aided by man ; but once introduced to more humid lands it profited by the plentiful food-supply and no doubt became more prolific. Yet the rabbit is still restricted to western Europe and its first appearance in northern Scotland took place only in the nineteenth century.

The migrations of two of the larger species of mouse tribe, viz the black and the brown rat, have placed them among the chief enemies of mankind. The black rat, a native of India, reached Europe in the thirteenth century and transmitted bubonic plague to this continent by the medium of its parasite, a flea. The stronger brown rat, however, had made an earlier entry from the eastern steppe, although it reached Britain only in the eighteenth century ; it has nearly exterminated the black rat there. The presence of rats and mice in human settlements of all kinds is a source of disease, and in addition they annually consume or spoil enormous quantities of grain and other foods in storage. Much less obvious than these pests are the field-mice and the other rodents of the countryside, hedgehogs, moles, and voles, all familiar in Britain, and the hamster of central and eastern Europe ; but moles and hamsters are taken for their skins.

We must now consider the birds, the insects and some other lower forms of life. The distribution of land birds offers many pointers to those of the humbler animals, as does that of sea-birds to the presence of fish, because so many species feed upon insects, worms, grubs, caterpillars and the like. Fewer but generally larger are the birds of prey (*Raptores*) which kill larger ground-animals. Other species again, especially among the smaller birds, are vegetarians, many of them subsisting upon seeds. In all cases birds are equipped in the first place for procuring their special types of food : e.g. long bills of the waders, for probing mud ; short strong bills of the finches for extracting and cracking seeds ; again the feet of the waders are obviously completely different from those of woodpeckers, designed for climbing trees. In every part of our region, then, there are assemblages of different birds to correspond to the environment ; but the proportions of the types must have changed greatly with the progress of cultivation. Thus birds completely dependent on trees, such as the crossbill living on pine-seeds or the woodpecker on insects in the tree-bark, must have decreased. At least as striking is the decline of the wading birds following upon the vast amount of artificial drainage, particularly in central and north-western Europe. On the other hand, as with the small rodents, the birds of the grassland must have increased greatly in range and

numbers in the later centuries with the continual turning and enriching of the
soil and the presence of cereal crops.

Because of the great mobility of birds—as of some of the flying insects too—
migration gives a seasonal rhythm to all bird life. Moreover, unlike the large
movements of fish in the sea, bird migration is visible to all who care to look.
It is true that even with the vast amount of study now devoted to this subject
it is not yet understood in all its aspects. But it is clearly related to the reproduction of the species : the impulse seems to come with seasonal development
of the sexual organs. But there are still questions unanswered about the
directional mechanism and the relations to the state of the atmosphere at the
time. ' As the crow flies ' is a common synonym for ' direct '. It would
probably be better to say ' as the pigeon flies home ', for this bird is now known
to fly along the arc of a great circle : the arrangement of the bird's ear seems
to serve the purpose of a gyro-compass in a modern ship. As for the routes
followed, these must provide for rest and food and water suited to the needs of
the species, and so except over the sea the direct course may not be followed.
As an illustration of the many enigmas, the migration of the stork may be cited.
These birds after the breeding season in Germany fly to South Africa ; those
nesting west of a middle line, roughly that of the River Elbe, go via the Rhône
and the coast of Spain to Morocco, and thence south-eastward over the desert
to the Upper Nile. Here they are joined by the eastern contingent who have
gone by the Balkan Peninsula, the eastern Mediterranean and the Nile
Valley.

It may be observed that migratory birds have their breeding places apparently at the coolest part of their range. Air temperature therefore during the
northern spring and summer may be correlated with the (generally) northern
limits of such birds. But how far this represents a direct response of the bird
itself or an indirect one as affecting the food supply is unknown.

It follows from these general remarks upon the geographical relations of
birds that there is a close accord between the zones of vegetation and the air-
fauna, but that the number and variety of birds occupying any one zone are
different in summer and in winter. Coniferous forest supports the most limited
range of types in view of the relative lack of undergrowth ; but even here, there
is more variety about the swampy openings. Southern Europe shows much
smaller bird-populations than might be expected in many areas for a quite
different reason. This is the merciless depredations made by man, who shoots
or nets birds of all sorts ' for the pot '—a fact that is perhaps partly explained
by poverty ; and there is certainly cultural significance in the contrast between
the islands of Heligoland (off the Elbe), and Cithera (off the Peloponnese).
Both are nodal points for bird migrations : the former has for long been used
as a scientific observatory for ringing (i.e. marking) and releasing birds ; the

latter is one of the chief sources of dead quails, taken in nets during migration, for the market.

The relative paucity of birds in the Mediterranean lands is most striking in regard to the sea-birds, a consequence of the absence of foreshore and shallows off-shore, as well as the poor distribution of fish. On the other hand there are many lagoons and deltas, including that of the Danube, where aquatic and wading birds concentrate, especially during migration. In such places the birds known in northern Europe may be seen mingling with the flamingo, pelican, ibis and other African species.

In southern Europe and overseas the indigenous animals have to compete with very large numbers of sheep and goats; for these domestic animals subsist chiefly upon wild herbage supplemented in winter by stubble after the harvest, for most of the flocks are moved seasonally. The forage of the two animals is somewhat different, the goats being the coarser feeders in that they devour foliage of the hard-leaved trees and shrubs as well as herbaceous plants. If wood-cutting and fires have been the prime causes of the destruction of the Mediterranean forests, it is the goat that has been mainly responsible for preventing their regeneration, and in the long run also for the further decline of the vegetation from maquis to garrigue and, in turn, to phrygana. The sheep, however, in many regions has taken part in this process. Moreover, it must be remembered that in Mediterranean countries the only domestic fuel is wood, used largely in the form of charcoal; and while the quantity needed is very much less than that consumed in northern Europe by equivalent numbers of people, this gathering of firewood depletes the bush seriously, especially near towns.

It is of interest, then, to get some measure of the probable effect of domestic animals on the rough vegetation which covers so much of these lands; so the average density of sheep and goats per square mile may be noted here, as it was in each of the countries in 1938. In practically all of them sheep exceed goats in numbers, but the proportion varies with the quality of the vegetation as forage.

In Albania, Bulgaria and Greece the mean density was over 200 per square mile; in Greece it was 250, a figure to be compared with that of sheep in Great Britain and Northern Ireland—282 in 1938—where sheep play an essential part in the arable system. For the Iberian Peninsula as a whole the figure was 140; for Italy, 94, and Tunisia, 91. The mean densities of the other lands vary widely with the amount of desert included, but all were lower than those quoted. These facts must be borne in mind in relation to the role of pastoral life, past and present, around the Mediterranean Basin.

The lower forms of animal life, despite their fundamental importance in so many ways, can be treated here only by means of examples. The beneficial influence of earthworms upon the soil is well known. Happily these worms are widespread and conditions inimical to them, such as waterlogging, are of local application only. Again, another organism, commonly called the boring- or ship-worm, although it is in fact a mollusc *Teredo*, exists in the sea around most of the European coasts. Yet its effect on human affairs in the past, though serious, has been local. The ship-worm, by riddling the wooden piles of the protective sea dykes in Holland, formerly led to many inundations, and so to the construction of dykes without timber. Venice also in the past has suffered from its attacks upon the piles supporting the buildings.

The place of insects in the human environment is difficult to assess briefly. On the one hand as the pollinators of so many indispensable plants a notable proportion are of inestimable value ; yet insects harmful to man himself, to his mammals and his crops are all but innumerable. One group of insects, the honey-bees, may be counted among the domestic animals, and at an earlier stage ' wild honey ' gathered in the forests formed an article of the earliest trade between the Baltic coast and the ancient Mediterranean world. The relationship of honey to zones of vegetation is obvious : for example, the Mediterranean bush-woods with their abundance of strongly scented flowers as offering the most varied source of nectar for the bees.

The most powerful enemies of man among the insects are the mosquitoes that bring him malaria and the locusts that devour his crops.

It is impossible to assess the damage done by malaria, but certain that only a small part of the evil is indicated by the annual death-roll from this disease. Besides this must be reckoned the effects of chronic malaria on human activity, including those of anaemia and physical and mental debility in malarial districts. Malaria appears to have become endemic in Greece by the beginning of the fourth century B.C., and it has been suggested that its influence upon the Greeks within the next century was sufficient to account for the decline in their culture. However this may be, the ravages in later times in other southern lands are well authenticated.

The anopheline mosquitoes include many species in our region, but only nine of these are known to convey the malarial parasite to man.[1] The disease is endemic, and therefore most serious chiefly around the Mediterranean and Pontic Basins. This is mainly because the climate there suits the life cycle of the mosquitoes concerned. The relationship to temperature and other climatic factors still calls for much research, and it must be noted that meteorological records are usually not made under the conditions actually experienced

---

[1] The parasites are protozoa of the genus *Plasmodium*, which pass a part of their existence in the body of the mosquito and a part in the liver, and then in the blood, of man. Transmission takes place by the bite of the female mosquito—males do not bite—which requires a blood-meal before her eggs can be deposited.

by insects. But it may be stated generally that transmission of the parasite starts effectively with the air temperature above 60° F. (16° C.). Hence the longer the warm period lasts the more endemic is the disease. Fig. 18 illustrates this factor geographically, and shows that most of the areas of high endemicity have mean temperatures over 60° for at least five months. In these regions

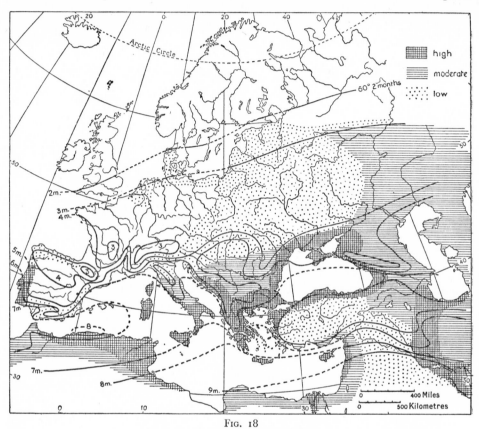

FIG. 18

Relationship of Temperature and Malaria

Lines show the number of months with mean temperature 60° F. (15.5° C.). Shadings show the degree of endemicity of malaria (up to 1943)

the malaria is termed 'subtropical', implying transmission throughout the summer but with a shorter 'epidemic season'. The latter, for example, in Sardinia was from June to September, and in most of Greece from July to September. It is certainly due to the shortened period of warmth farther north in Europe that the so-called 'temperate malaria' is much more easily subdued. This is endemic from the Netherlands eastward to Russia, where it merges with the more severe type.

Apart from temperature the most important aspect of environment is drainage, since the anopheline mosquitoes pass the larval stage in stagnant water, which may be brackish, or in slowly moving streams. With agricultural progress, leading to drainage, such breeding places have largely disappeared from much of western Europe, and with them malaria, formerly known in Britain as ague. But in the east this is only partly true, and in the south

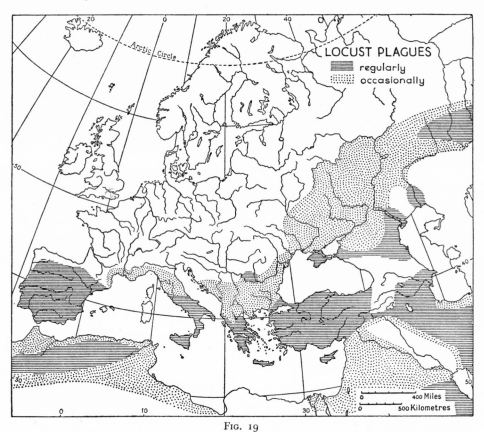

FIG. 19

the prolonged dry summer leads to the reduction of rivers to trickles or strings of pools suited to *Anopheles*, while the coastal lagoons are also hotbeds of mosquitoes. The disease, however, has now been reduced in many areas, notably in Italy, by artificial drainage ; but much remains to be done in this and other ways, such as application of larvicides to water and prophylactic treatment of the human population. Nevertheless final eradication may well be in sight, particularly because of the invention of the insecticide D.D.T. Armed with this, to kill the insects, and the other methods of eliminating the larvae, the health authorities of Cyprus were able to suppress malaria in the island within the two years 1947 and 1948. Similarly the battle has been won in Sardinia, a hotbed of the disease in the past; and in Greece, despite the effects of prolonged warfare, its incidence has been vastly reduced. So it would seem that once the population is persuaded to give full co-operation, these southern lands will be freed from the curse.

From ancient times there have been records from southern Europe and beyond of mysterious and sudden plagues of locusts and grasshoppers. The results of such merit well the term plague, since the millions of insects advancing either on foot or on the wing may, in a short time, strip from a large cultivated tract all the growing food for man and beast; whereupon famine prevails (Fig. 19). Such plagues were formerly unheralded, especially where flying locusts were concerned, for with a favouring wind these have been known to cover 300 miles in a day. As for the mystery, this has at last been cleared up by research. It has been demonstrated (by B. P. Uvarov) that certain species of solitary and usually harmless grasshoppers change their character and become gregarious locusts; there are not two distinct species, but two phases of the same species to consider. In a specially favourable season a vast increase in the number of individuals takes place in a given area, and the crowding leads to change not only of behaviour but also of form; thus some grasshoppers become swarming locusts. The destruction of woodland of the Mediterranean region in the past has doubtless favoured the general spread of the grasshopper family (*Acrididae*), including the four whose distribution must now be considered (Fig. 20).

The Moroccan Locust (*Dociostaurus maroccanus*) breeds on rocky slopes with an open vegetation of bush and thin grass in areas extending from the Canary Islands to the Transcaspian region; and swarms from the mountains have repeatedly ravaged the Atlas lands, the Iberian peninsula, Anatolia and Cyprus, Transcaucasia and Turkistan.

The Migratory Locust (*Locusta migratoria*) in the solitary phase is widely distributed throughout the Old World, south of 60° N., but the breeding grounds of this insect in the swarming phase are restricted to the deltas and swampy valleys around the Caspian Sea, to similar sites in Asia as far as Lake Balkhash, and occasionally north of the Black Sea, that is, to areas favoured by a humid local climate in a dry region. This species constitutes the chief locust-problem of Russia.

The Desert Locust (*Schistocerca Gregaria*) of the tropical and subtropical deserts is probably the most destructive of all. This is to be expected, from the huge extent of the deserts from which it comes to cultivated land in the early spring when already a swarming locust, but in the hopper stage, to be followed by other swarms in the adult stage. The need to combat such invasions of northern Africa and south-western Asia has led to vigorous research and measures of control in Africa and Arabia.

The so-called Italian Locust (*Calliptamus Italicus*) has a distribution similar to that of the Moroccan Locust, but is only occasionally a serious pest. Yet its attacks are notable as extending to western and central Europe, and the

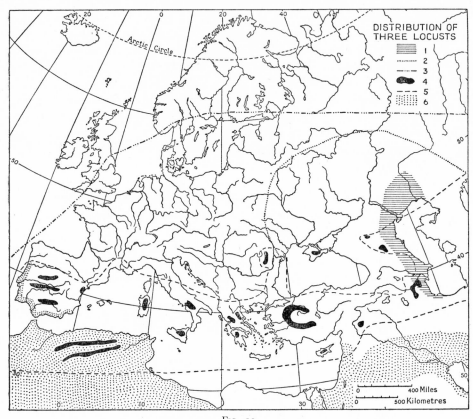

FIG. 20

Migratory Locust : 1 Area of solitary phase ; 2 Limit of its regular breeding ;
3 Limit of its occasional breeding
Moroccan Locust : 4 Breeding areas ; 5 Limits of its occurrence
Desert Locust :   6 Its distribution

damage is specially heavy since the insect may actually breed on cultivated land.

Thus the locust plague is a feature of the drier fringes of Europe, and investigation of the subject has demanded closer study of ecological conditions there than ever before. The behaviour of these insects at all stages is notably and directly responsive to temperature of body and so of ground and air ;

they even create a micro-climate themselves by crowding when on the march. They are active by day and in sunlight ; the Migratory Locust, for example, takes the road daily at temperatures from 59° to 71° according to age. Mass wandering begins when the temperature exceeds about 74°, the impetus being related apparently to body temperature. Once on the move the hopper bands in their countless crowding millions stop only because of weather changes, and not even streams form obstacles, since they can swim. After the final moult wings appear, but flight begins only with still another rise in temperature —with the Moroccan Locust to *c*. 90°. The subsequent migration by air may continue through the night, and is probably induced by physiological causes. Armed with much knowledge of this kind, entomologists and others acting with truly international support will inevitably succeed in preventing plagues of locusts in the future.

The farmers of all the eastern Bridgelands have to contend with another group of insects whose depredations may be compared with those of the locusts. These are bugs of the genus *Eurygaster*, widely known as the *sunn* or *sunna*, which destroy cereal crops. Like the locusts they migrate, spending the summer on the hills under stones, and then they invade the lowlands, subsisting on wild herbs until the seeds of wheat, barley, maize or millet have formed ; they suck these while still unripe.

CHAPTER 10

MAN AND HIS CULTURE

THE gradual peopling of Europe and its borderlands has been accompanied by slow modification of the landscape and all it means by many generations of men—that is, the process was slow until the nineteenth century, when it was greatly accelerated, principally in the west. The prolonged changes were those due mainly to the extended use of the land for agriculture and stock-keeping ; only in minor degree did they come from the foundation and growth of towns. The last century or so, in contrast, has been marked by the trans-formation of towns by the development of mechanical industry and by the spinning of a web of roads, canals, railways, pipes and cables linking the cities and towns and penetrating the settled rural areas and the intervening wastes alike. These modern changes began in the north-west, where the results now dominate large tracts, and they have been much less potent in the south and east. This artificial pattern, due to modern technology, and differing from all natural patterns, is the geographical evidence of the principal gift of western Europe to the world. Its eastward spread represents a reversal of nearly all previous currents of human progress ; for these flowed broadly from east to west, if we admit the existence of important eddies and occasional counter-currents.

It befits geography to devote its attention specially to those aspects of cultural advance which leave their imprint upon the face of the earth, and which may be most simply classified as rural and urban. We shall learn to trace under the existing man-made pattern of central Europe, for example, that settled country life which existed for ages without any towns. But we must also learn of the degree in which country has become tributary to town.

We need not pause to examine the theories adduced to explain why the north-western segment of the Old World is the home of the white race. The exploration of differences in racial types within Europe is also a difficult subject, and there are gaps in the evidence. But it seems to be clear that existing populations bear much closer resemblance to remote ancestors than is commonly realised ; that the people who first tilled the soil of some of our farms in the Neolithic Period really were, in part, our ancestors through perhaps 120 generations ; and that some of us may still carry the undoubted features of a still more remote Mesolithic hunter.

Without entering further into the complex problems of European racial origins and types, let us go on to examine other important aspects of man and his culture.

LANGUAGE

Of all the elements of a culture it is language which most distinguishes one people from another. Moreover, from the power which community of language and literature have exerted over human groups in the creation of nationality the distribution of languages must be considered as a causal element not only in history but also in geography, because of its relation to international boundaries and to the geographical organisation of states. On the other hand this distribution of languages as it now exists is directly the result of the history of the peoples concerned, and is only indirectly affected by geographical factors. A word of caution is perhaps in place here. While the racial composition and the language of a people are not necessarily unrelated, the term 'race' should never be applied to other than (average) bodily features, as is unfortunately often the case when a writer speaks of race when he merely means either general cultural characteristics—of which language is an important element—or else national, and so political, affinity.

Linguistic history is beyond our scope, but the probable cause, the approximate period and place of differentiation of the principal languages may be noted as relevant matters. Fundamentally, the cause of differentiation was comparative isolation of humanity, group from group at periods, more or less remote, when total population was small and communications necessarily poor ; and so linguistic units may be thought of in general as growing up while divided by forests or other barriers. The subsequent spread of tongues, once formed, like that of other cultural features, was bound up with migration, trade and conquest. Language has proved on the whole less permanent than other elements of culture such as agricultural implements and crops or types of rural houses and villages. Europe, however, abounds in relics of languages long dead or at least departed, and among the most fruitful sources for linguistic history are place-names. Of these, the oldest are usually those of physical features, especially rivers. Thus, for example, the names of the rivers of much of central Europe and of England possess predominantly Celtic names, and a common term for a valley in the western Alps and in Wales alike is *nant*.

The three great language-groups of Europe became differentiated between the fifth and the ninth centuries A.D. The Teutonic language originated in an area centred on the Danish Islands, and the Slavonic probably in some tract lying immediately north of the Carpathians. When thus evolved separately, each of them subsequently gained territory up to, and in parts beyond, their present limits because of the military strength and virile enterprise of the tribes. Hence, although the languages of the former Teutonic overlords of Gaul, Iberia, the Atlas region and the West Russian lands later gave way to the present languages, these still show many borrowings from the Germanic. The existence of the Romance group on the other hand is a consequence of the great power of the Roman Empire in the territories where these tongues are now spoken, and its persistence is due to the higher culture of Rome. But the variation of the Romance languages is explained partly by the fact that these lands were Romanised, at widely different times, so that the various languages derived from different stages in the development of Latin, and partly by the different reactions to Latin of the older tongues such as Celtic, Teutonic and Iberian.

Some of these languages and others not mentioned have persisted only because of relative isolation to the present time. Thus to take the oldest of all European languages, Basque : neither the antiquity nor the former extent of the tongue is known, but it has evidently remained about the western Pyrenees for geographical reasons. Comparable with this is Albanian, classed as an early Indo-European language, which certainly occupies the least accessible part of the Balkan Peninsula and no doubt had a much wider extension in prehistoric or later times. The Celtic tongues, again, which developed in and around the basin of the Rhine are now relics, on the Atlantic fringe ; they have persisted only in lands of farthest emigration. Their separation, Gaelic from Welsh, Cornish (extinct) and Breton is due to difference in period of arrival and to subsequent mutual isolation. Greek has survived a long and troubled history, and indeed it has reconquered territory from the Slavonic languages, largely on account of the strength of cultural memories, but also because much of the land where it was spoken was difficult of access.

Apart from Basque and several tongues on the outer fringe of Russia four languages are quite different from the Indo-European ; Lappish, Finnish-Estonian, Magyar and Turkish. Of these the two former antedate the Indo-European encroachments, the Finnish-Estonian was almost replaced by Russian over most of its former wide territory, but near the Baltic Sea developed as a literary language. Of the others Magyar, an interloper of the ninth century, was the speech of tribal nomads who crossed the Carpathians from south Russia to the Mid-Danubian plain, where it has remained ; it holds also in Transylvania since Magyars were settled there to resist further inroads from the East. Turkish is the language of the latest Asian conquerors. This, mainly spoken by the ruling classes in the Ottoman Empire, has never been the language of the majority on the European side save in colonial tracts of which only Thrace remains—an extension of the main body in Anatolia.

Turning again to the Teutonic, Slavonic and Romance groups in turn, we should note certain points about their subdivision. The original homeland of Teutonic is divided today between two of the chief branches—Scandinavian and German, with a small remnant of Frisian which is usually classed with the third branch, English. The distinction between Scandinavian and German can be attributed to three causes : severance by the Baltic Sea ; the inhospitable nature of the land between the mouths of Elbe and Oder ; the occupation of the south-western coasts by Slavs from the sixth to the ninth centuries. In the subdivision of Scandinavian the separation of Swedish from Danish and its kindred Norwegian dialects and from Icelandic was doubtless due to the isolation of communities by sea and by rough land, as e.g. between central Sweden and (Danish) Scania.

The chief Slavonic distinction, that between the northern and southern languages, comes from the historic penetration of the Mid-Danubian plain by the Avars, then in succession by the Germans and the Magyars. Since the original spread of the Slavs took them westward to the line from the lower Elbe to the eastern Alps, the present strongholds of separate northern Slavonic tongues are to be regarded as residuals. Czech and Slovak occupy between them a long mountain-girt refuge, while the minute remnant of Wendish, in the marshland of the upper Spree, was enveloped by the eastward advance of German. The much larger tract of Polish with Kasubian, almost entirely on the plain, now coincides chiefly with the basin of the Vistula. In the east the great Pripet marshland, to this day thinly peopled, led to the separate growth of Polish and Russian. This distinction, so important in European history, was confirmed by the accident of conversion to Christianity about the same time from different sources, Rome and Byzantium. North and south of the marshes much mixing took place between Poles and 'White' and Little Russians respectively. Boggy land and dense forest again favoured the differentiation of the east Baltic languages, Lithuanian and Lettish, both akin to Slavonic.

In the south Slavonic group Serbo-Croatian and Bulgarian pass into each other through their dialects, but in the west the division from Slovenian is clearly defined. The Slovenes, the smallest group of the southern Slavs, pressed well nigh out of the Alps by the Germans, occupy a strategic position between the Adriatic Sea and the River Sava.

The separation of northern and southern Slavonic tongues is completed by the large territory of Romanian, which in turn encloses small areas of Magyar and German speech. Except on the Danube and in the Carpathians its boundaries are not clear-cut. This is the only great outlier of the Romance group ; it has persisted north of the Danube while a similar language in the Balkan Peninsula has become obliterated except among the small remnants of Vlachs who still call themselves Aromuni. The Balkan Peninsula, the Danubian Lands and south Russia are all characterised by linguistic fragments, some of which mark refuges of older stocks, and some, deliberate colonisation by rulers, while others again record the haphazard displacements of former wars. Such are the fruits of troubled history on the approaches to the Bridgelands of Asia.

The other Romance languages form a single continuous block within which Italian, Rhaetic, Provençal and French have clear boundaries with the Teutonic group. German has for long had two firm bastions in the Alps—about the heads of the Rhine and Rhône and in the basin of Vienna ; between the former and the Strait of Dover the only mixture of German with French is in Lorraine and Alsace. The limit of the Walloon dialect of French with Dutch-Flemish language in the Low Countries dates from the fifth century ; it ends at the Strait of Dover and has had great importance for English culture which could draw so easily from both sources.

Whatever the earlier differences between northern French and the southern or Provençal language, they have been explained largely by the Teutonic rule of the Franks and Burgundians in the north and that of the Visigoths in the south ; the dividing line is farthest north in the Central Plateau, an indication of greater resistance to northern influence in this fastness than in the lowlands on its flanks.

In the Iberian Peninsula the threefold division into Portuguese (and Galician) in the west, Castilian in the centre and Catalan in the east reflects generally the course of the Christian reconquest from the Moors after the ninth century ; but the boundaries tend to follow inhospitable areas for the most part. The linguistic limit of Italian and French follows the main crest of the Alps with some exceptional French transgressions into Piedmont. The Rhaetic or Romansh language owes its preservation to isolation in a few remote Alpine valleys, and Sardinia is an example of an island which for long out of the main current of history, has retained a number of Italian dialects.

The languages of North Africa are Berber and Arabic. The former, much the older in this continent, is derived from the tongue of the ancient Libyans and Egyptians, and as now spoken it comprises varieties as wide perhaps as those of the Romance group in Europe. Arabic has displaced it completely in Egypt and partially elsewhere, as the language of the Koran and the speech of all descendants of the Arabian conquerors. Likewise on the fringe of Asia Arabic is the language from Egypt to Mesopotamia, its northern limit lying at the foot of the mountainous arc, where it gives place to Turkish, Kurdish and Persian—from west to east. These three with Armenian are the chief languages of the mountains and plateaux, but, as befits a region that has ever constituted the principal land passage of western Asia, there is evidence of intermingling ; and in the section standing between the lowlands of Syria and Russia, language changes almost from valley to valley. The great range of speech in eastern Anatolia, Armenia and throughout Caucasia is accounted for by the relief and the position of the region. Language fragments correspond in part to tribal groups whose ancestors sought refuge in glens aside from the alleys of the conquerors and especially in Transcaucasia between the Black and the Caspian Seas. Other remnants are due to the introduction of frontier forces from distant parts of empires, ancient and medieval, to defend this same land-bridge. Within the territory of Arabic to the south there is a lesser example of ethnic fragmentation arising from similar causes. A medley of tongues is found extending from Israel to the Tigris, but most obviously in Syria and the Lebanon where remnants of varied culture and origin occupy typical refuges. Israel, too, is linguistically unique, on account of the recent revival by the Jews of the ancient Hebrew tongue.

The linguistic map is thus seen to present an important component in the design of cultural and political nationality, and in so far as it conflicts with economic patterns or with the strategic aims of certain organised states it throws light upon some of the causes of international dispute. But ultimately numbers tell ; so the map of language should always be compared with that showing density of population. Nevertheless it is well to remember that although the existence of small units such as Wendish in the Spree-marsh or Rhaetic in the Alps is unlikely to affect world politics, some such outliers in critical places have provided at least excuses for great wars—witness the German language in the city of Danzig (1939) surrounded by Kasubian of Poland.

Religions and other Cultural Influences

After the mother tongue, the professed religion of a people has been the most important cultural characteristic. It has therefore had profound political effects, and it has frequently led to territorial changes. The evidences of the part played by Christianity in spreading other elements of civilisation in the past are to be seen in most regions of Europe, in the monasteries from which agricultural improvements developed, and in the churches of town and village ; but in the name of religion devastating wars have been fought which in fact retarded civilisation in some of these regions, as in Spain and later in Germany.

Even if there were no written history of Europe, the spread of the Christian religion could be traced by means of architectural study of the churches, cathedrals and monasteries. Ecclesiastical buildings, then, if regarded merely as prominent features of the landscape to which men have given of their best throughout the ages, have their place in any adequate appreciation of regional geography. The evolution of the architectural styles is associated not only with periods, but also with regions. The Gothic church, for instance, is seen at its best and purest in northern France where the style evolved, while English and Spanish Gothic each have their regional peculiarities. Again, the number

and the splendour of churches in a district give clear indications of the population and their wealth when the churches were built ; their presence can be
understood only as a part of the life of the region, and they give a measure of
its productivity.   But the geographic relations of the Church with the towns
and the countryside are not restricted to the distribution and character of
buildings, however dominant these may be.   We may recall that the oldest
churches were often erected on sites already hallowed by a more ancient religion,
and so at centres of still older routes.   Moreover, we may recognise the stages
by which church land was brought under cultivation for the first time under
the guidance of monastic pioneers.   For reasons such as these a map recording
the progress of Christianity should be studied in relation not only to the distribution of the later divisions of the Church, but also to those of languages and
other cultural elements.

Thus religion has to be reckoned as contributing to the geography of
Europe, and the distribution of its chief forms about the beginning of the
present century may be taken as a guide in appreciating its more recent
influence, notably upon political frontiers established after the First World
War.   As in all maps that concern human affairs it must, of course, be compared with that showing density of population, but with due regard to the
fact that quite small minorities holding strong religious or politico-religious
opinions have often initiated movements which spread rapidly under impetus
from other sources having more complex motives.

At the opening of this century the vast majority in all European countries
professed Christianity ; but this outwardly Christian continent was divided
into three parts.   Two of these had roughly equal numbers of adherents,
the Greek Orthodox Churches in the east with c. 104 millions, and the Protestant Churches in the north-west with 98 millions ; the Church of Rome
remained the largest communion, with c. 179 millions.   Added to these were
the Orthodox Christians, and the Armenian, Coptic and other Churches within the Ottoman Empire and Egypt claiming some 4 millions.   Behind the great
Schism of the ninth century between the Western and Eastern Churches was
the fact that the Latin language had never replaced Greek in the eastern part
of the Roman Empire, and that political power rested in Byzantium long
after the fall of Rome.   Hence the conversion of the eastern and southern
Slavonic peoples by missionaries from East Rome (Byzantium) led, among
other differences, to the writing of Russian, Bulgarian and Serbian in the
Cyrillic derived from the Greek alphabet.   Christianity reached the western
Slavs, the Magyars and the Slovenes from German and other western missionaries, and these peoples remained faithful to Rome.   Thus the cultural isolation
of eastern Europe from the west is of ancient origin.   That it has persisted
and even become intensified is due largely to oriental influence in the sub-

sequent history of eastern Europe, open as it was to pressure from Asia, with periods of rule by the Tatars in the north and the Turks in the south.

The Reformation of the sixteenth century chiefly affected northern Europe, and the complicated boundary of Protestantism in Germany and neighbouring lands is due largely to the varied partisanship of petty rulers during the Thirty Years War. The outliers in the Danubian countries and southern Russia represent later German colonisation, together with the indigenous Czech and Magyar Protestants. Thus religious divisions in central Europe have not *in themselves* had great influence in subsequent territorial matters, but the partition of Ireland, from 1922, must be attributed to this cause.

When the Muslim rulers were being ejected from Spain and from Sicily, Islam was gaining a new foothold by the Ottoman conquests ; but descendants of European converts under Turkish dominion remain only in the Balkan Peninsula while other Muslim remnants have maintained themselves throughout south-eastern Russia.

The Jews cannot be represented as occupying continuous tracts of territory in Europe, but their presence in great numbers in cities and towns must not be forgotten, since it came to have disastrous results after 1933, and this not only for adherents of the Jewish faith. We need not attempt to follow the migrations of the Jews before the present century ; but their distribution in 1910 has proved to be most significant, and it is therefore shown approximately on Fig. 21. The vast majority occupied the western states of the Russian Empire and Austrian Galicia with extensions in Romania, Hungary and Germany ; while notable outliers were the great cities of the west, especially Amsterdam and London. Similar concentrations of Sephardim Jews, descendants of emigrants from Spain, were those of Thessaloniki and Istanbul. But it is the tract of Europe between the Oder and the Dnepr, the Dvina and the Danube that held the main body of Jewry, crowded in the ghettos of the towns, from which, however, many sought the opportunity of emigration to the New World, while it still welcomed them. Since 1910 vast changes both in the status and treatment of the Jews have taken place. Most of their principal habitat was a theatre of the First World War, and it was devastated again in the Second War, which saw the culmination of the most vicious attack ever made upon this people, and more than half the Jews of Europe perished. The inset diagram on Fig. 21 indicates broadly the changes in distribution and numbers before and after the Second War.

On the African side of the Mediterranean the vast majority of the population are Muslims, for Christianity which flourished in the earlier centuries survived the Islamic invasion only in Egypt, where the Coptic minority never died out ; but colonial expansion and emigration from France, Italy and Spain increases the number of adherents of the Roman Church. It should be added, however, that devotion of North Africans to Islam varies greatly in degree, being complete where the Arabian tradition is strong, as e.g. among the puritan Senussi of the Egyptian and Libyan oases, but much more superficial among many of the Berber tribes of the Atlas mountains. Jewish communities are found in many of the cities where they have lived at least since the expulsion of their ancestors from Spain.

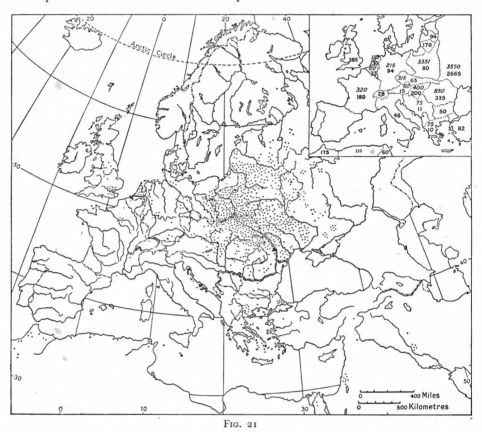

FIG. 21

Approximate distribution of Jews in 1910   (1 dot = 10,000 Jews)
Inset Number (in thousands) of Jews in 1939 (italic figures) ; in 1946–47 (upright figures)

Throughout the Ottoman Empire the Christian religion was permitted so long as it did not give rise to political unrest. Among the groups which continued as minorities, the largest consisted of the adherents of the Orthodox Church in the coastal districts of Anatolia, both west and north ; their Greek language as well as their faith kept alive the spirit of Hellenism abroad, until 1922, when they were expelled in exchange for a much smaller number of Muslims from Greece.

Several parts of Europe and the nearer East came under well-known influences that have been the subject of historical study, but are often insufficiently considered for their effect upon the regions ever since they were active. The most important concerning southern Europe and the Mediterranean are the rule of the ' Moors ' or ' Saracens ' and the rule of the Ottoman Turks ; both were exotic and alien in most of the elements of culture. The former affected Iberia and the western islands of the Mediterranean, and the latter, south-eastern Europe. In general it may be said that the degree of subsequent effect is proportional to the period during which the influence lasted, as shown on Fig. 22 ; but the Turkish influence in Europe is much more recent, since it began approximately when the Moors were ejected from Spain. Among the occidental influences in the east two may be mentioned, the Crusades, leading to the ' Latin ' principalities that were maintained for a short period in Syria and Palestine ; and the trading operations of Venice and Genoa which reached the same Levant coast. The insular realms of these mercantile republics embraced most of the isles of Greece and extended from the Adriatic to Cyprus. This influence continued during the earlier period of Ottoman rule in Europe. The Crusades were responsible for geographic elements not only in Syria but also in western Europe, notably the oldest castles to be built of stone and modelled on the oriental pattern.

In northern Europe certain characteristics of cities and seaports are traceable to the activities of the Hanseatic League, so the extent of the trade carried on by this powerful organisation (Fig. 22) must be noted as contributing to the character of the northern cultural region. Similarly the medieval influence of the Saxon miners has had lasting effects, notably upon the eastern limits of German speech and culture as they were, at least until 1939. The map shows only the principal areas where these pioneers worked in Germany, as well as in other countries at the invitation of foreign rulers. Comparable with these distributions but not suitable for plotting on a small-scale map, are the numerous and widely scattered areas of swamp that were drained for the first time by Dutch engineers, again usually at the instance of ruling princes, especially in northern Germany. In many of these districts there were also Dutch farming communities.

While some of the effects of these historical influences may be properly and fully discussed in relation to specific regions, there is one consequence of the Turkish conquests that must be referred to here, the spread of the Gipsies in Europe. This oriental folk, who seem to have retained their ancestral traits under the Byzantine Empire, must have seized the opportunity offered by the unrest that accompanied the Turkish advance to move westward.

They made their appearance in Germany early in the fifteenth century, but they have continued to occupy the former Turkish dominions in far greater numbers. At the end of the nineteenth century they numbered 176,000 in the Balkan Peninsula, 230,000 in Romania, and 275,000 in Hungary, while perhaps another 175,000 were scattered in every country of Europe. From

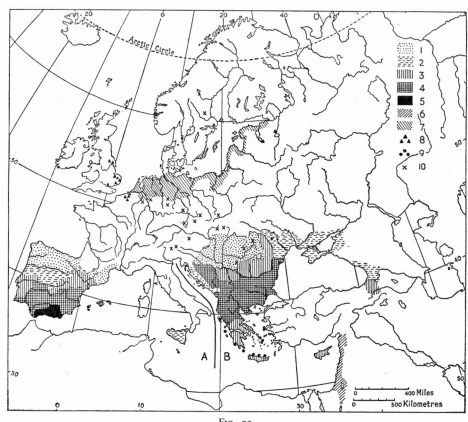

FIG. 22

Distribution of certain alien and other cultural influences

A	*Arabian rule (west)* :		B	*Turkish rule (east)* :
1	less than 170 years		1	less than 200 years
2	170 to 370		2	200 to 300
3	370 to 470		3	300 to 400
4	470 to 570		4	over 400
5	570 to 780		5	—

6 principalities of Crusaders in twelfth and thirteenth centuries
7 commercial territory of Hanseatic League
8 foreign depots of Hanseatic League
9 possessions of Venice and Genoa in Turkish sphere
10 chief areas of German mining settlements

(Note that the Arabian rule in Africa is not shown)

earlier migrations the Gipsies had reached Egypt and spread throughout North Africa, but their numbers outside Europe were not really known. Because of their nomadism and other habits, few of these people have ever been regarded as normal Europeans, and they have often been persecuted by their hosts ; during the Second World War under Nazi rule they perished in large numbers. Yet they must certainly be considered an important element of the population of the south-east, and from their music at least they must be credited with a contribution to European culture. The south-eastern Gipsies, when settled, have tended to occupy distinct and usually sordid quarters on the outskirts of towns and villages.

CHAPTER 11

THE HUMAN IMPRINT

By his occupation and use of the land man has made his mark chiefly by tilling the soil and by his buildings of all kinds, and these works, comprising the human imprint, may be regarded as a geographic pattern. It is extremely complex and varied, not only on account of considerable differences in present practice from region to region but also because every region still bears traces of former stages of material culture ; and these are to be considered not simply as features of the landscape that bear witness to older ways of life, like objects in the cases of a museum, but as real dynamic elements in the existing scheme of social geography. For just as the present system of life—economic, political and spiritual—of peoples is to be understood only in the light of history, so their mode of occupying and using the land has been guided, and often hampered, by features created as a result of the habits of the previous generations, or even those of quite remote ancestors. Thus, for example, the network of roads and bridges planned and built for use by horse-drawn vehicles proves inefficient for motor transport ; and this applies also to farms and fields designed for the horse or the ox when these give place to the motor tractor. Yet the old pattern cannot be easily eliminated, nor do the settlements that grew up to suit it simply disappear without trace. Hundreds of seaports famous in the days of sail have lost their trade to the few that have proved specially able to cope with large vessels, and the old coastal towns have had to find new functions. Towns which owe their location to some long-forgotten circumstances prove to be badly sited for their present function. Political boundaries, national or local, established perhaps in a forest or on a disused Roman road, prove inconvenient under modern conditions. It is for reasons such as these, then, that geography must delve into the past if it is to attempt exploration of the composite patterns of man and his works that it aims to study and describe. In this way the map of any part of a continent that has been occupied for many centuries is found to reveal in its man-made lines a pattern composed of bits and pieces differing widely in the period of their origin. The process of study may be compared with that of examining an ancient parchment which bears not merely the clear script of its latest use but also one or more palimpsests incompletely erased by the latter scribes.

ROADS

The system of roads built by the Romans throughout the Empire, when viewed as a whole (Fig. 23), must surely evoke admiration for an achievement which as a means to control subject peoples and to tap resources could hardly be improved by modern engineers provided with accurate maps.

The importance of this network in the geography of modern Europe is

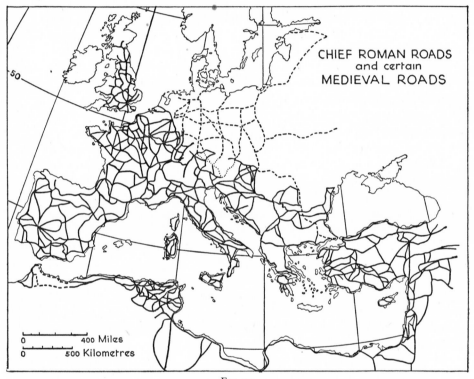

CHIEF ROMAN ROADS
and certain
MEDIEVAL ROADS

0   400 Miles
0   500 Kilometres

FIG. 23

partly indirect, in the numerous cities and towns whose origin is so closely bound to the connecting system. But the Roman roads themselves are followed more or less closely over long distances either by more modern roads or by railways, and often by both. In other words the pattern of communications in western and southern Europe in its main lines comes to us from the Romans. Furthermore where the old roads have disappeared their straight trace is left in many landscapes as an age-old division of fields and woods, or it may be recorded as a boundary of land preserved through all the changes.

The mesh of the Roman net is widest in the Balkan Peninsula, with a frame following the coasts and the Danube, and inland roads along the two furrows which converge on the Morava, and so the Danube. In addition to these there were four bold mountain routes across the Balkan Mountains and five through the western ranges.

A remarkable symmetry marks the system of the Iberian Peninsula ; each coast has its road, except the north where the mountains keep the route inland —the one used in the Middle Ages by the pilgrims of Santiago ; parallel to these, but on the plateau, is a smaller quadrilateral with diagonals crossing at Toledo. These elements do not have complete counterparts in the modern nets of main roads and railways, since the Spanish road system now radiates from Madrid ; but railways in many parts correspond with Roman roads.

The striking features of the network in Peninsular Italy are the coastal roads and the ways radiating from Rome, three of which are now followed generally by railways crossing the Appennines.

The modern communications of Tunisia and eastern Algeria show a close correspondence to those of the ancient provinces, Africa and Numidia, but they are in parts less complete than this remarkable net of Roman routes.

Throughout the northern and greater part of Gaul the roads are rather closely and evenly spaced—but with the notable gap in Flanders—and enclosed by a semicircular way from Cape Finisterre to the mouth of the Rhine. It should be possible to follow this arc today almost completely by train, and again, a railway journey from Lyons to Köln would be almost as direct as that on the old road. It is notable that within this northern arc the chief centre of routes is not Paris as in later times, but Reims.

The road-pattern in Asia Minor is not unlike that of Iberia ; here, again, there was an inner quadrilateral with diagonals on the plateau ; these cross at Ankara, but far to the east Sivas was the centre of eight roads. In Syria the parallelism of main roads is imposed by relief, and the eastern one is now lost in the desert.

Many of the Roman roads must certainly have replaced much older tracks, and similar early trade-routes existed beyond the frontiers of the Empire ; no doubt the commercial use of these increased in Roman times ; among them were the ancient salt-roads among the hills of central Europe and the 'amber roads' and waterways leading south from Jutland and the eastern Baltic coast. Some of these gradually came to be knit into the system of routes that grew up in the Middle Ages with the revival of trade and the development of mining and the crafts. None of these roads was built throughout like the roads of Rome, but as the system was extended eastwards with the spread of German culture they came to be well organised and of more or less standard widths. The more important medieval roads have been added to the map (Fig. 23), and it may be noted that they form a network composed of east-west and north-south elements. Unlike the Roman system, however, these roads seem at first to have mainly served local or regional trade and only gradually became continuous European roads. The lower Rhineland was linked via Dortmund and Bremen to the Baltic at Lübeck. From both Köln and Frankfurt roads led to Erfurt in the Thuringian basin, which was linked via Leipzig to the upper Oder at Breslau (Wrocław), whence the route continued by Crackovie (Kraków) to Kiev, passing from the Vistula along the southern edge of the Pripet marshes. From Würzburg one road led to Praha and Kraków, a second to Nürnberg and the Danube, and a third to Augsburg. Five routes from south to north developed progressively, and so Nürnberg, Praha and Wrocław became important nodes in the system, and much of the trade on these was directed upon the Brenner Pass via Augsburg or upon Salzburg and Villach on the Drave. The most easterly route followed in part the ancient ' amber road ' from the Baltic, and at Pest on the Danube it joined with the Transilvanian road to Byzantium. A comparison of this medieval system with that of the post-roads of central Europe at the end of the eighteenth century brings out the continuity of use in most of these routes.

CITIES AND TOWNS

Civilisation, especially Western civilisation, is unquestionably marked most clearly and widely by cities and towns, and this despite the squalid appearance of many. These centres of organised life have necessarily been bound by communications, since it is from them that external relations have developed, and towns have either grown out of certain earlier villages or they have been founded deliberately at intervals along the fringes of natural features which acted as barriers in greater or lesser degree—the sea-coast, mountains, rivers, swamps, forests or deserts. Moreover, since they were tempting repositories of wealth, almost all towns had to occupy defensive sites with walls or other fortifications varying with the period. Historically then, cities were born in Egypt and Mesopotamia on the banks of the rivers by which they communicated, and near the fringe of the desert. These were followed by others first between the mountain foot and the desert, connected by well-marked but unmade trails for animal transport, and secondly on the hill-girt coasts of the Mediterranean. These depended upon coastal sea-ways to a very great extent and colonial towns multiplied as sea-borne commerce increased. Then came the great expansion of urban life under the Roman Republic and Empire, and towns for the first time were an integral part of a widespread system of made roads for wheeled traffic. But as Roman roads gradually disintegrated so also did very many towns decline, though a comparatively small proportion disappeared. A new impulse in the foundation of cities beyond the former Roman frontiers in Europe came from Charlemagne, and the process was carried eastward during the Middle Ages. But these cities were largely dependent upon the sea and on river-borne trade ; western and central Europe had to wait until the eighteenth century for networks of roads comparable with that of the Roman engineers, while such development in much of the southern and eastern part of the continent was postponed for almost another century and indeed hardly preceded the arrival of the railway. The growth of power-driven manufacturing, the new means of rapid transport by land, first on rails and then on the road, as well as the vast development in shipping, have of course led to great increase in the number and size of cities. But this complex of cause and effect must be left for special treatment.

Thus the city is as old as Western civilisation and has existed in Egypt and throughout south-western Asia for at least fifty centuries, and the length of its life as an institution elsewhere should be borne in mind, viz : around the Mediterranean, some twenty-five centuries ; in the remainder of the Roman world, eighteen ; beyond these frontiers, progressively less in an eastward direction to central Russia, with only about eight centuries of urban life.

Many ancient towns have perished, but few have left no trace ; mounds of accumulated debris of successive towns are scattered over the Nearer East, and ruins have been actually an economic asset in many other parts ; their relation to the modern ' tourist industry ' begins with the fashion of English ' milords ' to take the Grand Tour. These remains as well as the monuments of living cities are recognised as objects of archaeological and historical study ; but the character and functions of towns are equally facts of geography, and the long-continued life of a town, together with its special function in the past, have real bearing on its present aspect and the part it plays in its region. The historic spread of cities may be summarised at this point, even if the detail be largely avoided (Fig. 24).

Historic Spread of Cities

Of the great cities of ancient Egypt and Mesopotamia none has persisted, yet in Egypt, Memphis and Heliopolis have a successor in Cairo, standing between their sites at the head of the Nile delta, and Alexandria, founded *c.* 330 B.C., replaced the older Canopus near by. Similarly Mosul corresponds to the more ancient Nineveh across the Tigris, while Basra, probably of Roman origin, no doubt still performs some of the functions that belonged to Ur from which the Persian Gulf has receded by 150 miles since it flourished.

Before 2,000 B.C. the Hittites, having learned much from Assyria, probably had built many towns in Anatolia ; those which survive are Marash in the

foothills of the Taurus, Birecik (the classical Zeugma) on the upper Euphrates
and Aleppo. About the same period Troy had been founded in a key position
commanding the Hellespont, and the nucleus of a maritime realm in the
Aegean had been formed at Cnossus in Crete. Both cities are in ruin—the

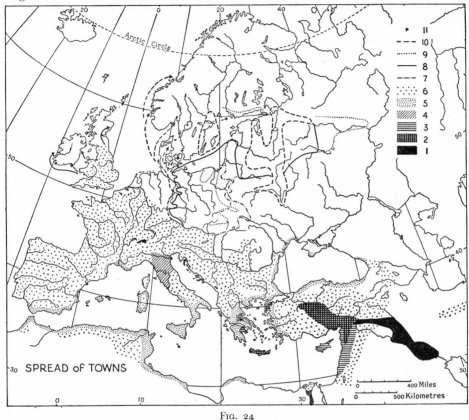

FIG. 24

Towns existing by :
1 3000 B.C., Mesopotamia and Egypt
2 c. 2500 B.C., Troy, Cretan and Hittite
3 c. 1500 B.C., Aramean, Cyprus, Mycenean
Medieval towns by :
7 1100 ;   8 1200 ;   9 1300 ;   10 1400 ;   11 outlying towns at each stage.

4 c. 900 B.C., Etruscan
5 c. 500 B.C., Greek, Carthaginian
6 c. 150 A.D., Hellenistic, Roman

former in several strata, but Byzantium was later to arise, and to remain, at
the other entrance to the Straits ; and again, about 1500 B.C. cities, presumed
to be daughters of Cnossus, were founded in Greece—Orchomenus in Boeotia,
and in Argolis Tiryns and Mycenae, which yielded place to Argos, and this
town still stands. The position of Syria made it a habitable and a coveted
bridge between the river-bank empires and between the desert and the sea,
and so an early focus of urban life of which the Arameans seem to have been

notable promoters. Thus the inland cities of Damascus and Jerusalem stand out on account of their long-continued occupation and importance ; and such cities have ever been in close relation with the seaports of the Phoenicians. Nearly all of these still exist, some still continuing to occupy the old sites as at Tyre (Sur) and Sidon (Saida) and some being now mere villages. Two that were relatively small at the earliest stage, but which attained great importance in the Roman or other periods are Beirut and Tripoli, while Akka, a small place now, stands opposite the large modern port Haifa. The Phoenicians by their ever bolder voyages accelerated the spread of oriental knowledge and culture. Thus by 1100 B.C. they had founded their western outposts of Utica and Gades, so that the latter (Cadiz) is the most venerable city of western Europe, and although Utica gave way to Carthage which dominated the narrows of the Mediterranean from the African side, and this city in turn was destroyed, its successor, the Arab city of Tunis, still occupies the same gulf.

The early centuries of the first millenium B.C. saw the town-building of the Etruscans in Italy, and the founding of many city-states in Greece. The Aryan Greek invaders were adapting themselves to a town-life already established in Greece, but one which they developed greatly. A large majority of the Etruscan cities still stand ; and this applies also to most of the Hellenic cities of Greece. Like the Phoenicians, the Greeks later planted trading posts and then colonies overseas. Thus many towns of Hellenic origin, or their ruins, are to be found along all the Mediterranean coasts of Anatolia and in Cyprus, and beyond Byzantium around the Black Sea ; while southern Italy and eastern Sicily became ' Greater Greece ', and there was an African colony in Cyrenaica. Westward expansion led to the Greek foundation of Nice (Nicaea), Antibes (Antipolis) and Marseilles (Massalia) about 600 B.C., and other towns were built along the Iberian coast as far as Cape de la Nao. Similar progress, first by the Phoenicians and then by the Carthaginians, completed the ring of Mediterranean cities along the coast of Africa from the Gulf of Syrtis to the strait of Gibraltar, and that of Spain from Cadiz to New Carthage (Cartagena), while their insular realm included the Balearics, Sardinia and western Sicily. All this commercial and urban expansion had taken place by the fourth century and before the intervention of the Romans. Large numbers of these towns have survived even where, as in many cases, the reason for survival is not easy to perceive. Others have been replaced by later towns at a short distance from the early sites. Except in Asia and in Etruria, most of them are seaports or possessed harbours near them. While the relief of the land and the form of the coast lead to infinite variety of character in detail the towns have many features in common, such as the hill-fort or acropolis that often became the site of temples, and later of churches ; the lower town close-built even where space is not lacking, but centred on a market-place. Many of the towns which tended to grow were termini of land-routes, and others commanded the larger tracts of good agricultural land.

With the rise of Roman power there dawned a new era marked by the growth of inland towns, all of which were nodes in a network of roads that ultimately extended from the Euphrates to Britain (Fig. 23). Many were built on the sites of military camps chosen for strategic or tactical reasons, and subsequently developed as centres of provincial or local administration ; and some were probably replacements of villages or towns that had already been fortified, as notably by Gallic tribes. But economic motives were often present as well ; indeed the planting of colonies as part of a policy of agricultural expansion determined the location of these amid good farmland.

At the end of the second century A.D. there were about fifty large cities in the Roman and Hellenistic world ; the seven greatest, with their population (in hundred thousands)—estimates that must, of course, be accepted with caution—being Rome (10), Alexandria (3), Antioch, Carthage, Ctesiphon (2), Corinth, Ephesus (1). With Roman decentralisation certain cities which still exist grew in size ; good examples are Byzantium, Antioch, Milan and Trier.

While the period of Roman rule varied greatly, and lasted very much longer, under East Rome, in the Balkan Peninsula than elsewhere it was from Roman Gaul and the upper Danubian provinces that urban life eventually made further advance into the Germanic lands. The persistence of the town in face of the barbarians and its subsequent eastward development are related to the spread of the Christian religion, and this fact affects the character and appearance of a great many towns even at the present day. Thus with the conversion of the Roman world, cities became the centres of a new type of organisation, that of the Church, especially those chosen as the seats of the bishops ; and in many towns of France the episcopal residence and the cathedral adjoining the market place are evidence of the close association of church and town which seems to have enabled the latter to continue its existence, however miserably, after the fall of Rome. In western Britain and in Ireland early Christianity persisted in the Celtic form, but in England it would seem that with the pagan invasions the life of the Roman towns—perhaps even London —came to an end. Hence, as Fleure has pointed out, the English cathedral stands in its close apart from the town as it was in the Middle Ages. Towns of medieval origin are usually marked either by a castle or by an imposing town hall, the one indicating the influence of some feudal notable, the other the growing power of the gilds of merchants and craftsmen. The extension, then, of towns beyond the old Roman Empire when recorded on the map (Fig. 24), is seen to have been marked by slow progress till about 1200, followed by rapid advance with German conquests of the Slav peoples in the next century, which in turn became slower after 1300. This map of eastward growth, however, fails to indicate the great number of foundations of towns of the several types : bishops' seats, the burgs of large numbers of princes, and especially the strongholds of civil freedom, typified by the seaports and river ports of Flanders and the northern plain where the Hansa League prevailed (Fig. 22). Again, the growth of similar types of town may be traced throughout Britain and in Scandinavia. Moreover, in Russia there grew up a network of towns much more widely spaced and bound to the banks of the rivers, which formed the avenues of the trade that began with the Scandinavian ' Rusmen '. Starting from Kiev, the ' mother of cities ' in the south, they extended to Novgorod in the north, and then with later advances eastward as in Germany, to Moscow and Nizhni Novgorod.

At the end of the sixteenth century the largest cities of Europe and the Mediterranean region seem to have been Constantinople with some 400,000 inhabitants and Naples with 200,000, while the following may have had about 100,000 citizens : Rome, Milan, Palermo, Lisbon, Paris, Moscow, Fez, Tunis and several towns in Persia. But the next century saw much growth among western towns, which led to a change in the order of population (in hundred thousands) : Paris (5), London (4), Naples and Constantinople (3), Amsterdam (2), Vienna (1).

Many of the medieval towns had previously been villages, and this origin is often betrayed by the lack of regular plan in the old nucleus, whereas the original kernel of a town of deliberate foundation generally reflects this by the regular arrangement of streets and market place. But in general the expansion of towns was hampered by the encircling walls, or as in the northern plain the defensive moat or canal ; and again with military changes in the seventeenth and eighteenth centuries came the construction throughout the continent of broader and more complex ramparts, prolonging the restriction. Then, as modern artillery rendered such works useless, their removal allowed for rapid growth, and often gave the towns a ring of pleasant parks or boulevards in their place.

The attachment of the Jews to town life throughout central and eastern Europe (Fig. 21) and their religious and social isolation, and so restriction, led to the ghetto as a separate quarter, a characteristic and usually sordid feature of many towns of commercial importance, particularly in the Russian Empire.

We have seen that the spread of medieval towns followed the advance of the Germans, and in the plain east of the Elbe it was thus the result of deliberate colonisation amid Slavonic or other peoples. It will be noticed, however, that the expansion by 1300 and again by 1400 was greater in the mountainous south, and this calls for remark, since it was due in the first instance to the Saxon pioneers in mining and metallurgy exploiting the ores of Bohemia and the western Carpathians (Fig. 22). Thus mining towns arose, most of which still exist even where the minerals are exhausted. Many still show by their grid-like plan that they were created by the ruler, while others owe their irregularity to the haphazard manner in which buildings were placed among the workings which in those times were numerous and small.

It is for historic reasons that towns have developed little and late in southern Russia and the Danubian lands. Security was lacking on these open grassy plains ; Transylvania with its hills and forests was the exception, for historically it was an outlying stronghold used by the Romans, and again in the Middle Ages. The inland towns of the Russian steppe, then, are by origin modern colonial and agricultural centres, scarcely having real urban life until industries arrived later on. Bucharest, although a capital city, is modern, while the large and loose aggregations of houses that count as towns in Hungary east of the Danube were originally agricultural colonies created when Turkish rule ended ; and they still have this character.

Regional Features of Urban Architecture

The present aspect of the towns of southern Europe and other regions of ancient civilisation for the most part records a process of growth and decline, in some cases repeated more than once ; but about this no rule can be discerned. Yet history has left its mark more clearly upon the towns than upon the countryside, and with pronounced distinctions from region to region. The economic strength and the cultural leadership of Italian towns, especially those of the north, is abundantly stamped on many places that date back to the Etruscans, and others of later origin. The trading outposts of Pisa, Genoa and especially of Venice are still distinguished from other coastal towns of the eastern Mediterranean (Fig. 22). But more widespread than such Italian influence is that of Islam, whether produced by the Arabian rulers from the Muslim conquests onward or by the Turkish conquerors, in Asia Minor from the eleventh century and in Europe from the fifteenth. Thus in Spain cities mainly founded by Rome have been changed by building to suit an oriental mode of life, and this in proportion to the length of the Moorish occupation, so that the change is most marked in the south-east and least in the north-west. In the Balkan Peninsula Byzantine towns were largely rebuilt under the Turks, but the domestic architecture seems to have been altered chiefly as required to suit the seclusion of Muslim women ; in some ways the Turkish influence was greater in the village than in the town.

From this sketch it is clear that towns reflect cultural influences directly, while the effects of geography upon the style and character are largely indirect.

Nevertheless in one respect it is possible to discern the more direct effects of the physical environment, the nature and use of building materials. For humble dwellings sun-dried clay has been used at all ages along with wood in small or large proportion—in Egypt and Mesopotamia restricted to palm-beams to support the flat roof. Sun-dried brick, also very ancient, has ever been the only material for large buildings in Mesopotamia, whereas in Egypt building stone has always been largely used for this purpose. Throughout the Mediterranean lands local stone, chiefly limestone, has been used for a very long period, while marble and other special rocks for noble structures were brought from long distances by sea, and even by land, in Classical times. Nevertheless it has been shown that the architecture of temples and the like, from Persia westwards, began with timber as the sole material, and masonry therefore developed as the woodlands receded to the more remote mountains and timber came to be subsidiary. Strong beams are still needed for the low-pitched roofs of this region, since the commonest covering is of red tiles, semi-circular in section, and these are heavy and set in mortar. The distribution of this tile, which was doubtless spread under Roman influence, extends across the lowlands of western and southern France from the estuary of the Loire to the lower Saône valley, while there is an outlying northern area in Champagne and Lorraine. This heavy tile, however, tends to be replaced now by a lighter rippled variety which is laid without mortar. The Romans were probably the greatest of all inventors in building, and they used burnt brick, stucco, and especially hydraulic cement made from a mixture of lime with a special volcanic ash, later called pozzolana.

Mediterranean towns are almost infinitely varied in aspect, not only on account of the setting of rocky hills, small plains and the sea, but from the long time-range in the origin of buildings as illustrating much of the history of architecture, and from the considerable age of even humble dwellings which often indicate pronounced individuality in the builder. But common to all are the mellow pale-red roofs, and the general use of limewash of many tints on the plastered walls. Moreover, all the southern towns, from the desert fringe to the foot of the northern mountains, have been built with a view to coolness in summer; streets are narrow and houses relatively tall, walls are thick and windows on southern walls are small.

South of the Mediterranean the flat roof prevails generally, and it is obviously adapted to the rainless climate of Egypt and the Saharan oases. But it is found also along the Levant coast, on many islands of the Aegean, in Sicily and in the Salentino or 'heel' of Italy, as well as in south-eastern Spain and the Algarve in Portugal. On the other hand, it is replaced along the northern fringe of the Atlas Lands by ridged roofs of thatch, cork or tiles. Rainfall may perhaps be regarded as the limiting factor in its distribution wherever the construction is flimsy, such as earth supported by palm fronds or reeds ; in and near the Betic mountains of Spain the occurrence of this roof has been found to coincide with that of a suitable earth which absorbs most of the rain. In towns, however, the terrace is usually built solidly and provides a drying floor as well as a social amenity.

Around the Mediterranean a feature of many villages and small towns is the cave quarter, composed of houses in which only the front wall is artificial, although some excavation may have been made behind it. This habit of living in walled caves has persisted because these are cool and sheltered from wind and dust, and also because the wall is easy to build with little wood ; moreover, the place is easy to defend. While such dwellings are to be found in many districts of France and central Europe, usually in limestone cliffs, it is in the dry lands of the south that they are commonest, generally where the rainfall is less than 20 inches (50 cm.). In these parts wind erosion is active, and has made many of the caves, and as there is little water to percolate from above the houses are dry. The great majority of the cave-dwellings are found surrounding the ends of the Mediterranean Basin ; thus, in the drier half of Spain, on both the Castilian plateaus, in the Ebro basin, and especially near the south-eastern coast and in Andalusia, where the town of Guadix, for example, includes some 3,000 troglodytes ; a comparable Italian case is Matera in Basilicata. Similarly they are characteristic of Morocco on both sides of the Middle Atlas, of Tunisia, and, to a phenomenal extent, in Tripolitania. They are common, again, in Palestine and the interior of Anatolia.

Comparable with cave-dwellings are the pit-houses dug in loess or other soft material, as on the plain of Valachia, where, in 1910, they housed about 250,000 people, and across the Danube in Bulgaria. Similar dwellings are common on the plateau of Armenia and in eastern Georgia, many being occupied only in winter when protection from low temperatures is needed.

Throughout Europe north of the mountains timber has been so abundant in the past that domestic architecture developed generally with wood as the main structural material, but along with clay, burnt brick or stone ; the skeleton or frame of timber was commonly as essential for the walls as it still is for the roof. It is only on the fringes of the natural woodland of Europe that houses have had to be made almost without timber ; clay walls (adobe) in Castile and southern Russia, or very thick double walls of dry stone with earth between in the Hebrides. On the other hand the block-house of solid timber is still characteristic of the coniferous forests of the north-east. Naturally the older ways of building disappeared earlier from towns than from the countryside, and frequent destructive fires in medieval towns led to the gradual reduction in the use of wood. Yet many fine examples of timbered houses remain, even in the heart of large cities throughout the Continent and in England ; and they include not only dwellings but also public buildings such as town halls and, in the north-east, churches.

A special word is due to the roof, the most conspicuous part of most buildings, the most difficult part to build and repair, and the one most closely related to the climate. The slope or pitch has been determined probably by the materials available for the cover ; straw thatch for example may have called for a steeper roof than was needed with more permanently waterproof coverings ; but it would seem that in snowy regions such as the Alps and Scandinavia the low pitch may have been designed to retain the snow as an insulating cover ; unexplained tradition must also be recognised. Throughout central and much of eastern Europe the slope is steep and the pitch high ; it has been noted further that while the roof in the west is usually straight, ending in gables, there is a steady increase in the number of hipped roofs eastward. Among the roofing materials thatch and shingles have for long been virtually absent from towns. Slates until modern times were restricted to districts where quarried, but tiles once known could be made in almost any land. Their use in some northern regions may have persisted since Roman times, but there is evidence of a medieval spread of tile-making in central Europe northwards from Italy. This was not however the semicircular tile of the Mediterranean but the flat variety now the most widespread. The curved pan-tile probably originated in Flanders, whence it spread to be still characteristic of the coast around the North and Baltic Seas. Wooden shingles have always been a favourite material in the regions of coniferous forest, and the variations are unimportant. Finally the technique of thatching has differed with the material to some extent, especially as between reeds and straw, and the use of the latter has continued longest where rye is the chief cereal, on account of the length of this straw.

The great architectural masterpieces of western and central Europe include only fragments of Roman origin. On the other hand the so-called Gothic church was developed from the earlier Romanesque style in northern France. The brilliance of design and of the masonry exemplified in great churches built in both these styles was surely encouraged by the presence throughout this region of easily worked but durable stone, notably the limestones of Tertiary and Jurassic ages. This applies also to England with its oolite and other similar rocks and to southern Germany, while the architects of the Rhine valley had the red sandstones of the lower Triassic for their material. On the northern plain remarkable adaptations of style had to be made to allow large churches to be built of brick while the rubble walls of many village churches consist of glacial erratic boulders.

Most historic towns are dominated by certain public buildings that have outlived the original dwellings and which show special creative effort. They often record brilliantly the rise and geographical spread of the builder's art of various periods, and they stand at the heart of old towns in witness of a function that dominated urban life for centuries. By far the most universal motive for their building has been religion. Thus the temples of the ancient cities throughout the eastern Borderlands are still the most noble ruins, but in these lands it is the Islamic mosque that displays the highest form of oriental art still intact, while rarely, as in Spain, a stately synagogue has survived. Christian churches are much more widespread, not only in the towns but in almost every European village and, in the case of abbeys, even in places remote from both. The Mediterranean lands, again, still contain great architectural works, chiefly Roman, for which the motive was civic amenity or imperial glorification : bridges, aqueducts, and triumphal arches, baths, theatres and amphitheatres—the latter still used or imitated later in the bull-rings of Iberia and southern France. This civic motive reappeared in the Middle Ages linked to commerce in the noble town-halls and gild-houses. Distinct from these in all ways and often dominant on account of its site is the stronghold, often grim yet beautiful in its strength and balance.

The geographical distribution of churches in relation to their date and style of architecture offers not only a record of their place in history but also a valuable indication of the routes by which commercial and cultural contacts were maintained. Although it is impossible to treat this subject adequately here, even without reference to the early Church in the Borderlands, a few salient points may be mentioned.

In the south there is a greater variety of architecture than in the north, and there Roman temples and halls of justice—basilicas—were converted to Christian use. From the Basilican style there developed two others, the Byzantine in the east and the Romanesque in the west. The former has been retained ever since by the Eastern Churches, and so it prevails as the architecture of churches and monasteries among the Bridgelands of Asia where, however, many such buildings have become mosques, and also throughout the Balkan Peninsula and Russia ; the most famous example is probably St Sophia of Constantinople. The Byzantine style unites Greek and oriental features in massive brick buildings with domes and cupolas, marble facing, mosaics and frescoes. The Romanesque churches are also massively built and are marked by vaulting and semi-circular arches ; many of those in the south were made fit to withstand attack from Muslim forces ; there are special features in each country including England where the most glorious example is Durham Cathedral. Unlike the Byzantine style the Romanesque was replaced by the Gothic—a misleading name. While the first Gothic architects seem to have derived the pointed arch from Burgundy and the ribbed vault from England, it was in the cathedrals of northern France that this remarkable style arose.

It is typified by high thin walls with large windows and many buttresses, which are essential in the construction, and fine carving within and without. As this form spread throughout western Christendom regional varieties developed, and because of the Crusades there are examples in the east, notably in Rhodes and Cyprus. With the Italian Renaissance came a reversion to the Greco-Roman style which again spread throughout the west for new churches, with local variations, and then with more and fantastic ornamentation attributed largely to the Jesuits as this Order expanded. These modified styles are named Baroque and in the extreme form—notably absent from Britain— also Rococo.

We have traced the slow spread of the town throughout the lands, and noted its historic development down to the eighteenth century. But the onset of the Industrial Revolution accelerated the process enormously ; with England as the place of origin and money as the motive, it affected north-western Europe in the first instance and thence, with less speed and more sporadic incidence, the eastern and southern parts of the continent. Villages rapidly grew into towns, groups of villages were ultimately swallowed up by larger cities ; architecture was at a low ebb while unplanned utilitarianism prevailed. Hence the urban sprawl of factories and mean dwellings at the centre, surrounded by solid but often pretentious suburbs which deteriorated with further outward growth. Such is the all too common heritage of the nineteenth century. It is seen at its worst in Britain where the phenomenon began, for the longer the outward industrial ripples were delayed in Europe, the greater the chance of the enlightened planning of towns, even where the only aim was increased output of manufactured goods. Nevertheless, even in the period reviewed there were remarkable exceptions where noble and far-sighted plans were made and carried out. In general this was due to a powerful government as in the case of the Napoleonic re-planning of Paris, but in other cases, as in Edinburgh, the credit must go to the city fathers of the period.

This chapter has been concerned with an immensely long process of up-building, as generation learned from generation and one region learned from another ; there were disasters here and decadence there, but on the whole a steady geographical spread and historical improvement of cities. But what of the twentieth century ? The Europeans having acquired a new weapon of war, and conducted two wars involving almost the whole arena of our study, have annihilated much of the material evidence of all this cultural progress. The geography involved in this wholesale devastation is of a very different order—dealing with direct distances, atmospheric conditions and the like, for the cities and even their individual buildings became mere targets to be ' pin-pointed ' with precision and were ruthlessly destroyed.

CHAPTER 12

FRONTIERS AND STATES

IT will be necessary soon to turn to matters where statistical comparisons are useful, and therefore, if only because such data are compiled by governments, we may first review the extent and distribution of states both as they exist and as they were during the nineteenth century. While this aim does not involve consideration of the evolution of political territories and changes of frontiers before the last century it will be useful to record the relative permanence of certain boundaries even where some of them had disappeared before the Congress of Vienna in 1815. The noteworthy cases are these : the Pyrenees, between France and Spain ; the frontier of Portugal ; the boundaries of Bohemia ; the northern Carpathians until the partition of Poland ; the present frontier between Norway and Sweden except for a changeable part on the Kattegat ; the boundary between Danish Scania and Swedish Gothland until the eighteenth century ; the lower course of the River Sava and that of the Danube below its confluence with this river, which formed a frontier during long periods from Roman times onwards. In Britain the boundary of England and Scotland has not changed substantially since the thirteenth century. The prolonged existence of most of these lines is evidently attributable to the separation of peoples by mountains or by rivers difficult to approach and to cross. But, as has been indicated, dense forest irrespective of relief had this effect in former times ; and there are many instances of such origin among the internal boundaries of modern states. Among the frontiers just cited for their permanence density of the forest was doubtless more important than the relief in the cases of the Böhmerwald, between Bohemia and Austria, and the southern part of the frontier between Norway and Sweden. Many boundaries, again, upon the northern plain seem to be marked by quite meaningless twists that originated when they were simply the limits of private estates, and had no great significance. Such cases may be found in the frontiers of Belgium and the Netherlands and among those of the German states; when they have achieved international status by treaty, they have evidently been wasteful of supervision and defence.

The creation of new boundaries took place after the First World War as the result of deliberate attempt to establish accord between territorial and linguistic limits throughout east-central Europe, as befitted the aim of the victorious powers in relation to the national aspirations of the various peoples in these regions. While this in the main brought great satisfaction to large majorities of many peoples, the application of the principle in detail often damaged the economic interests of those who were fated to live near the new boundaries. This part of Europe, lying between the Baltic and Aegean Seas, has been described as the political ' shatter-belt ' of Europe, and the political map created in 1919 again suffered drastic changes as a result of the Second War. Nevertheless it is useful to discern some of the main divergencies from the ethnic limits in the political map of the period, and to note the causes thereof.

After language, economic factors played a great part in the boundary settlements. In the first place it was vital that the new or recreated states be provided with adequate railways and other routes ; and this often involved transfer of territory inhabited mainly by people belonging ethnically to the neighbouring state. Thus, Czechoslovakia could not gain access to the rivers Morava and Danube and acquire continuous railways without including some Austrian population and a large minority of Magyars. Hungary, again, lost border territory and numerous nationals to allow Romania to have the marginal railway system. The ' Polish Corridor ' was created with a German minority, but leaving Danzig as a Free State, in order to give Poland direct access to the sea. The question of international rivers and their uses had to be incorporated in the treaties of peace. Mineral resources affected the boundaries of Czechoslovakia, both north and south. There had been a more spectacular case of this in 1871 when the new German Empire delimited the boundary in Lorraine, with the defeated France, in such manner as to include in Germany the entire iron-field as it was then known. But a modern industrial district was partitioned for the first time in 1921, when the boundary between Germany and Poland in Upper Silesia was settled, after great difficulty. On the other hand it was mainly on strategic grounds that the very old frontiers of Bohemia were virtually retained, despite the inclusion of a large German minority in the new state.

It is only in the Borderlands that international boundaries are straight lines traversing empty spaces. In Africa these are former administrative divisions of the Ottoman Empire, but those in the Syrian desert date from 1922 and 1926. In this region, too, there is the case of the Turkish frontier following the Aleppo-Baghdad railway exactly for some 230 miles ; and again, more recently, a river boundary, the Jordan, has raised difficult questions between Arabs and Jews.

International boundaries are marked discretely on the ground by pillars erected at intervals after precise surveys. Unfortunately works of defence on both sides of many frontiers have absorbed much effort, and have frequently sterilised considerable areas of land. Apart from such military works the frontier becomes visible where movement across it on roads and railways is controlled; but the customs posts on each side are symbols of the differences that have come to mark the organised life of peoples throughout the entire territory of adjoining countries. Outwardly there may be nothing else to indicate these contrasts. Two farms, for example, within hail on either side may support similar families; yet these will be subject to systems of law and government and standards of life that differ profoundly. While the two farmers are concerned with their fields in the same way, in all other matters their outlook differs since it is necessarily directed away from the frontier. Thus the boundary is a barrier, often quite artificial, and the zone in which it lies may show signs of economic stagnation, with consequent reduction in the density of population. There are notable exceptions such as the frontier between France and Belgium, where the governments have reduced its significance so far as to allow for daily or weekly movement of workers across the line; moreover, the three Benelux countries, Belgium, Netherlands and Luxembourg, aim at the gradual elimination of economic hindrances caused by their mutual frontiers. The degree of obstruction, then, reflects the temper of the nations and their governments, and accordingly it may be subject to rapid change since it rarely depends upon physical factors. It must be noted, however, that at the two ends of the continent physical barriers have been erected in so far as movement by rail is concerned. The normal railway gauge prevails throughout Europe on main lines except in U.S.S.R. and in Spain and Portugal, where broad gauges were adopted; so there can be no international movement of trains beyond their frontiers.

Because of the virtual stability of national territories in western Europe for at least eighty years, except in the case of Ireland and Iceland, it is possible to examine the measurable changes in human affairs there with statistical accuracy. But this is much more difficult in regard to the rest of Europe and the Borderlands. Thus the (second) German Empire of 1871 was over one seventh larger in area than the Republic of 1919; the Austro-Hungarian Empire disappeared in 1918, and the Ottoman Empire suffered truncations throughout five of the eight decades. Some of the states created in 1919 have ceased to exist and the frontiers of Poland have been greatly altered.

CHAPTER 13

AGRICULTURE AND RURAL SETTLEMENT IN SOUTHERN LANDS

OF the man-made features of the European landscapes the most universal is the farm with its cultivated land and ordered pasture ; and here the effects of revolutionary changes in agricultural methods within the last two centuries have not been sufficient to eliminate all trace of systems that may be as old as the Neolithic period. If the digging stick or antler has disappeared, the loy, a narrow curved spade used in Ireland resembles it closely, and the foot plough, still used in the Hebrides, can be matched by an almost identical implement in northern Iraq. Again, the primitive practice of intermittent or shifting cultivation following the cutting and burning of wood or heathland —the usual method throughout inter-tropical Africa—was still common fifty years ago in the Ardenne and parts of the Central Plateau of France ; and while the seasonal movement of flocks between highland and plain, fundamental in the pastoral systems from earliest times, is in gradual decline, it is still characteristic throughout most of the mountainous countries.

The soil of the settled farmlands has been tilled in much the same way for very long periods, but with an important divergence between the methods in regions where the summer is respectively wet and dry, with the corresponding difference of soil. As explained (p. 68), the soils of the Mediterranean region must not be cultivated deeply ; the small plough is therefore adapted for scratching and not for turning the earth. It has been a common practice also to plough first along and then across the field, the better to break the soil and reduce evaporation. It is perhaps partly for this reason that the fields are rectangular and often square. They are divided by low dry-stone walls or by hedges of the American succulents, the prickly pear (*Opuntia*) or the agave ; the purpose is defence against animals, but the divisions reflect the individualism of the cultivator.

The heavy European plough with wheels seems to have been invented in the Italian plain and then developed by the Celts north of the Alps. It was clumsy but effective in turning the deeper, damp soil ; to do so, however, it needed a yoke of four oxen abreast and often others in front. This meant co-operation, an essential in the village system to which it belonged. It was difficult to turn such a team and plough, hence a furrow as long as the beasts could haul without rest—the *furlong* of the Anglo-Saxons ; hence the narrow fields, originally 40 by 4 *rods or perches* (200 × 20 metres) enclosing one acre (0.4 hectare) ; hence, too, the absence of walls or hedges between the strips which would hamper the plough. Here, then, in the nature of a plough and its team, perfected over two thousand years ago, we see an important element in the origin of the rural landscape as it is today—or as it was quite recently— from the River Loire in the west to the heart of Russia. Nearly all the cultivated land surrounding the village consists of open hedgeless champain country, divided up, often minutely, by the motley strips under different crops or grass, and ending abruptly in rough pasture or at the forest edge. No longer, how- ever, do the fields have the same uniform dimensions, since the ' open field ' agricultural system of the Middle Ages, with its collective servitudes, gave way to ownership of scattered strips by individual peasant farmers ; and then to eliminate inconvenience and wasted time strip-fields have been reassembled into compact groups, although only in limited areas. But many of the original boundaries remain, and the general effect is as described ; moreover, in many regions this improvement of peasant farming has not been effected. Conversion to broad acres under one crop denotes usually a different system of land-tenure, often the existence of large estates. On the Continent this is common in certain tracts, and in Britain the obliteration of the strip fields is complete, owing to the enclosure of farm land as well as common grazing land at several periods, but especially during the Agricultural Revolution of the eighteenth century.

Broadly the two systems by which farmland is divided correspond to distinct types of climate and soil. But this was not always so, because western Europe received its culture from the Mediterranean Region, and the light wooden plough was the first to be introduced to the moist lands of Gaul and the British Isles ; and it may well have been suited to the drier areas there in the better climate that prevailed during most of the Bronze Age. Moreover, it continued in use, with little improvement, in the remoter western highlands until modern times, and in Ireland the Mediterranean practice of cross-plough- ing also persisted. There, too, the small squarish and walled fields still prevail ; but in the south of England it was the air-camera which led to their discovery on the chalk downland, which later reverted to grass and permanent pasture. On the other hand, throughout most of the farmland of Britain, and especially that of the English Midlands, the effect of the strip-cultivation by the heavy plough is visible in the parallel undulations of the fields, largely independent of the present hedges or walls.

AGRICULTURE

Since the southern peoples doubtless derived much of their agricultural knowledge from the oldest civilisations of the river banks in Egypt and Mesopotamia, it will be useful to note from the earliest archaeological records in these lands the plants that formed the object of cultivation and the animals that were either associated with agriculture or formed the basis of pastoral economy.   It is easy to forget that the great ages of human discovery are pre-historic, and it is therefore useful to remind ourselves of certain facts about the cultivation of crops and the domestication of animals.   Thus the earliest husbandmen of the Nile valley, whose remains have been examined and who probably lived over ninety centuries ago, grew two-row barley, millet and flax and possessed two breeds of cattle as well as the zebu, pig, ass, sheep, goat, dog and gazelle.   Lower Mesopotamia at this stage reveals cultivation of barley, a kind of wheat and the date-palm, and domestication of similar cattle, with the pig, sheep, goat and dog.   More than half of this long period was to elapse before a comparable assemblage of crops and animals flourished in the heart of Europe, among the pile-dwellings of Swiss lakes—rye and oats being added there.

Ever since agriculture became established throughout the Mediterranean lands it has had two distinct aspects that are imposed by the climate : the cultivation of grain and other annual crops which depend upon rainfall during the cooler half-year, and that of fruit trees or bushes which, like the indigenous woodland, persist and benefit from the heat of summer.   The emphasis on arboriculture is the most distinctive feature of Mediterranean husbandry, and but for the propagation of the two xerophytic trees, the olive and the fig, in the third millenium B.C. and their gradual westward spread, most of these lands could not have supported dense populations.   With the olive oil and dried figs, providing essential foods in supplement of the cereals and legumes, went the grape-vine, which although deciduous is well adapted by the length of its roots to resist drought.   Bread, oil and wine, the triad of the ancient civilisation, are still the basic diet ; the shimmering olive grove and the vine-yard form the background of the wheat or barley field, and the former often veiling it with a thin canopy.   This dependence upon trees has provided an element of stability, since an orchard is a valuable investment, and its destruc-tion, as by an enemy, a disaster.   The planted olive, for example, requires seven years to mature and twenty to come to full bearing, so the olive branch was the appropriate symbol of peace.   Similarly the skilful use of water for irrigation, whether from springs and streams or lifted from wells, has further attached people to the favoured localities, since these installations allowed them to extend the period of growth into or throughout the dry summer.   By such means it became possible to grow plants belonging to regions where rain falls in summer, as such plants gradually became known, and so there were added, at widely different periods, cereals like millet, maize and rice, sesame for its oil, cotton or sugar-cane, as well as various fruit trees, notably the orange and the lemon. Moreover, a little irrigation sufficed to provide during the year a great variety of vegetables which have thus been introduced to the European table. Hence the Mediterranean peoples at an early period became gardeners and fruit-growers of noted skill and ingenuity. Comparable with these developments near the coasts is the still older practice of cultivating the date-palm and growing annual crops by irrigation in the oases of the desert ; and it was this which led to the entirely exceptional settlement of people along the southern rim of our region.

Although wheat, spelt and barley were first cultivated in the Nearer East and then spread around the Mediterranean basin and beyond, southern agriculture has made no great subsequent contribution to the growing of cereals ; the climate and historical circumstances have combined to keep the raising of field crops at a low level of productivity in nearly all of these southern lands. The farmer with fruit trees also produces grain and some legumes such as beans and lentils for food and others for fodder, but there are far greater areas where grain and legumes are the only crops ; and there the people dependent on agriculture are fewer, yet they generally live at a very low standard.

Owing to the proximity of the high mountains on the one hand and of the desert on the other, the pastoral element comes into the rural life of the southern lands. This is probably older than agriculture in the Mediterranean scene, and it has remained distinct from it, being essentially marginal, and in many ways hostile to it ; the integration of stock-keeping and cultivation that has developed progressively elsewhere in Europe is still largely lacking. This derives from the fact that it is more or less nomadic in character.

We may now examine each of these rural activities in turn, first those typical of the foothills, slopes fronted by small plains, with their orchards ; secondly those of the greater plains with their extensive grain-land ; and thirdly the pastoral life of the mountains and of the semi-desert. The respective domains of these three forms of life differ greatly in extent. The first, which is much the smallest, consists in a large number of small districts whose appearance from a distance is that of woodland. The second comprises many large continuous tracts, but also innumerable patches more or less cleared from the greater area of scrubland. The third embraces much of the remaining natural forests and the far greater expanses of maquis and garrigue, generally on the mountains but always on land of rough relief, as well as wide uninterrupted plains and plateaus of the Borderlands often referred to as ' steppe ' (cf. pp 87-8.).

Tree Crops and Intensive Agriculture

Among the fruit trees and shrubs that had been added to the olive, fig and vine before our era a few require no watering, notably the carob with its rich fodder in the locust-beans, and of more local importance, the almond, the pomegranate and the pistachio. These, therefore, may be found with the other three among the orchards or scattered groves that occupy two characteristic types of site near the centres of population : first the slopes, either rocky hillsides with stone-built terraces or natural pockets of soil, or on the upper and stonier parts of alluvial fans just below the gullies ; and secondly, on the plains beyond the limits of irrigation. But these orchards and vineyards are by no means excluded from more favourable ground, although they are not usually in the dampest soil. Another series originating mostly, like some of those already mentioned, in the Bridgelands of Asia, include the apricot, quince, apple, pear, cherry and walnut. These require somewhat moister soils, and the last four can do with lower temperatures and so form orchards in the valleys of the mountains where the natural oak forest has often been replaced largely by the sweet chestnut, a tree encouraged because its fruit offers an alternative to a cereal diet. Mention must be made, too, of the peach and the mulberry ; introduced from China, the latter, spread around the northern fringe of the Mediterranean where groundwater or some irrigation is available, provides in its leaves the food of the silkworm, and so is pollarded to permit easy picking. Finally, the citrus fruits, lemon, orange and mandarin, introduced by the Arabs from monsoonal Asia, are greedier of water than any other trees and more sensitive to cold, so they are restricted to places where irrigation is abundant and where the risk of frost is slight. The management of all these fruit trees not only demands skill in such operations as pruning and grafting but it also provides work for many hands and extends the season of employment. With such a range of woody species as well as many herbaceous vegetables at their disposal the Mediterranean husbandmen, as they multiplied and needed more ground, undertook the hard labour of building and maintaining the terraces that are required if the soil is to be held on the steeper slopes. To work the higher terraces, or the lower if the village is above, also calls for great exertion and loss of time ; so it is not surprising that they now tend to be neglected, especially where alternative employment is available, as for example on the steep Ligurian coast of Italy.

Associated with arboriculture, annuals are grown between and under the trees in variety according to their demands, either as 'dry crops' or receiving some watering ; and this combination, the intensive *coltura promiscua* of the Italians, requires the most continuous attention and so typifies the most densely peopled districts. Space is restricted and the implements used are simple, the hoe and the mattock often entirely replacing the small plough.

Many of the lesser works of irrigation are very ancient and owe their existence to perennial springs or to rivers emerging from the foot of limestone hills, a very characteristic feature throughout the eastern Mediterranean ; the most impressive example is probably that of Damascus, which owes its greatness as an oasis to the abundant flow of its river from the natural reservoir of the Anti-Lebanon. But the Arabs of the Middle Ages, while spreading the knowledge, developed and regularised the use of irrigation wherever they settled ; thus, for example, the system of weirs for diversion, channels and underground conduits on the coastal plain of Valencia are almost replicas of those at Damascus, and so are the rules for the collective usage of the water. They introduced also the wheel, driven by the current, for lifting water on to the river-bank. Moreover they found, or developed, the means of raising it from wells in the water-table of alluvial plains by use of the animal-driven wheel, the *noria*, known also as the Persian wheel, and in Egypt as the *sakieh* ; and where the groundwater under sloping land was deep and meagre they dug the tunnel-like *foggara* to concentrate the supply for a channel, a system widely used in Persia.

Apart then from the Nile valley and the lower plain of Mesopotamia and that of northern Italy, all special cases, it was by these various means that intensive agriculture came about in southern Europe and the Borderlands. Only in the last half century has the intervention of governments or investment companies led to the greater expenditure of capital involved in the building of storage reservoirs and sought to extend irrigation to greater areas of the Mediterranean lands. The conditions so far described are applicable to the districts with the greater amounts of rainfall, which are generally those with considerable relief. They are the conditions which most obviously attach the peasant to the land and make him an individualist. His aim until most recent times everywhere has been self-sufficiency, and it is in such areas that the small, or very small, farm is typical ; such peasant holdings predominate, for instance, throughout the hill country of southern Greece.

Grain Crops and Extensive Agriculture

We have now to review the much larger tracts where fruit plays a negligible part in the economy. Their aspect is generally monotonous, since they are devoted largely to wheat or barley interspersed here and there with one of the leguminous crops, such as beans, chickpeas, vetch or sainfoin.

Whatever the crops, at least one-half of the cultivated land is bare, for this 'dryland' is very largely farmed on a two-field system, by which a given field is cropped every second year, the fallows being ploughed to keep weeds down and reduce evaporation by maintaining a loose mulch. This is the rule where farming is good and rainfall moderately so ; in wetter districts the fallow period may be reduced to one year in three, but toward the semi-arid margins extended to two, three or more years. The methods correspond to those of modern dry-farming as developed in the drier regions of North America and elsewhere, but the implements used are simple and traditional. The return generally varies inversely with the rainfall, and the seed is sown closely or sparsely according to the rainfall expected ; but it is everywhere low by northern standards, since little or no manure is used. Fallow fields are ploughed repeatedly to retain moisture and keep down weeds. After the sowing in the shallow furrows, with the autumn rains the fields are not harrowed, the seed being covered by dragging either a levelling beam or even branches across the ground, or again, as in Spain, by ploughing between the furrows, when the plough is furnished with pegs at the sides for this purpose. The grain is cut from May to July, according to the climate, by scythe or more generally by sickle ; and it is threshed on the village threshing floor, a circle of beaten clay. On this the implement is pulled round by an animal ; it is either a sledge, the Roman *tribulum*, studded with iron or flints, or consists of striated rollers of stone, as in Spain, or wooden ones as in Turkey. The grain is then cast in the air for the wind to winnow, and the straw, chopped during the threshing, is used as fodder or to make bricks or, again, when mixed with dung, as fuel.

These, then, are the common traditional and primitive practices by which grain is grown. Certainly there are many degrees of care or lack of it, perhaps depending partly on nearness to the village. The farmer may live a long way from the fields (cf. p. 142), and much time is spent in transit. The grain, again, may be ground in windmills which are situated generally on hills, often high hills, so transport is laborious. Furthermore, in the drier regions of Turkey and in the Borderlands grain-growing is apt to be regarded as an incident in a semi-nomadic life, the fields being visited only at the sowing and the reaping. The question of land tenure is closely bound up with the economy of the ' dryland ' country. The greater areas of grain are in the regions where large estates prevail, and this in the southern lands has meant lack of initiative and general backwardness. These conditions are at their worst along the outer fringe from Iraq to Morocco, as is to be expected ; but they apply also to plains where rainfall is adequate at least for biennial cropping, such as those of southern Portugal and Andalusia as well as much of southern Italy and Turkey. The evil is of long standing, since the great estates began to be formed, as *latifundia* under the early Roman Empire, and each successive military conquest has been followed by the granting of large holdings to the leaders, to religious orders and others. Feudal rule prevailed widely and, while this was not necessarily bad so long as the owner lived on his estate, many of the modern landlords reside in the capital and maintain an intermediary, who is often none too scrupulous, on the spot. Hence from the earlier times, when slavery was the rule, the agricultural workers have had a low economic and social status. While many of these estates are worked directly for the owner, probably the majority are subdivided among tenants, with a great variety of tenures in which some form of share-cropping is the commonest ; and in general it would appear that the worker's share is only just sufficient to keep him and his family at a low standard of physical fitness and wellbeing. Thus there are vast tracts reckoned as agricultural land which give very low yields of grain or other crops and where poverty prevails, and this condition has come about owing to the course which history has taken in a region where the summer drought is long and the winter rains less regular. The evil has been recognised in recent times by governments as they attained enlightenment, that is for nearly a century by France in Algeria, for much less than that in the case of Italy, Turkey and Spain ; but French experience soon showed the difficulty of reform in the direction of peasant ownership, viz that a typical farm without irrigation and devoted to grain and forage to be an economic unit must extend to 100 hectares or 250 acres in area.

Pastoral life

Many descriptions of pastoral life in early times have come down to us that throw light upon its character ; the Homeric poems, for example, indicate the relative importance of cattle and of the eating of meat, which were also features of the life of the tribes of central Italy, while large herds of swine were fed in the woods before the virtual disappearance of this source of forage. For the Nearer East the Old Testament has abundant illustrations of the value placed upon the flocks of sheep and goats ; and it is these two animals that now predominate in all the southern lands, for the degradation of forest and lush grass have reduced the keeping of cattle and pigs to almost local import-ance, with certain exceptions. Pastoral life still implies movement ranging from complete nomadism on the desert's edge to seasonal transhumance that may mean only a day's journey twice a year. But since the industry is entirely extensive, being dependent on the natural vegetation supplemented by weeds growing on fallow land, movement of the flocks is obviously necessary in a climate of Mediterranean type. On the European side and in the Atlas lands and Anatolia the great variation in altitude with corresponding seasonal changes in plants makes it possible to maintain large flocks by moving them up in summer and down in winter. Elsewhere in the Borderlands, to compensate for lack of high mountains, the distances covered are generally greater and the movements more frequent. It is mainly the descent for the winter and the outward movements from the desert which have ever led to strife between farmer and herdsmen, since the irruption of large flocks to the neighbourhood of sown crops and plantations is almost bound to lead to illicit foraging. Here and there fallowland may derive some benefit from the dung, if the flock be folded ; but this practice is far from common, and the destructiveness of the goat especially is widely recognised. Hence stock-rearing is almost completely separate from husbandry, as conductedd it in by men whose homes are generally in the highlands near to the summer pastures. Many of the flocks are owned by these independent highlanders who live by selling cheese, wool, hair and surplus stock. But at various periods the migration of the flocks has been regulated as a matter of state policy, especially when powerful individuals or corporations were the owners of vast flocks, as in medieval Italy and Spain. From this fact and from the need to placate the farmers systems of broad drove-roads were created between the main summer and winter pastures, and these are still prominent features of the landscape ; they are the *cañadas* of Spain, the *tratturi* of Italy and the *drailles* of southern France ; but in these countries rail and motor transport have now reduced their use. In the Balkan Peninsula and Anatolia transhumance still takes place on the hoof and, although there are no similar roads, the routes are prescribed by tradition, if not by law. The herdsmen even today constitute a separate element in most countries, with their own customs, keeping to their own calendar, and for their principal activities to certain saints' days, while some groups in the Balkans, the Vlachs or Aromuni have their own language. It is these pastoral peoples who maintain villages at the highest altitudes and in remote places and who keep up the traditions of the southern mountains.

Trade

In the past the aim of farmer and herdsman has been the direct support of the family, coupled generally with some selling of produce in the neighbour-hood ; and this probably still applies to the great majority of those dependent on crops or stock throughout most of the southern countries. But there are many regional exceptions to this general self-sufficiency, and so there have been at various former periods. Trade in agricultural produce has been carried on from very early times, especially by sea but also overland, as on the Roman roads. The economy of the Roman Empire indeed depended upon movement to the capital of large quantities of grain, olive oil, wine, wool, flax and many other things from the outlying provinces. Again, the medieval mercantile states like the Venetian and Genoese Republics were importers of these products, although their trade was chiefly concerned with the more valuable manufactured goods from the Orient ; yet their northern customers came to know the finer wines of the Mediterranean. Hence over limited areas there has been a commercial aspect of agriculture which flourished while, and where, navigation of this sea was moderately safe from piracy.

It is fortunate for the Mediterranean farmer that much of his produce can be easily preserved or converted into commodities of reduced bulk and high value, such as dried fruit, wine, oil and tobacco. The demand for these things has led to their export to ever more distant markets, some of which have served rapidly growing populations of industrial countries where such goods are scarcely produced. More recently the same consumers in the north have been ready to pay for fresh fruits, then for fresh vegetables and even flowers, as means of rapid transport have developed. In response to these demands the growers in many districts have improved their methods so as to obtain better fruit or tobacco or to make better oil or wine, and particularly to supply produce of uniform quality. Further, a few districts have devoted more and more land to raising one or other of the commercial crops, and in so doing have risked disaster when the distant market has failed.

The Vine

Although the making of wine is the typical industry, it is quite unevenly distributed throughout the Mediterranean region. In many areas that are suitable the vine has been little cultivated since the Muslim conquests, because the Islamic code forbids the drinking of wine ; but the grape has been grown for eating fresh or dried, and, as in Turkey, for making sweetmeats. Again, in the eastern lands wine is made almost entirely for home consumption, mainly because in these parts the ancient practice is retained, that of adding resin to make the wine keep well ; and this is distasteful to the foreign palate.

The large content of sugar developed in the grapes where summer temperatures are high contributes to the character of famous wines from the Douro valley, with its ' port ', from the western plain of Andalusia, with its ' sherry ', as well as to that of the wines exported from the southern coast of the same province through Malaga, and from the Sicilian district of Marsala. All these wines and some other Italian vintages have long-established foreign markets.

The Olive

Since Roman times Spain has been the great producer of the olive. The trade in olive oil is largely local or national rather than international ; the northern peoples, long accustomed to use animal fats, have demanded it mainly as a table delicacy. There are districts where the aim is to produce oil of fine quality, for instance the lower valley of the Arno, and governments now play their part in the maintenance of such standards. On the other hand there are districts, as in southern France, where olive cultivation has declined in face of competition with tropical oils for industrial uses. Yet for the Mediterranean peoples in general the olive harvest is still of paramount importance, since it provides an essential part of their diet, notably in Greece, Spain and southern Italy.

Fruit

Before the modern agricultural changes in California and similar regions the Mediterranean lands had a virtual monopoly of trade in dried grapes, as raisins and currants, and dried figs which, like dates from the southern oases and prunes from the northern margin, had become almost indispensable to the ' civilised ' table. The intensive cultivation and drying of these fruits is still characteristic of the Aegean area, especially in the southern mainland and islands of Greece and in western Turkey. Figs and raisins, including the ' sultana ', are exported from many ports of this region, where Greece alone raised one-third of the world's total crop of grapes for drying before World War II, a proportion since reduced by the growth of United States production. Currant vines are restricted to the north and west of the Peloponnesus and the Ionian Islands, and nine-tenths of all currants still come from the district. The development of this small seedless grape, in the Middle Ages or earlier, seems to mark a triumph of plant breeding.

The foreign trade in dates during recent times has been marked by the dominance of Iraq, the home of the date-palm ; and about three-quarters of all the exports of this fruit are shipped from Basra. But among the other districts partaking in this trade are the oases of Algeria and Tunisia, which are famous for their ' choice ' fruit.

Among the fresh fruits by far the most important are the orange, the lemon and the mandarin. The three leading Mediterranean producers are Spain, Italy and Israel, the last being a new rival of the other two.

As compared with the citrus fruits, the other fresh fruits are much less suited for transport to distant markets. Nevertheless the export of grapes from the Almeria district in Spain, packed in cork dust, and that of apricot pulp from the neighbouring huertas, are examples of initiative that will doubtless be followed widely in the future. Moreover, fruit growers have begun to learn the advantages of the most recent development in commercial agriculture, the trade in table vegetables. Since buyers in the north were ready to pay for the freight of fresh produce during the winter and spring the southern gardeners have realised a new means of exploiting the climate, where facilities for rapid transport are available. The French name *primeurs* expresses well the essential feature of the business, to get the crop to market as long as possible before the local product is ready. The French, too, have been the pioneers both in France and in North Africa, followed by the growers along the east coast of Spain and the Canary Islands.

Flowers

The wealth of scented flowers in the evergreen vegetation have given rise in various districts to the distillation of the essential oils for making perfume. But there is greater commercial importance in this industry where it depends upon gardens rather than on wild flowers. The making of rose oil is due to the Turks, using petals from gardens long established in western Anatolia and at the southern foot of the Balkan Mountains, now in Bulgaria. But the most varied and valuable essences are those made in the French Riviera, where much capital and skill have been devoted to the industry.

While many plants are cultivated for the making of drugs, this is of only local importance, except perhaps in the case of opium. The purple poppy, *papaver somniferum*, yielding this drug from the sap of its seed capsule, is indigenous and, until the spread of Islam to the Monsoon Lands, Asia Minor was probably the only source of the drug. Much labour is needed to gather the exudation from the punctured plants separately, in the early summer ; and this has so far been procurable in the chief poppy-growing districts, western Anatolia and Serbian Macedonia. The opium, small in bulk but costly, is required for medicinal use, but since it offers great temptation to those who would abuse it, the production is now restricted by international convention to Turkey and Yugoslavia, and the trade is controlled.

Tobacco

The cultivation of tobacco in the southern lands is of geographical interest, especially in relation to Anatolia and the Balkan Peninsula, not only because the leaf is a great source of revenue to the states concerned, but also from a biological reason. 'Turkish' tobacco comprises varieties that have been evolved by the climate and the Turkish peasantry, and this long before the days of scientific plant breeding. The adaptation of this American herb to Mediterranean conditions, and more precisely to a marginal variety of this climate since its introduction, after 1600, has led to the growth of small thin leaves with a particular aroma. Furthermore the finest types are produced only in certain sites, usually on foothills, where the soil has the right physical and chemical character. As with opium, much labour is involved, together with care and skill which reflect the best qualities of the peasant. The international renown of Turkish tobacco dates from the popularisation of the cigarette in the second half of the nineteenth century ; but the foreign taste for it influences the trade greatly. It is most favoured by American and German smokers, and there is a large import into Egypt, where none is grown, for the manufacture and export of cigarettes. Hence, while tobacco is raised in most southern lands to supply the various national demands, as is the case also throughout central Europe and France, the famous brands of commerce still come from the oldest tobacco districts. These are in Anatolia, especially the north-east and north-west, in Thrace and Macedonia and with less importance, Syria. To the tobacco exported from all countries of the world in 1934–38, the southern lands contributed over one-fifth, chiefly from Greece, Turkey, and Bulgaria. The proportion from former parts of the Turkish Empire in the year following World War II remained the same, but with Turkey as the chief supplier in the area.

RURAL SETTLEMENT

In some of these areas of commercial agriculture the British visitor is likely to note one familiar feature, the cottages and farm buildings scattered among the crops, or near them. But this is exceptional, and it is usually a modern development that has come with the new commerce. Yet it is in such places alone that the visitor has the impression of dense rural population, although the density is remarkably high in many fruit-growing districts, where the people live in the normal way, withdrawn from their lands in large compact villages. These, then, are the typical southern settlements, and they stand characteristically on hilltops or at least on the upper edge of basin or valley, and often backed by a craggy hillside. The village generally looks like a small town, and indeed the distinction may be a narrow one. There are several possible explanations of this marked concentration of dwellings ; but it would seem that the former need for security against attack by land or sea has been the general cause, supplemented locally by unwillingness to use precious farm land as building sites ; while in districts of uncertain water supply good springs may well have influenced location. But this last reason has been sometimes too generally applied ; innumerable villages on hilltops have quite insufficient water, and the people are accustomed to carry it from sources at lower levels. Moreover, the aspect of these old villages, and their siting in detail, indicate that defence was a powerful motive ; entrances are narrow, and the outer edge appears as a serried mass of high walls above a steep slope. It is very probable that many of the high villages are on or near to sites that were occupied before our era ; and likewise, the watershed roads that connect them are doubtless very old. But whatever their age, they belong to periods when villagers had to defend themselves. Originally their high situation was favourable to the pastoral interest, and their maintenance is now partly explained by the difficulty of establishing new settlements amid lands subdivided under complex tenures, as well as by habit and a strong attachment to the old home. Nevertheless in recent times many of them have declined or have been entirely deserted in sympathy with a general downward movement of population. Perhaps the most striking fact about the distribution of the older villages is their general absence from the coast ; and this is clearly due to fear of piracy and, on marshy shores, also of malaria. Frequently the less convenient places now have daughter villages situated on main roads, on railways or on the coast, and the tendency is for such to outgrow their parents. Many of the seaports have arisen from mere boat landings, for fishing or trade, the Greek *skala* and Italian *marina*, which less than a century ago had no permanent dwellings.

But it must not be thought that old villages are confined to defensive sites. There are many also on plains and in open valleys, and they include the largest settlements. Some of them have certainly originated during periods of greater security. Thus it was the policy of the Roman Empire to get the subject tribes down from their highland strongholds and attract them to the vicinity of the villas ; so many of these became the centres of villages. This process has been repeated during peaceful periods, and no doubt many lowland settlements have been deserted and reoccupied more than once.

Dispersed settlement is exceptional, whether as scattered homes or as hamlets. It reflects, of course, the natural inclination to obviate waste of time and effort in reaching field or garden. It develops when permanent houses replace the flimsy shelters that are commonly used to store tools or as temporary abodes, and therefore especially where labour is needed most continuously. Hence, as already mentioned, the most widespread dispersion of modern times is that which typifies the irrigated gardens of eastern Spain. But there are two large regions where it is very much older. The first of these extends from the Basque lands in the Pyrenees along the margin of the Iberian Peninsula to the Douro, and as a narrower inland strip to the Tagus. This has a medieval origin, from the twelfth century in Galicia and northern Portugal, where it accompanies extreme sub-division of the land. The other is the north-eastern part of peninsular Italy, where the process began about the sixteenth century as the result of colonisation by landlords and crop-sharing tenants. But, apart from such exceptional regions, the husbandmen around the Mediterranean normally live at very close quarters and, as a rule, they lead a sociable life. Their homes seem to northerners to be very cramped for farming people ; they are satisfied with small buildings whether in a village or not. But their form of husbandry calls for no large establishment, no farm court, byre, midden and store of hay are needed ; a single building of two storeys can generally house the family and the few working beasts, the grain and fruits, the cart and the simple implements.

ALLUVIAL LANDS OF THE SOUTH

Three special regions in the south have been mentioned as requiring separate review; they are Lower Mesopotamia, the Nile valley in Egypt, and the plain of northern Italy. All three are large alluvial tracts, which have vast sources of water, but they differ in most other respects and notably in their size. Lower Mesopotamia has an area of some 41,000 square miles (106,000 sq. km.), more than two-thirds that of England and Wales; about one-fifth of this is in Iran and the rest in Iraq. The area of the settled part of Egypt, comprising the valley and the delta, is about 12,000 square miles (31,000 sq. km.), and that of the plain of Italy, about 16,000 (41,000 sq. km.). Only a small part of the first-mentioned is under regular cultivation, certainly not more than one-quarter, whereas the other two are almost wholly productive.

Lower Mesopotamia

The alluvial plain at the head of the Persian Gulf saw the beginning of agriculture, in the lands of Sumer and Akkad, and its development in Babylonia and Elam, and again under the Califs of Baghdad. Although it has been a populous region, the fact is that agriculture can flourish here only when the rivers are under control, and this requires a powerful organisation such as has been absent since the conquest by the Mongols in the thirteenth century. Since human settlement began the Tigris, the Karun and the Euphrates by their changes during the annual floods have discouraged permanent settlement in many parts, especially in the lower areas. Nor is the flood sufficiently regular to be ideal for irrigation; it may be a menace, as in the case of the Tigris. Again, renewal of the soil by an annual coating of silt is generally good; but here deposit may be too great and too coarse; that from the Tigris is four times greater than the load brought to Egypt by the Nile. Moreover, the imperfect drainage and the intense evaporation in summer combine to render much of the land unfit for cultivation, since the surface becomes impregnated with salts, and the lowest tracts are swamps. Formerly these defects were met in part by an elaborate system of canals connected with earthen dams on the rivers, but for the past six centuries most of the plain has been left to Nature: a desert of baked clay and dust from September to February, thereafter inundated except for the higher riverside strips, and all becoming green as the flood subsides. Apart, therefore, from properly irrigated areas, the plain supports mainly the kind of agriculture that is found throughout the higher ground along the so-called 'fertile crescent', extending to Syria, based mainly on cereals, legumes and oilseeds, with meagre yields.

But where the soil is still damp throughout the summer, sorghum, maize, sesame and some cotton are also grown, while the swampy edges are devoted to rice ; yet for the most part this form of agriculture does not rise above the standard of subsistence, except for the date gardens described below. An important element of instability among the cultivators is the annual influx of nomads from the southern desert, attracted by the pasturage after the floods.

Reclamation of the plain began at the end of the Turkish period when a modern sluiced weir was built on the Hindieh branch of the Euphrates, to bring flow again to the old arm that once watered Babylon ; this extends the area, but not the period, of irrigation. On the other hand, a new diversion of the Euphrates farther upstream will regulate the flood and store water in the natural basin of Habanieh. A barrage on the Diyala provides irrigation for dates, other fruits and cotton on the fan of this tributary of the Tigris, while on the latter the new weir at Kut greatly extends irrigation, though not perennially, and the increasing use of oil pumps along the river banks helps in the period of low water. In the future it is likely that virtual control of the main rivers will be achieved when they have been dammed within the mountains ; but such a plan involves international co-operation. When this happens the plain will be made to produce much food and cotton and it will support a large population.

Meanwhile, as already indicated, Iraq makes one valuable contribution, in the fruit of some thirty million date-palms. The majority of these grow near the banks of the lower channels where the very ancient art of date-growing probably arose ; and there the physical conditions are unique. The large delta of the Karun, growing westward near the head of the gulf, impounds the water of the two greater rivers to form lagoons, and it has narrowed the outlet to the bed of the united effluent, the Shatt-el-Arab. But the fresh water of this river and of the inland swamps is subject to rise and fall in sympathy with the tides of the gulf. Thus the date-palms are naturally watered and drained twice a day, as well as the varied gardens amongst them. The growers learned from their remote ancestors the proper proportion of male trees to female and the way to pollinate the latter by hand. Nature again favours them in the absence of rain thereafter, which would prevent fertilisation of the flowers. Western science is needed only in preparing the fruit for export as each autumn the great harvest is brought in to Basra.

The Nile Valley

The valley and the delta of the Nile in Egypt offer to man a sharply restricted amount of land to cultivate, that of the strip of silt limited by the rocky walls of the plateaus. Near the two ends of the strip are parts which, so far, have defied complete exploitation ; in the south because the ground is rather too high to be reached by modern irrigation, and in the north where the lower part of the delta cannot be easily drained owing to lack of tides in the Mediterranean. Elsewhere, with but small exceptions, perennial irrigation has become the rule during the present century, with revolutionary effect upon Egypt. The population, omitting that of the cities and the desert, increased from ten millions in 1897 to sixteen in 1947. As national production is almost entirely agricultural this has meant a demand always for more water from the Nile during more weeks in the year. For millenia Egypt depended directly upon the flood, starting in July and subsiding between November and January. This allowed crops to be sown in the mud in November and reaped in April, the same group of crops that grow during the winter around the Mediterranean under rainfall. After the harvest the soil became baked and cracked (except on the very limited areas that could be watered from the low Nile or canals, lifted by hand or animal power). The soil, bettered by the cracking, thus received its renewal from the silt in the next flood. To promote this deposition the ground was divided into mud-walled basins that held the water nearly stagnant. As population grew this method of ' basin-inundation ' spread gradually to new land with the building of the ancient canals ; but these could not extend the season of cultivation. The method persists, as noted above, on the higher terraces in Upper Egypt and in patches along the lower valley. One of the old winter crops should be mentioned as originating in Egypt, and always more important there than elsewhere ; this is *bersim*, a clover, which is still the main source of fodder.

The present century has seen the agricultural year extended from one of five or six months to twelve ; and the benefits of this have now reached about nine-tenths of the farmland. The main engineering works which have thus made continuous irrigation possible are, first, the Aswan dam, built on the First Cataract, which makes the Nile into a lake extending up to the Second Cataract near the frontier ; and secondly, the five principal barrages, three in the valley and two in the delta below Cairo. These serve to raise the river surface to the height of irrigation canals, and the latter are, of course, connected to drainage canals at lower levels. Given water during the hot summer, almost any tropical plant can be grown. But in fact those adopted as important summer crops number only four : cotton, maize, sugar-cane and rice. Of these it is cotton which dominates Egyptian commerce, providing fibre of high quality. Cotton-seed, too, is an important export. The real producers of all this precious fibre are the hard-working peasants, the *fellahin*, whose ancestors had to fill the Pharaoh's granaries, who live in crowded mud villages, and multiply so rapidly that their land is subdivided into minute strips. Others again work on larger estates owned by city dwellers. The vast majority are miserably poor.

The North Italian Plain

The plain of northern Italy is lavishly watered, but imperfectly drained by the River Po and its tributaries and, in Venetia, by independent rivers. Unlike the other two plains it receives rainfall throughout the year, and while it has a hot summer it is subject to frost in winter. The plain has been cleared of the broadleaved forest that originally covered most of it, and progressively has been devoted to agriculture and the feeding of stock. Along with these changes, and closely related to them, hydrographic control has been nearly attained, first by embanking rivers and making canals for drainage, irrigation and navigation, and in the latest phase harnessing the rivers for hydro-electricity. The whole process has been influenced, and generally favourably, by the fact that this is a terraced plain ; for throughout most of its extent the rivers have cut into the fans which they had made in the earlier stages, chiefly during the Quaternary period.

The present aspect and the rural economy of the plain represent the results of several distinct phases in its history—Etruscan, Celtic, Roman, medieval, Renaissance and modern. Thus the rectangular pattern of farm and field along the Emilian Way still reflects the Roman colonisation. Many of the older canals in Lombardy were built by the civic authorities of the Renaissance ; their construction marked not only the vigorous commerce of that period, but also the prolonged wave of agricultural development in the central part of the plain, largely initiated by the medieval monasteries and including the elimination of the bare fallow. The mulberry tree introduced by the Venetians with sericulture in the fourteenth century became widespread, to recede only in the twentieth ; the cultivation of rice, begun in many lower parts in the fifteenth century, had its distribution localised in the west in the nineteenth ; while maize, brought to Venice about 1550, is to be found all over the plain. History and geography have combined to favour progress in the central area. It is there that the building of the higher canals during the past century has led to the greatest changes, notably the concentration of rice-paddies in one part, the formation of irrigated meadows with sown grasses in the adjoining tract, and the growth of intensive dairying. Elsewhere traditional subsistence-farming is more common, while at the extremities of the plain, in Piedmont and Friuli, there is much permanent meadowland, and less intensive cultivation. The rapid increase of population in the towns with the further development of long-established manufactures has served to emphasise this agricultural contrast, especially by the promotion of market-gardening and dairying. As in Egypt reclamation of the lowest parts near the sea had to wait for large capital expenditure, and the result is a regular landscape of large fields and new crops such as sugar-beet, quite unlike that of Mediterranean agriculture.

But everywhere the differences are those due to some specialisation that is suited to the soil and, even more, to the amount of water. It is therefore a region of varied production and great output, the result of labour that has improved the soil over a long period, and in which the practice of fallowing was replaced by rotations, including sown legumes at an early date. Moreover, the growing of crops is fully integrated with the keeping of cattle, horses, pigs and poultry. Yields of wheat, maize and other crops are high, and there is great output of hay, especially where irrigated. In short the husbandry in this plain is closely akin to that of the well-farmed northern regions of Europe. It is therefore not surprising to find that rural settlement differs widely in its character from that of other southern regions.

Not only the location of manufacturing industry but the character of the agriculture in the western sector of the North Italian Plain make for greater aggregation of population in centres of more than 500 inhabitants, while to the east of the line Parma–Mantova–Verona the population is for the greater part scattered in smaller settlements. The characteristic unit of rural settlement in the western plain, along a zone with its axis from below Cuneo, through Torino and Milano to beyond Cremona, is the *corte*, or farm court. This consists typically of a farmyard, high-walled and surrounded by the living quarters of the occupier and the permanent labour, the byres, stables, machine-sheds and workshops, with haylofts and granaries on the upper floors ; adjacent to it the threshing floor forms a second quadrilateral. Generally several of these units are grouped, frequently near road-crossings. It is from these units that the large irrigated holdings of the western plain, with high specialisation on rice or on dairy-farming, are organised. In the eastern section of the plain, in a triangle with its apex at Parma and its base stretching from beyond Venice in the north-east to beyond Ravenna in the south-east, rural settlement is for the most part disseminated, with frequent roadside villages. In these areas agriculture is either less specialised or, where industrial crops have been introduced, especially in the more recently reclaimed sections, depends on a large permanent labour-supply, and small or medium-sized tenant holdings, with much share-tenancy in the south-east, prevail.

Separating these western and eastern sections, is a strip of territory from Mantova through Vicenza to Treviso, in which isolated farmhouses are the characteristic form of settlement. To the south-west of this strip a high density of cattle and to the north-east vines, mulberries, fruit and vegetables make heavy demands on the family labour of the small holdings.

CHAPTER 14

AGRICULTURE AND RURAL SETTLEMENT IN NORTHERN LANDS

THROUGHOUT the remainder of Europe the arts of agriculture and stock-rearing may be seen at the most varied stages of their development, from primitive shifting cultivation following burning of vegetation to the most productive arable farming on scientific principles and the raising of cattle to give prodigious amounts of milk or of meat. These differences are, as a rule, not explained by soil or climate. The methods of the husbandman of Polesie in the present century have differed little from those of his Neolithic ancestors because this marshland of the Pripet has been avoided by all cultural streams. A bull bred in the not very clement climate of Aberdeenshire in Scotland may fetch 10,000 guineas, first owing to the skill of the breeder and secondly, because the beast's fine progeny are badly needed in other continents. These extreme cases serve to indicate the importance of location as more or less open to economic stimulus ; in the case of agriculture such stimulus generally arises from growth of urban population requiring food, and this has been brought from near or far according to the period and ease of transport. Without such external influence local self-sufficiency has prevailed and traditional methods lasted long.

North of the Mediterranean lands nature has offered great opportunities for agriculture, some of which have been indicated in former chapters making it sufficiently clear that cultivation is possible throughout most of the lands. But it reaches its cold-limit in the north-east and its dry-limit in the south-east, while in the north-west it is almost suppressed by rain and wind. Within these natural frontiers the soils are generally thicker than in southern Europe and they are much richer in humus ; although often difficult to work, they repay this work since, when properly managed, their fertility is maintained. More-over, they include, in the belt of mid-latitudes, the deep loams and the brown forest soils which are unrivalled for the growing of cereals and, in modern times, of other important plants also such as sugar-beet. The retention of moisture in the soil rarely presents difficulty ; on the other hand much of the land has had to await the invention of field-drainage before agriculture could become fully productive. Again, throughout the maritime fringe and the regions of the northern coniferous forest the cultivator has had to overcome the defect in the soil—podzol—caused by excessive leaching of the upper layer.

Throughout the huge area under consideration in this chapter there is of course much variation in the physical environment ; but in every part the keeping of domestic animals and especially cattle has been in some measure related to the system of husbandry, although not until modern times could full integration be achieved by a balanced production of food and fodder and then by some importation of the one or the other.   Nor was this attained simultaneously in all parts ; indeed the stages of agricultural progress from Neolithic times to the present day have been reached at periods widely different from region to region. In this fact lies one of the causes of diversity in the rural scene and economy as these now are in the various parts of the continent north of the Mediterranean. For it must be borne in mind that advances have often been made in method without corresponding changes in rural landscape and human abodes ; in such cases the improvement of technique as applied, for instance, to new crops or improved stock has been hampered by the outmoded framework of village, farm and field, which nevertheless remains.   Hence these visible features can only be understood by references to practices of former times.   Thus, for example, while British farming has almost everywhere reached a high pitch it is set in a rural frame that varies greatly in date.

The Atlantic Fringe

There is a pronounced contrast between the farmland in most of north-western Europe and that of the vast inner regions ; it is the contrast of enclosed and open fields as well as that of dispersed and concentrated settlements.   This usually implies different emphasis in agricultural aims and products, since enclosure is associated with the keeping of animals, especially cattle.   There is therefore good ground for seeking the first reason for its distribution along the Atlantic fringe in the mildness of the climate which allows cattle to be out in the winter and in the relatively even rainfall that favours lush grass.   At the present day the lands with enclosed fields include those where the density of cattle is highest and, apart from the Alps, it embraces those where the yield of cows' milk is the chief object of husbandry, and where the dairy industry has reached perfection, as well as the chief areas of beef production.   In the past the human response to conditions favouring cattle has not been uniform, and the enclosure has been effected at very different periods.   The *bocage*, as such hedged land is called in France when marked by hedge-trees (cf. English 'bosky'), is perhaps oldest in Brittany and west Normandy ; in the former it certainly seems to antedate the Roman conquest, probably by many centuries.   Again Julius Caesar commented on the hedges in the Belgic country between the Meuse and the Schelde, and a Norman pact of the twelfth century refers to the contrast between *bocage* and plain.   The antiquity of enclosure, too, is indicated by the word 'haw' or hedge-thorn, the equivalent of which occurs in most of the old Teutonic languages. In England the part south-east of the Wash was enclosed at an early period, but the rest of the lowland remained largely open farmland until the eighteenth century, and in Denmark open farmland remained until the modern dairy movement there, while in the adjoining part of Germany hedging has been extended to reduce the effect of wind upon arable land. Throughout highland Britain and in Ireland, where the old Celtic system of stock-keeping prevailed, with limited enclosure near the hamlets, the present aspect of the countryside is even later in origin than in the Midlands of England. Thus in maritime Europe from the Douro to Denmark the hedge dominates the landscape, with trees or without ; the partition however varies from a massive bank of earth and stone, as in Brittany and Cornwall, to the simple hedge and ditch, and with great differences in the amount of hedgerow timber. Moreover, these are replaced as in Galicia and highland Britain by stone walls, or by ditches in the reclaimed coastal marshes from the Strait of Dover to Slesvig.

The association of enclosed country with dispersed settlement is fundamental, since both features record the individualism of the inhabitants, control of certain fields by a family or a small group of families living in a hamlet, and control of their own animals : in complete contrast to the communal obligations of the medieval village in the champain. Complete dispersion may be either an old phenomenon, as in much of southern France and in Flanders, where it has evolved from still older settlement in hamlets, or it may have emerged from a loose aggregation of farms worked on a communal basis as in north-western Germany and the eastern Netherlands. Both these forms of settle-ment may still be seen in the same districts. In parts of France, again, large planned villages are found like islands in a sea of scattered farms ; in the Garonne basin these *bastides* were built as refuges during the Anglo-French wars, while others in Burgundy are thought to have a more economic origin in relation to vine cultivation. In Britain where scattered farms are a modern feature they replaced hamlets in the Scottish Lowlands, but on the English Plain they were added to the old villages which belonged to the open country of former times.

The High Mountains

Conditions like those of the maritime fringe prevail among the high mountains. Space is restricted at heights where crops will ripen, and this even in the Alps which owing to their great breadth have specially favoured local climates, so that cereals and fruits flourish at levels much higher than elsewhere in Europe. Hence there has ever been dependence upon livestock with seasonal movement of herds throughout the mountains from the Cantabrians and Pyrenees by the Alps to the Carpathians and the Balkan highlands, and again in the Caucasus. Relief and climate combined to compel the people, as their numbers increased, to use the whole area up to the permanent snow, where this exists. The deep glens give some ground for crops and none can be spared for fodder ; so forest has been cleared and replaced by grass used as hay to maintain animals in winter, and the herds ascend, following the melting snow, to the herbaceous pasture of the alp above the treeline. Thus the aim of mountain communities was almost self-sufficiency in food and sale of surplus animals and some of the dairy produce. In the past this was cheese alone ; now, where routes permit, butter and milk may be exported. The extent to which the total area is used depends upon the density of population and their stock, while the proportion of the people actually moving with the herds varies in the different mountains and their parts. At its best this pastoral life has led to improvement of pasture by diverting streams through the folds of the summer stations to irrigate and manure ; by communal effort, too, aqueducts have been built to augment the supply of hay by irrigation. Among the stock cattle are kept in preference to sheep wherever pasture is adequate, but sheep predominate in the drier eastern part of the Pyrenees and the south-western Alps ; and, again, throughout most of the Carpathian arc and the Balkan highlands cattle range in the lower clearings of the forest, while the much more numerous sheep are driven to the high pastures which include most of the summits ; in the wooded parts of Yugoslavia pigs also take part in these seasonal movements. While cattle play a leading part in the economy of the south-western high mountains their density is much greater among the plateaus, hills and plains to the north, and in northern Italy. Near the summits of these lower highlands seasonal transhumance still persists from the central plateau of France to the Riesengebirge, but the rearing of cattle is generally now integrated with arable farming and, except locally and in Switzerland, the emphasis is on the production of beef rather than milk, while in many districts cattle perform the farm-work.

Rural settlements throughout all these mountains and other highlands are characteristically either hamlets or completely scattered homesteads, as they are in the maritime zone. But where considerable tracts of smoother land lie among the highlands these are generally marked by villages, of several types, that belong to the great plain in the north and which developed with its agricultural systems. In the high mountains special features imposed by the relief and mode of life must be mentioned. The larger places are usually loose aggregations of hamlets, and dependent upon these are subsidiary clusters at a higher level, some occupied permanently, others temporarily as for haymaking. Still higher are the scattered summer stations—the chalets of the French Alps. Everywhere there is preference for the sunny slope, and in many of the glens places subject to avalanches are avoided. During the last half-century or more some notable changes have taken place in the economy and the aspect of the mountains. Many mountaineers have been attracted to the lowlands, so abandoned homesteads and hamlets are common. Also, with increasing and more widespread demand for dairy-produce and greater ease in producing food from a distance, much of the lower arable land has been converted to meadow or devoted to fodder crops. Finally, new or enlarged and altered settlements are to be seen in many of the principal valleys, owing to two causes : the penetration of the mountains by modern industry and the enormous influx of tourists.

The outer coastlands of Europe, in the British Isles and Scandinavia, are mountainous as well as having a maritime climate. With cool, rainy and cloudy summers and leached soils, they lie near the limits of profitable cultivation, and there is great dependence upon stock-keeping, supplemented by fishing. In Ireland, Wales and Scotland seasonal movement of cattle has now ceased, but this practice is still common in Norway, and the continued occupation of many of the high summer *saeter*, or shielings, is assured by use of a simple modern device, the wire ropeway by which churns of milk are sent, by gravity, to the roadsides in the deep glens. Central Sweden, notably the Indal, furnishes an example of a pastoral system that may well reproduce medieval happenings in Central Europe. Modern colonisation of the forest there involves movement of the settlers' cattle in the summer to pastures specially cleared for them ; and as these clearings may later be cultivated the animals are an advance guard of permanent settlement. But here again the system seems to be in decline as roads are built. Finally in this review of dependence upon stock it is fitting to note that in Scandinavia beyond the cold limits of agriculture is the migrant society of the Lapps, whose mode of life has been determined by the feeding habits of their reindeer. These people form the counterpart of the pastoral nomads in the southern borderlands of Europe. In Wales and Scotland the summer shielings lie in ruins and the hills are browsed mainly by sheep, reared for meat and wool to the detriment of the pasture—in Scotland also by wild deer. This change was marked by depopulation, which may perhaps be countered in part by the reintroduction of more cattle. It must be noted, however, that the British Isles maintain a huge stock of sheep because they form part of the mixed farming system ; there is close interdependence of the hills and the highly farmed lowlands.

An exception to the general dispersion of settlement on the Atlantic fringe is found along the North Sea coast. The Low-German word *dorp* (village) probably derives from *terp*, a mound, and the oldest Friesian villages, in Netherlands and Germany, are clustered on ancient mounds that were raised to provide their sites in the marsh. Next, there are street-villages built in the polders as these were formed, followed by the dike-villages, which are long strings of houses behind the successive sea-dikes, and lastly, dispersed farms occupying the newest polders. Such is the general succession found throughout the land gained from the sea, lakes and estuaries between the Netherlands and Jutland, although not all the types are found in the same areas. Farther inland and at a higher level the peat bogs have been largely reclaimed for agriculture by the people of the so-called fen colonies ; these are villages aligned on the straight canals by which the cut peat has been removed.

Open Fields and Villages

It was suggested at the beginning of this chapter that the open countryside with its strip-fields is associated with the village as opposed to the hamlet or the isolated home ; and these two principal elements in the landscape throughout most of the European Plain are, in the main, equally old, neither having changed much in aspect since the Middle Ages. The pattern was formed when the land was worked communally by the villagers, and it is often still possible to trace the bounds of the three large open-fields of the village, one of which in a given year was under autumn-sown corn, one under spring-sown corn, and one, bare fallow ; or again in some parts vestiges can be found of a two-fold division of a village field-system, not necessarily older, however. The western limit of this champain with villages spaced evenly upon it lay for long at the Welsh border, but in England now, while the villages remain, the land is enclosed and redivided among the scattered farms ; and this also applies to Denmark and southern Sweden. So the western limit runs from Dieppe to the bend of the Loire and thence passes east of the River Yonne to Dijon and the eastern Jura Mountains. From Seine and Saône to the Volga and Black Sea the open farmland of Europe spreads out, with its clustered villages. There are exceptions in and near the mountains as we have seen, and some also on the plains ; but such is the general character of the European grainlands, growing specially wheat for white bread in the west, and rye for ' black ' bread in the east, and again wheat in the south-east. The oldest form of the village is usually held to be the unplanned aggregation of farms clustered more or less compactly round a church, but with gardens and many winding lanes. This type predominates in France, central Belgium, the Swiss plateau and Germany up to the lower Elbe and the Saale, but also on the plains along the Danube. It certainly derives from a prehistoric village, but since the reason of its origin is much debated, we may note simply that the general distribution suggests connection with the later spread of Celtic civilisation in the Iron Age while, on the other hand, the continuous occurrence of such villages from the Seine to the Saale associates them naturally with the Germanic Saxons, Franks and Allemanni and with their movements into the Roman Empire. Many villages again may have had Roman villas as nuclei and, finally, the type coincides in many areas throughout the whole expanse, with the distribution of loess or similar deposits which favoured the original agricultural settlements in the Neolithic Age. So the compact irregular villages may represent foundations of different periods with subsequent accretions.

The other kinds of village can be related, much more certainly, to the penetration of forest, marsh or moor on the one hand and to ethnic differences of the founders on the other. Linear villages are associated with colonisation of land formerly waste ; the houses, originally and generally still being farms, built along the single street, with the fields of each farmer extending in a single strip from his home to the forest, which has of course in many cases been felled later, and replaced by farmland of newer villages. In hilly land the road, and so the village, tends to wind along the valley ; on the plains it is usually straighter, but in a distinct type it divides in the village to enclose a green, the church and often a pond. These planned linear villages may be traced to the several waves of forest clearance of the Middle Ages in western and central Europe. But on the great plain east of the Elbe and Saale history has been complicated by the contest between the Slavs and the Germans who, after the tenth century, gradually gained mastery of these lands up to the frontier which they held until 1918. Hence there are many small villages, originally Slavonic, which are either linear or almost circular, and among them the planned settlements of the Germans. In the zone first conquered, about 120 miles wide, the Germans seem to have copied the Slavonic round or oval defensive villages, but with more regular plan, while their long villages, with or without greens, are widespread throughout the whole territory. Around these settlements traces of the German three-field system may be found ; but the rural landscape over wide areas was dominated until recently by the modern large estates of the *Junkers,* with their big square fields and new settlements around the owners' mansions. Although these began to appear in the sixteenth century, they date mostly from the nineteenth. Similarly the drainage of the broad marshy valleys, effected especially in the late-eighteenth century, led to the building of planned villages like those of the coastal marsh. Since 1946, with the abolition of the great estates, further changes have occurred.

The peasants of the plains throughout eastern Europe are essentially villagers whose settlements differ widely in date of origin, since the process of colonisation has suffered interruption in many parts through wars and insecurity. The northern forest, however, has been cleared progressively for cultivation, so innumerable hamlets grew up in the morainic belts and larger street-villages where bigger areas of suitable soil were available ; the older settlements are generally near waterways, and in the far north the pioneers are still found sporadically with their homes and fields aligned on the river banks. Fire has ever been the menace for all these log-house villages, and most have been rebuilt many times. In southern Russia and Romania it was unsafe to live out in the open steppes until the late eighteenth century, so the villages are not older than this ; and they are most distinctive. They lie in the valleys, above flood-level but hidden from the plateau, thus having shelter and relatively easy access to water. Strings of villages so placed have more or less coalesced, to give a highly concentrated population in the valleys. The houses are built mainly of dried sods and are lime-washed. The mid-eighteenth century again saw the recolonisation of the Great Alföld of Hungary, which had suffered large reduction in population during two centuries of Turkish occupation ; and the result has been the creation, after the liberation, of villages unique in Europe for their great size ; many have the population of large towns, but are, or were until recently, entirely agricultural in function. Most of those in the northern part of the plain are irregular in shape, but in the southern part many consist of a vast assemblage of cottages in gardens, built on a grid-plan at the instance of the Habsburg crown for the German, Serbo-Croat and Romanian colonists who were introduced. Similar dice-board villages border the Danube in Romania. These great villages are much too widely spaced for convenience, hence the growth in the present century of isolated farms between them. In the Balkan Peninsula new villages were formed in the lowlands as the Turkish landlords withdrew. In many parts these are evidently aggregations of hamlets which represent the traditional settlement of the southern Slavs, with each hamlet, spaced very openly, occupied by a group of blood-relations, the *zadruga* or enlarged family. But in the southern part of the Peninsula as well as in much of Serbia east of the Morava, the Turkish feudal estate-centres, the *chiftliks*, became enlarged to form villages.

The revolutionary changes in the agricultural system that have taken place in Soviet Russia, and similar alterations in neighbouring countries under Russian influence, have undoubtedly affected the arrangement of settlements throughout eastern Europe, but it is most unlikely that the older imprints on the landscape have been erased.

TRANSPORTATION

At this point we may pause to consider how the inhabitants of these varied settlements move about on their daily round and carry the produce of their land. The impact of modern means of rapid transport upon life and upon the landscape has varied greatly in the degree of its effect in the different regions. Although it is now unlikely that many people exist who have not seen an aircraft in flight, there are vast tracts where planes do not normally land. Railways during the nineteenth century came to penetrate all kinds of country and to multiply with a general correspondence to increase in the density of population. But, from their costliness, the aggregate length of railways is now very much less than that of roads which carry motor traffic. The subject of the use of rivers as waterways has been mentioned (p. 73), as well as the historic spread of roads ; and the regional density of routes by land, water and air, and the intensity of their use will be reviewed later. But it must be emphasised that such routes, essential as they are to organised life, are related to the movement of goods by other means throughout all the land that lies between them. The age-old methods of transport by animal traction and even human carriage remain important, whether they feed the rapid carriers of modern times or are independent of them. They are practised by millions of people as part of their everyday life, and the efforts of these are of importance to the greater masses not personally concerned who need food or raw materials from the land.

Human porterage has persisted throughout certain large regions, as around the Mediterranean and in the mountains where it is common among the great mass of country people, even where other means of carriage are in use as well. Moreover, it is still found elsewhere, in both country and town, associated with special occupations such as peddling fish and vegetables. There is much interest in the local variety, both of the simple utensils for the load and of the manner of bearing it. The sack, the creel or the wooden container is generally hung from the shoulders ; but it is curious to find the brow-band in use near the two ends of Europe, giving support from the head to the fisherwives' heavy creels around the North Sea on the one hand and to the assorted and heavy loads of the town porters of Turkish coastal towns on the other. The ancient mode of carrying water, the earthen jar upon the head—aslant when empty, upright when full—continues to impart grace to the female gait, not only throughout the Arab and Turkish lands, but also in their former realms, as in the Iberian Peninsula, although the distribution of the practice there suggests an origin older than the Moorish occupation. The use, however, of twin petrol cans, shoulder borne, tends to oust this mode in many parts.

The different animals employed for pack or draught purposes correspond in general to the physical environment, but tradition or prejudice as well as local wealth or poverty play a part in determining the actual distribution within the various climatic zones, from that of the hot desert with the camel predominant, to that of the cold desert with the reindeer. In the Mediterranean zone and in the neighbouring high mountains the ass and the mule are universal because they are easily fed and are suited to rough tracks and steep slopes ; but horses of the smaller breeds are also used for loads, and oxen for ploughing where sufficient fodder is available, as in the wetter northern parts of the zone. Owing to the Moorish and the Turkish occupations of European lands the camel is still found in the driest parts of Spain and the Balkan Peninsula, and the water-buffalo, too, in small numbers on the wetter plains of the latter. Dogs are used as draught animals to pull small carts here and there in flat lands, but especially in Flanders.

Throughout the greater part of Europe, where there is seldom any lack of fodder and where slopes are generally not excessive, the horse has predominated for use on road or track until the days of the motor ; for work in the fields, however, it has gained slowly upon the ox, and then only where agricultural implements and methods and the economic status of the farmer have combined to make it the more suitable beast. So for a thousand years the evolution of horse breeding, notably regional in character, proceeded all over the European lowlands and especially in the west, but also in Hungary, the home of the last horse-nomads to adopt a settled life. In the contest for the plough between the ox and the horse, an important factor has been the increasing demand in western Europe for good beef and fresh milk, which could be met most easily where grass grows throughout the greater part of the year. Thus gradually the horse came to replace the ox from the British Isles and Brittany in the west to Poland and Scandinavia. In contrast with these lands is south-eastern Europe, where the typical breeds of cattle are tough and muscular, grey long-horned beasts, capable of much work but yielding little milk. Between these zones, as in central Europe or south-western France, this ox-horse competition was decided regionally or even locally ; indeed, there and elsewhere it may remain unresolved at the full advent of mechanical power which has been accelerated by the Second World War, bringing as it did huge losses of animals and wide familiarity with the motor.

If we disregard the cycle, the steam train, the electric train and all forms of the automobile, we may still find the most interesting regional variation in the vehicles of Europe and its margins. There is, of course, first, the distinction of runners and wheels. The sledge has its special use on snow, and so, in various forms, is the winter vehicle of the Eastern Plain and Scandinavia ; but stout sledges of simple form are also used where snow is absent, on rough ground, if only for short hauls. Space forbids discussion of the manifold wheeled vehicles, but reference must be made to the important distinction between those with two wheels and those with four. From England and eastern France to Russia the typical road wagon has four wheels and, except in England and Flanders, it is long and narrow, suited to the straight farm tracks of the plain, but not to twisting roads, and it is also lightly built to avoid sticking in the mud ; similar wagons are used on both sides of the Pyrenees and in northern Italy. The two-wheeled cart, on the other hand, which evolved in the Mediterranean lands or beyond, prevails there still as well as in France, Ireland, the English uplands, Scotland and Scandinavia. It is probable that the detailed distributions of the wagon and the cart would be found to be explained by historic changes.

A good example of the adoption of a western invention by the towns of the south in Europe and beyond is the spread of the light four-wheeled carriage known in Britain as the victoria. The selection of this as opposed to the many other types evolved during the nineteenth century may well be due to chance, but the victoria is certainly better suited to the fine weather of such places than are most of the other carriages.

We must resist the temptation to follow this brief study of land vehicles by examining the varieties of other inventions as they are distributed, such as boats, fishing gear, wind- and water-mills, agricultural implements, or even household furnishing and traditional costumes. But the foregoing examples of things in common use may suffice to indicate that many of the data gathered by ethnologists which in some measure reveal the nature of man's response to his environment are to be integrated with facts that are more usually regarded as primarily geographical. The full geographic synthesis of a vast body of ethnological lore remains to be attempted. It would seem certain, however, that regional variety in all these things will now decrease very rapidly for two reasons. These are, first, the prevalence everywhere of goods made in factories, and, secondly, the fact that Europe is on the move as never before ; not only did the vast temporary movements of troops and of civilians during the Second War have their effect on most countries, but the habit of travel has been acquired and with it greater opportunities for exchange of ideas ; and the greatest leveller of all may well be the motor-bus, which has become an almost universal means of transport.

CHAPTER 15

AGRICULTURAL POPULATION, CROP
DISTRIBUTIONS AND PRODUCTIVITY

BEFORE examining further the various farm practices, their distribution and results, it will be well to give some attention to those who labour in the fields, and particularly their numbers and the general effectiveness of their work. It happens that the material for such a review and comparison exists for a period between the two World Wars, as a result of inquiries made for the League of Nations.[1] They were based on the censuses taken variously between 1926 and 1934, and the average agricultural statistics for the years 1931–35, and from the results the facts illustrated by Figs. 25 and 26 are selected as disclosing in a striking way the part played by agriculture in the life of the nations except Russia and Turkey. Unfortunately no such thorough analysis of more recent conditions has yet been published, but the probable nature of the subsequent changes will be indicated below and in Chapter 19, which also deals with the growth of population during the previous century.

The degree in which the populations are directly dependent on agriculture (Fig. 25) is seen to increase from its lowest in England with 5 per cent, southward and eastward as the opportunity for other employment decreases, to exceed 40 per cent upon the fringes, with 70 per cent or more in Lithuania, Romania, Bulgaria, Yugoslavia and Albania. The second cartogram (Fig. 26), which is on a provincial basis, shows the production per person dependent on agriculture expressed as percentage of the European average, taken as 100; 'production' means the volume of agricultural produce actually available for food and industrial consumption. It is clear from this diagram that the efforts of the farming people are least successful in eastern and southern Europe, and most successful in Great Britain and Denmark, where the index is over three times the European average. It will be evident that these distributions roughly concentric upon the North Sea are to be explained largely by the economic, political and social histories of the various countries review are closely related to those of demography, and especially to the relative rates of reproduction of the countries during the preceding period. This rather than the factor of physical geography. Moreover, the facts under matter must be discussed later ; but it should be noted here that during these inter-war years the net reproduction rate in central and western Europe,

---

[1] By W. E. Moore of the Office of Population Research, Princeton University, and published as *Economic Demography of Eastern and Southern Europe*, Geneva, 1945.

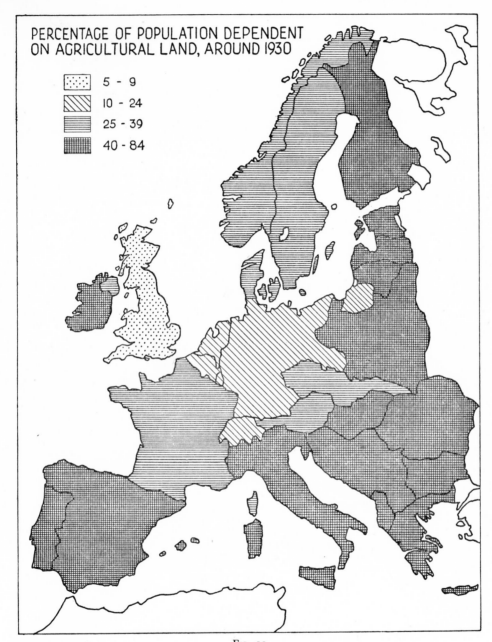

PERCENTAGE OF POPULATION DEPENDENT
ON AGRICULTURAL LAND, AROUND 1930

5 - 9
10 - 24
25 - 39
40 - 84

Fig. 25

161

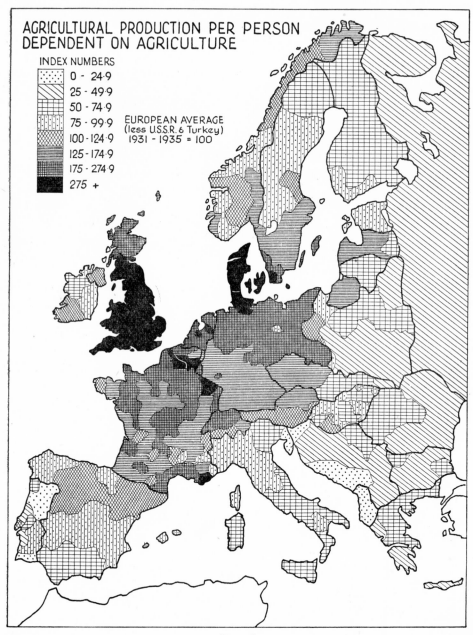

FIG. 26

except Ireland and the Netherlands, was lower than the average rate for Europe, while the rate in the Mediterranean and eastern countries exceeded the average.

The fertility of the peasantry of eastern Europe, coupled with conditions of land tenure there, mainly accounts for their population density, which is shown on Fig. 27, again as a provincial cartogram. The figures upon which this is founded have involved the invention of an abstraction called the ' arable equivalent ', which makes it possible to compare reasonably land that is devoted to very different purposes, such as grain fields, orchards and rough pastures. Hence the cartogram shows with fair reality, for administrative areas, the density of population upon the land which gives them a living. Nevertheless there is no uniform explanation of the variation in these agricultural densities as between countries that differ widely in their national economies. But in respect of the south-east from Poland to Greece, where eighty or more farming people are seen to depend on the produce of one of these ' adjusted ' square kilometres, a general and simple deduction may be made. These lands were overwhelmingly agricultural, and the production per person was very low ; so also was the standard of living and there was a real ' land-hunger '. It was these agrarian and over-populated countries together with Italy, Spain and Portugal which provided the last great wave of emigration to the Americas ; but this had virtually ceased before the period of these statistics.

Since the principal task of these farmers is to provide food, the subject of dietary may be mentioned at this point.

Consideration of the feeding habits suggests that there is a broad causal relationship between climate and diet. This certainly exists, and it is indicated by the great difference in total weight of food taken in the north, as well as the high proportion of food of animal origin and probably the higher total calories, as compared with southern lands. But it is also probable that the relative poverty of the southern peoples has a great deal to do with their diet ; at any rate it is certain that the dearer foods are not shared among the population. Again it should be noted that habits change with opportunity and purchasing power. But whatever the causes of variety, the main facts stand out clearly. National diets less than half composed of cereals and potatoes mark north-western Europe. In Poland, Germany and the Netherlands the proportion of potatoes greatly exceeds that of cereals. The bread grains by weight are at least three times as nourishing as potatoes, but the latter give vastly greater bulk from the same area of cultivation—up to ten times. The sugar quota is variable, and is doubtless influenced by the amount raised locally and by purchasing power. The use of dried pulses increases where foods of animal origin are scarce.

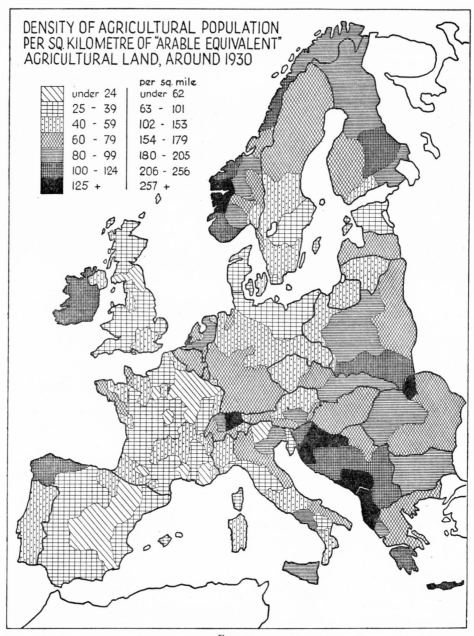

DENSITY OF AGRICULTURAL POPULATION
PER SQ. KILOMETRE OF "ARABLE EQUIVALENT"
AGRICULTURAL LAND, AROUND 1930

	per sq. mile
under 24	under 62
25 - 39	63 - 101
40 - 59	102 - 153
60 - 79	154 - 179
80 - 99	180 - 205
100 - 124	206 - 256
125 +	257 +

FIG. 27

European governments make ever greater efforts to increase agricultural output and so to meet home requirements, but the industrial countries have long depended upon imports, and the degree of variation in this respect will be referred to in due course. It is therefore in these lands that commercial farming is most highly developed, with specialisation in the products to which they are geographically best suited and reliance upon import of others. The special and valuable products are exported, the dairy produce of Denmark

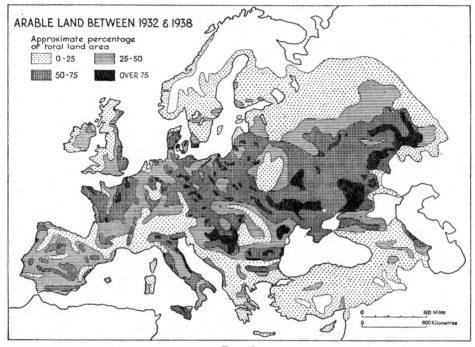

FIG. 28

and the Netherlands, the wine of France and Mediterranean lands, while grain and fodder are imported by the first two of these, mostly from overseas. Moreover, there is a large international trade in mineral fertilisers. This commercial agriculture is typified by Britain, Denmark and the Netherlands, but is also characteristic of Sweden, Norway and Switzerland, and in lesser degree of France, Belgium, Italy and Germany. All this is bound up with the intensity of farming, and hence with its output per unit area ; and variety in these respects must be assumed while reviewing the general agricultural distributions.

The degree in which Europe was under cultivation before World War II is illustrated on Fig. 28. This map, although not statistically accurate, is believed to give a reliable impression.[1] The natural limitations of agriculture imposed by climate, altitude, rugged relief and swamp, as in the Pripet, are at once obvious. In addition there is the higher proportion of arable in the part of Poland that previously was Prussian, and similarly in the Baltic States as compared with adjoining Russian territory ; and again within the U.S.S.R. the most continuous arable belt is seen first along the main rye and potato belts which coincides with the axis of greatest population, and secondly near the south-eastern limit of the steppe, essentially the spring wheat and sun-flower zone, which always has a large proportion of fallow land. Then to compare the proportions over the smoother lands as a whole, the relatively high status of the eastern plain or of Spain on the one hand and northern France or Denmark on the other serves as a reminder that maps of this kind may be deceptive. Thus at the period in question one-quarter of the arable land in European Russia lay fallow, and in Spain one-third ; in the Atlas Lands the proportion was about one-half, whereas in France and Denmark it was negligible. It has to be borne in mind also that in north-western Europe large areas which had been, or could be, ploughed were kept permanently under grass for the very productive animal industry ; in the British Isles such land was almost equal to the arable area.

DISTRIBUTIONS OF CROPS

The distributions of the leading crops and domestic animals over Europe and the Borderlands may now be reviewed generally, with the help of Figs. 30 and 31. These maps have been derived mainly from the detailed ' dot-maps ' prepared by the United States Department of Agriculture,[2] and they have been drawn boldly so as to allow them to be viewed together, and with only three grades of intensity. Their chief weakness is in the lowest grade, which, because it has been extended to the extreme limits of cultivation or of stock, represents a great variety of values. The maps show distributions as plotted from three-year averages of various years from 1932 to 1938 ; later data for the U.S.S.R. are not available. They show the relative areas under the respective crops and the relative densities of the animals ; the shadings of all but three of the maps are intended to be comparable, but those of potatoes and root forage crops represent areas only one-half, and that of sugar-beet only one-fifth, of the acreages of the other crops.

[1] It is founded on the ' dot-map ' of arable area and the cartogram showing arable percent-age of total land areas in *Agricultural Geography of Europe and the Near East*, U.S. Department of Agriculture, 1948, referring to three-year averages between 1932 and 1938.
[2] *Agricultural Geography of Europe and the Near East*, Miscellaneous Publication No. 665, 1948.

CEREALS AND PULSES

Barley

As has been indicated in Chapter 5, the climatic requirements of crops cause them to be distributed in approximately latitudinal zones. By far the broadest of these is that of barley, which in its several varieties extends from the cold limit to the dry limit of agriculture, owing to its relatively short period of development. Roughly one-half of the barley is raised in the Mediterranean lands or beyond, and probably over three-quarters with the south Russian crop included. But the high yields are obtained in the north-west, where, because of slower ripening, the grain is more starchy, and this is good for malting. Barley then is the chief source of alcohol in beer and whisky, a fact which accounts for the considerable area devoted to the crop ; and the chief brewing countries also make large imports. The United Kingdom is the leader among them ; it has produced in a year—as one of the sinews of war in 1945—over 27 gallons (123 litres) of beer per head of the population. However, this beer-population ratio has been exceeded consistently in Belgium, a great importer of barley ; in Britain the crop forms about a quarter of the grain harvest. In Denmark it is the principal grain and serves the animals as well as an important brewing industry. In central Europe barley is prominent in the regions that also grow sugar-beet since it likes the same soils and, as a spring-sown crop, forms a suitable element in the rotation practised.

Oats

Oats is the prime fodder crop of northern Europe, but the main concentrations lie first in general along the latitude 50° from the Paris Basin to the Vistula, secondly in Russia, from the vicinity of Kursk north-eastward to that of Molotov (Perm), i.e. along the fringe of the northern forest ; and thirdly in the British Isles and along the south-western coasts of the Baltic. Oats are the principal cereal in the harvests of all the northern countries from Finland to Eire, except Denmark.

Rye

Rye is now primarily the food grain of the boreal continental climate, since it resists frost better than other cereals ; but formerly its use as a bread grain extended to the British Isles. In France rye is grown upon the poorer soils, but the main tract of its cultivation begins at a sharp limit almost coincident with that of the German and Flemish languages ; and everywhere on the plain east of the Elbe except on the Baltic coast it is the principal cereal until it overlaps the wheat-growing tract of the south-east, where its limit lies near the isotherms of 59° for May and 68° for July. Rye forms over a quarter of the German grain harvest and half of the Polish ; in Russia, since it is the principal food, its distribution corresponds closely to that of population (Fig. 34). The distributions of the two principal bread grains, wheat and rye, will tend more and more to reflect the quality of the soil since everywhere there is evidence of growing preference for wheaten bread. Rye, therefore, will prevail only where the yield is more reliable because of its tolerance of sandy and acid soil and because of its winter hardiness.

Wheat

It may be said that in every country efforts have been made to augment the production of wheat and to meet the ever-growing demand for it so far as possible. Everywhere wheat is given the best soils, and the most productive regions are naturally the plains. Again where possible the grain is sown in the autumn since a higher yield is thus obtained. While the average quantity of wheat gathered varies, like other crops, with the intensity of husbandry, the variety of the grain itself is less obvious ; yet this affects its use greatly. The chief distinction is that between, first, durum wheat, suited only to the making of pastes like spaghetti, and grown in the relatively summer-dry climates of the Mediterranean and south Russia ; secondly the hard wheats, high in gluten and the best for modern milling and bread-making, grown largely in the Danubian lands and Russia ; and thirdly the soft wheats of north-western Europe. These last, while prominent in French bread, are now used in Britain largely for biscuit-making or for blending with imported grain.

After Russia, France and Italy are by far the greatest producers of wheat, which is usually over half and over two-thirds of their respective grain harvests. Approximately the equivalent amount is produced in the Danubian lands as a whole. Wheat is the principal grain in Europe and the Borderlands.

Maize

The maize plant has many uses for the farmer, apart from its seed, but it is grown where climate permits primarily for its high yield of fodder or food. It has an important function in husbandry comparable to that of the root crops, but it is spring-sown. Ideally maize should have heavy rain from May to July, with over 4 inches (100 mm.) in June and July, and some rain until September ; the temperature should rise to a July mean of about 70° F. (21° C.). Hence this crop is limited to regions with very warm summer-rain climates, but with southern outliers under irrigation. The great producers of maize are Yugoslavia, Romania, Hungary, Italy and Egypt. As a fodder it is specially important for pigs and poultry, but it is given also to milk cows and horses. It is the chief food-grain in Egypt and probably still in Romania. There and in Italy it is eaten as a pudding or moist paste (*mamaliga* and *polenta* respectively) ; and the lack of vitamin B in maize accounted for the former prevalence in some districts of the disease known as pellagra (= Ital. ' raw-skin '), which has a high morbidity.

Rice

The growing of rice in the Mediterranean lands under irrigation has been mentioned earlier. The areas are widely dispersed and relatively small, but the principal ones, those of Italy, Spain and Egypt, are marked by their high yield of grain. In one part of the Borderlands, the alluvial plain of the Caspian Sea in Iran, rice is grown as in its homeland under natural semi-aquatic conditions, yet the yields obtained are much lower.

Legumes

Leguminous crops are raised in great variety and in all countries to provide green fodder, and they are beneficial to the soil and to the other crops that follow them in rotation. In addition to those a number of pulses are grown for food, most of them whether beans, peas or lentils being preserved by drying. While the extent of such cultivation (Fig. 29) is almost as wide as that of wheat, its relative importance is greatest in the south, and especially in Italy, the largest producer, Iberia, France, the Danubian countries and Ukraine. In all of them beans of several varieties greatly exceed peas and lentils in amount.

VINES AND HOPS

Wine

About three-quarters of the world total is produced in the Mediterranean countries, and half in France and Italy alone ; Spain produces a tenth, Algeria, Portugal and Greece follow. The northern limit (Fig. 15) is in general climatic, but in detail economic ; it has oscillated in the past, and in the Middle Ages wine was made in England. The Romans introduced the vine to the Rhineland by way of the Mosel valley, and at various later times it has been planted throughout the Danubian lands and the southern fringe of Russia. Where the plant attains the higher latitudes as in Germany it is grown on slopes with southern aspect. In France and the other outlying areas where long established its cultivation and wine-making give a special character to the agriculture and economy of the favoured districts, increasing land values and density of population, vineyards as a rule being held as small properties. France shows much greater specialisation than other countries in the production of wine ; the vineyards give both higher average yields and larger variety of fine wines. The plain of Languedoc is notable for the huge area devoted to vines, and the great volume of its wine which is largely made in co-operative factories, while among the other southern districts those of Burgundy and of the Gironde are famous for their many choice vintages. But France also imports much wine from Italy and Spain, and also receives most of the produce of Algeria from the vineyards of French growers in the northern valleys. It is only in France that the industry plays a great part in the national economy.

It must be noted, too, that the vine is subject to many diseases ; the most serious of these have followed the bringing of American species to Europe, and with them *phylloxera*, a grape-louse, as well as several fungi. The attacks of the former in the second half of the nineteenth century caused the ruin of vast areas of vineyards, which had to be renewed by planting American vines that had acquired some degree of immunity. The constant fight against mildew and other pests calls for regular spraying with copper salts and sulphur ; and this, incidentally, has introduced new elements of colour to the summer landscape.

Hops

The cultivation of hops resembles that of the grape-vine in many respects ; both plants are deep-rooted perennials ; the hop garden looks not unlike some types of vineyard, while the oast house for drying the flowers corresponds to the installation for grape pressing. The use of hops in beer began probably in Germany, and became prevalent by the sixteenth century. Although the area devoted to the plant is a minute fraction of Europe, the crop possesses real importance for many millions of consumers, as is evident from the statistics of brewing given above. The gardens are found always on rich soil such as that of the brick-earth in Kent, which is so treated that English yields are the heaviest ; and so again in Flanders, Alsace, Bavaria and Bohemia, thus partly within the zone of the grape-vine.

POTATOES, ROOTS, OILSEEDS AND FIBRES

Maize and potatoes have been described, with reason, as 'revolutionary crops' of the sixteenth century, but the cultivation of turnips and clover as parts of a rotation marked an even greater change in agriculture. Although this took place in Flanders in the fourteenth century, most of Europe has only taken advantage of these discoveries much later. The present productivity of the soil, however, is closely related to the use made of roots and green fodder crops, including the nitrogen-fixing legumes, and so, too, of course, is the integration of stock-keeping and arable farming. The production of roots and tubers and of hay from sown grasses and legumes makes it possible to maintain large numbers of cattle and pigs mainly by stall feeding, and even flocks of sheep in Britain, to obtain the foods of animal origin needed by the teeming population and at the same time to ensure that a great proportion of this vegetation returns to the soil as dung, the best of all fertilisers. Space forbids discussion of all these plants separately, but two may be selected as of special interest : the potato, which is primarily a staple food ; and the sugar-beet, an industrial crop always treated in a factory. The principal root crops grown primarily for animals are turnips, yellow and Swedish, mangolds, which need higher temperatures, and so do not extend so far north as these, and the beets. While the latter have lost importance as fodder, one variety has been evolved and grown on account of its sugar, the residual pulp and the leaves have also feeding value.

Potatoes

The remarkable adaptation of the Andean potato to almost every soil and to most kinds of European climate has affected the diet of a vast population. But it is grown for other purposes as well : as fodder, especially for pigs, and as a principal source of starch and alcohol. Without potatoes, pigs and herrings in great quantities to feed the workers, the industrial revolution in central Europe could scarcely have taken place ; nor would Ireland without the first two have become over-populated and then suffered famine owing to failure of the potato crop in 1845. So this American plant has become predominantly European. In regard to the distribution, it is simplest to mention its relatively small importance in eastern Spain and the Carpathian and Balkan lands. The eastern limit of great cultivation lay for long at the German and then the Polish frontier, but now although the crop is slight in White Russia and on the southern steppe, the potato is widely grown throughout the central part of the plain. The dependence of Germany and Poland upon the tubers is very striking. In the past a substantial fraction, perhaps one-tenth, of the large German crop has been devoted to industrial uses such as the manufacture of starch and alcohol, and the factories are situated near the main producing areas.

Sugar-beet

There is no such widespread growing of the sugar-beet. In the first place although this again is essentially a European crop, the total amount is very much smaller ; secondly it is much more exacting as regards both soil and climate than the potato, and lastly dependence upon the factory for processing the beets means that farmers must grow them within districts where the sugar industry is organised. The soil must be deep and stoneless, the loams of the loess are thus perfect for it, and the great bulk of the crop is raised within the zone of such soils between northern France and Ukraine. Ideally the mean temperature during the summer months should be not far from 70° F. (21° C.) ; but with the longer daylight cultivation is extended northwards to Scotland, Denmark and southern Sweden. Beet usually takes part in rotation with wheat and barley, and its main distribution lies within that of winter wheat cultivation, but for reasons both physical and economic the leading areas are quite distinct : first, north-eastern France, the Low Countries and lower Rhineland, together with eastern England ; secondly the plain west of the middle Elbe with those of Bohemia and Moravia ; and thirdly Ukraine, especially the western part.

Fodder Roots

From Scandinavia to France substantial areas are given to roots for feeding animals, particularly cattle. Denmark devotes one-seventh of the arable land to this, chiefly now to kohlrabi, but with sugar-beet also raised for this purpose. In other countries the chief roots are as follows : In Norway, kohlrabi and turnips ; in the British Isles, turnips, swedes and mangolds ; in France, turnips and swedes ; while from Belgium to Hungary the mangold is the favoured plant.

Oilseeds and Fibres

The plants producing oil in Europe and its Borderlands include olives, sunflower, cotton, flax, hemp, rape, and sesame. Nearly all are raised in the south and east ; Spain and Italy produce most of the olives, and Egypt most of the cottonseed, the sunflower seed comes from the southern part of the Russian steppe, with a small quota from the Danubian plains, while Russia leads with flax and hempseed. The rest of Europe must meet the need for oilseeds by imports. When their customary supplies became insufficient and vegetable oils were required, as for margarine and soap, the manufacturers were able to tap the tropical sources of oil from the coconut palm, the oil palm and the groundnut, which yield far greater quantities than the surplus of the olive yards. This also applies to the vegetable fibres of which flax alone is widely grown, but much less so than was the case before the commercial rise of cotton. The main fibre-flax area lies in White Russia, and thence eastward as a narrower zone between latitudes 66 and 68, where it is determined by growing season and other climatic factors, and by the availability of labour with traditional skill such as this crop exacts. The yield and probably the quality have recently been improved by the use of machinery and by change in the system of rotation. Flax of the finest quality has always been produced in the Low Countries, especially Flanders, where the techniques of cultivation and of retting, in the River Lys, were evolved. This Belgian lint is sought specially by the makers of fine linen, notably in Northern Ireland.

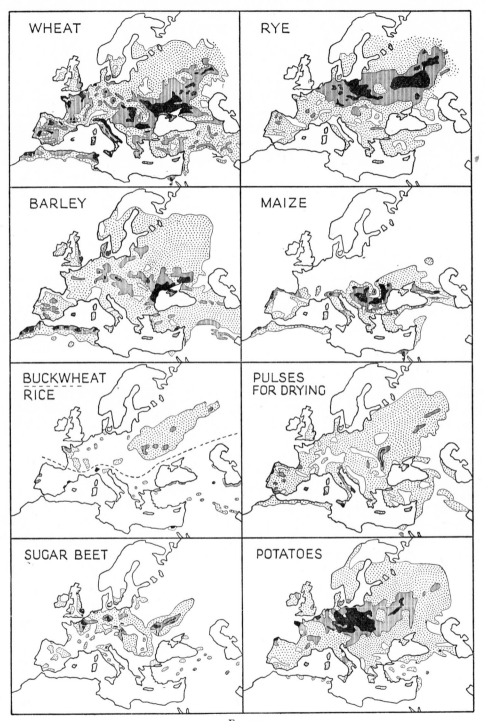

WHEAT   RYE

BARLEY   MAIZE

BUCKWHEAT
RICE   PULSES
FOR DRYING

SUGAR BEET   POTATOES

FIG. 29
Distribution of Crops
173

LIVESTOCK

The interdependence of crops and stock is partly revealed by some of the distributions given in Figs. 29 and 30, and the maps of oats and root fodder are placed with those of animals for this reason. In the case of oats the correspondence would probably be more obvious with a map of work animals, but the relation between roots and cattle is very clear, as is to be expected, since these bulky crops must be grown near the beasts that they feed. Cattle, again, as well as sheep in western Europe, have a share in the crops of sugar-beet at least by consuming the pulp. Where pigs are kept in large numbers they are dependent first upon potatoes, as is obvious in the case of eastern Germany, Poland and France, and secondly upon the by-products of the dairy, especially from Denmark to the Netherlands. Unfortunately the most important link between cattle and their food cannot be illustrated from lack of data in convenient and comparable form. A map based upon the returns of 'grassland' would show this as of equal importance, for example, in the lush meadows of western England or Ireland and on the mountains of eastern Spain. Furthermore, no adequate distributions are available for sown grass and the large range of other green fodder that is so important in the diet of cattle and especially of dairy cattle.

Cattle

Most of the cattle are in three areas : first and greatest, the coastal zone from the Danish Islands to the Garonne, secondly southern Britain and Ireland, and thirdly the zone of plateaus and mountains from central France to the Moravian Gate. There are also two outliers, in north-western Iberia and the northern plain of Italy. Thus the ancient disposition of the Atlantic seaboard for pasture is fully maintained under modern conditions.

Cattle are reared for their meat, their milk and over much of the continent still, for their work. But commercial agriculture is now usually marked by specialisation upon either dairy or beef production and, at least in Britain, breeding is directed by one or other of these purposes. The art has been brought to a very high pitch, especially in Britain, where modern breeding began in the eighteenth century ; hence the very high prices obtained by skilled and enterprising farmers for prime bulls, and the establishment of pedigrees that pay higher dividends than those of distinguished men ! Scientific breeding is practised with the other domestic animals as well as cattle, but the pecuniary rewards are less save in respect of horses, especially where the thoroughbred racehorse is concerned. Unfortunately the data are not available to show where, and how far, the domestic animals of various kinds throughout Europe have been improved by scientific breeding. But one may conceive

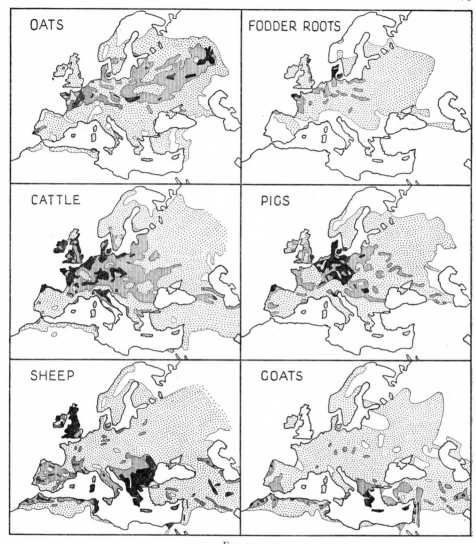

FIG. 30
Diagram showing the interdependence of crops and stock

a map showing the distribution of cattle, for example, which also represents the courses taken by streams, as it were, of aristocratic blood, throughout the herds of different regions. Many of the streams would have their sources in Britain : Shorthorns in Teesdale, a breed good both for beef and milk, the beef breeds such as Herefords and Aberdeen (or polled)-Angus, and dairy breeds like the Ayrshires, Jerseys and Guernseys. In the three years 1950–52

Scotland alone exported 2,030 pedigree cattle, the majority going to the Americas, and of this total 1,262 were Shorthorns and 409 were Aberdeen-Angus beasts.   Famous milkers, again, emanate from Denmark, the red Jutlands, while the black and white Holstein or Friesian cattle are now widespread upon the northern plain, including the Netherlands and in Britain.   Among the French 'blood-streams' two stem from the northern edge of the Central Plateau, the Limousin and the Charolais, while two of the Swiss breeds, the Simmenthal and the Schweiz, have spread to all the neighbouring countries, including Italy.

In stock-rearing there are two kinds of movement, besides that of the nomadic herdsmen near the desert.   The first, now called transhumance, has already been described : the seasonal movement to and from the mountain pastures.   The other is the movement of beasts by stages from their birthplace to the areas where they fulfil the main purposes of the industry.   By this means two kinds of region and two types of land-use are linked and interdependent —extensive grazing on semi-natural pastures with intensive feeding on rich permanent meadows or sown fodder, or with stall-feeding indoors.   This is commonly a link between hills and plains, and it operates with cattle, some breeds of sheep and, in places, also with horses.   A simple and spectacular example was the droving of the small black cattle from the Highlands of Scot- to feed the Lowland, and especially the English market ; this traffic flourished from 1750 to about 1830, and there was a similar movement from Wales.   The Scottish beasts were sold at the autumn tryst or market of Falkirk to the number of perhaps 150,000 annually from 1800 to 1825, with sheep in addition. The cattle were fattened in Norfolk and other parts of England.

For nearly a century Ireland has been the great source of these 'store-cattle' in Britain.   The young animals reared in the hills of the Atlantic side are moved to the east, where some are fattened on rich pastures, as in Co. Meath, but the majority are exported to be fed on British farms ; they have exceeded 800,000 in a year at the beginning of the century.   About one-quarter usually go to Scotland, and their diffusion by rail from the ports is to the eastern arable farms rather than the dairying west.   The same sort of movement takes place on the Continent and notably in France, where young cattle converge upon the arable tracts of the Paris Basin and the extension of this champain along the limestone belt to the Charentes; they come both from the Central Plateau and the whole Armorican region of the west.

All these movements are intermittently and greatly hampered by outbreaks of foot-and-mouth disease.   This is the most serious affliction of all the cloven-hoofed beasts, highly contagious and mortal.   In the British Isles the incidence is less than on the Continent, but it has serious results since slaughter of diseased animals is obligatory. There is no certain solution to the problem of its arrival in Britain, but infected mud on the feet of migrating birds, especially starlings, is suspected.

Dairy-farming

The dairy industry steadily becomes more specialised as farmers appreciate the possibility of raising the yield of milk by breeding and by management of the dairy farm. Moreover, there is a special incentive to this from the attention to hygiene and the suppression of tuberculosis that is demanded. All this calls for an abundant supply of water and, where possible, the use of electricity. The relative success of dairying in north-western Europe may be seen from the high yields of milk per dairy cow. The proportion of the milk that is consumed liquid and used in other forms varies with the countries ; it depends partly upon facilities for transporting fresh milk and partly upon other economic conditions. Thus for the Netherlands and Denmark milk products are an important part of the national exports. But one tendency is common to all countries with progressive dairy industries : butter, cheese and other products become the business of the factory rather than the farm. This leads to uniformity which, in the case of cheese, is regretted by many.

Pigs

The rearing of pigs is associated, as already noted, with dairy farming, owing to the by-products, skim milk, butter milk and whey, as well as with the growing of potatoes on a large scale and accessibility of foreign feeding stuffs from the seaports. But there is another link : that between pigs and peasants, for the pig has been called the 'small farmer's bank' on the ground that it eats his scraps. The herding of swine, still common in southern Europe, has long ceased in the north, and the pig fed in the sty and as the product of careful breeding differs greatly from its ancestors and gives much more meat.

Sheep

The two regions of Europe distinguished by the vast numbers of their sheep are the British Isles and the Balkan Peninsula. Since sheep also extend throughout the Carpathians in densities almost as great, south-eastern Europe stands out as the chief domain of the animal ; but it prevails throughout all the southern mountains except the roughest and most arid, where goats exceed sheep in number. Elsewhere there has been a steady decline in the flocks as modern agriculture developed and extended. Only in Britain, north-eastern France and parts of Germany do sheep have a large place in a system of mixed farming. In contrast the farmer in southern lands usually does all he can to keep sheep away from his fields except when fallow ; so Balkan and British sheep-rearing are scarcely to be compared, save perhaps in respect of those flocks in Britain which depend wholly on rough highland grazing. Even so, while the practice of milking ewes died out in the British highlands some two centuries ago, about half of the profits of the Balkan shepherd are still derived from cheese and other milk products. The attention given to the breeding of sheep in Britain is almost unique. Since the eighteenth century many highly distinctive breeds have been evolved, always with the aim of improving weight and quality of both wool and mutton. In regard to the latter, it must be noted that the people of Britain alone among the industrial nations continue to welcome and even to prefer this meat whether home-grown or from New Zealand. On the Continent, however, the taste for lamb continues to hold. It is of interest to compare the production of wool before World War II in Britain and in Italy as a Mediterranean country. One ton of wool was produced for every 368 sheep in Britain and for 649 sheep in Italy, but it would be useless to compare the mutton by weight in view of the much better quality of the British meat.

DIFFERENCES IN PRODUCTIVITY

Since agriculture is far from being equally successful throughout Europe, it follows that maps based on volume of the harvest differ considerably from those representing area, but this cannot be shown effectively on a small scale. The variation in efficiency, however, has already been demonstrated in relation to the population dependent on agriculture. This involved use of the 'arable equivalent', and the same data may now be used to paint a good general impression of the productivity of land in Europe about 1930 without the U.S.S.R. and Turkey (Fig. 31). While the calculations involved allow for many factors, there are certain assumptions that are not equally valid for all regions ; moreover, in northern lands no adequate division between forests and pastures could be made, and for this reason part of Norway is omitted. But the map brings out strikingly the economic importance of intensive cultivation properly integrated with a well-managed and specialised animal husbandry. Hence the leading positions of the Low Countries and Switzerland, with Denmark, the British Isles and Germany following closely. The importance of cattle is obvious in France, which as a whole stands just above the European average, and in the Iberian countries which have the lowest averages ; the yields of most field crops there are very small, and at least a third of the farmland is in bare fallow. The lack of differentiation in western Germany and England and Wales may be criticised, while some

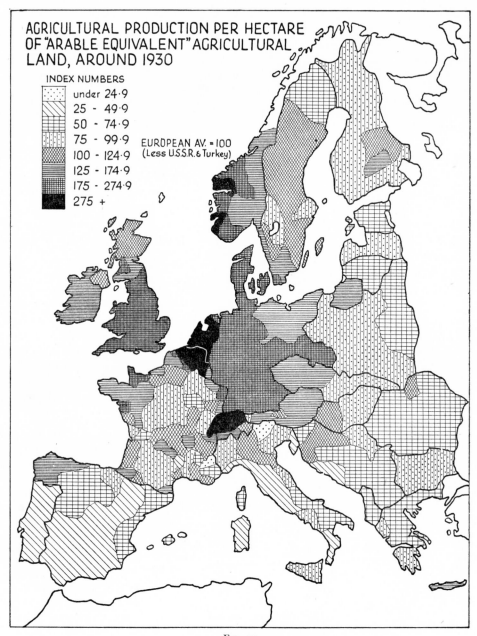

AGRICULTURAL PRODUCTION PER HECTARE OF "ARABLE EQUIVALENT" AGRICULTURAL LAND, AROUND 1930

INDEX NUMBERS

under 24·9
25 - 49·9
50 - 74·9
75 - 99·9
100 - 124·9
125 - 174·9
175 - 274·9
275 +

EUROPEAN AV. = 100
(Less U.S.S.R. & Turkey)

FIG. 31

179

of the assessments are perhaps puzzling. A simpler comparison between twenty-four countries may be made in respect of their average yield of the four grains—wheat, rye, barley and oats—for the period to which the crop maps refer. The countries are found to belong to five categories. In the Netherlands, Belgium and Denmark over one ton of these cereals per acre was raised (1934–8). In the second rank there were five with over three-quarters of a ton, Switzerland (0·83), Sweden, Germany, United Kingdom and Norway (0·79), while Egypt showed the latter yield for wheat and barley. In grade three were Czechoslovakia (0·65), Finland, Austria, France and Poland (0·56) ; in grade four, Italy (0·50), Hungary, Bulgaria, Turkey, Spain and Syria ; and in grade five Yugoslavia and Romania (0·33), Portugal and Algeria (0·25). Parts of many of these countries are of course much more productive than appears from the average—northern Italy for instance —but production generally in countries about the North Sea was three or four times that of the outer fringe, with the exception of Egypt, where a teeming peasantry works under unique physical conditions. During the Second War agricultural production, including animals, declined in most countries, and very greatly in those that were battlefields. Britain, having to reduce imports of food, was a notable exception, and by 1950 total production was over a third greater than prewar, and the few countries that had surpassed their prewar output belong mostly to the first or second grades mentioned above. It follows then that for our present purpose there is an advantage in using the earlier statistics referring to these more favourable years. Britain alone greatly extended the arable land at its 1944 maximum by about 49 per cent above prewar. This was done mainly by ploughing the farmland previously under grass ; this inevitably had the disadvantage of reducing the number of livestock that could be grazed. In Finland, where the farming population of territory lost to the U.S.S.R. had to be absorbed, a remarkable colonisation of the forest has taken place.

The causes of the great differences in productivity are physical, economic and social, some of them a heritage of the Middle Ages. Physical reasons for low yields include poverty of soil, which may occur anywhere within the geographical range of the crop, and unsuitable climate, that usually marks the marginal parts of this range. Occasional poor harvests due to bad weather may be gathered anywhere in a given year, but they lose in significance when averages are considered. The maintenance of fertility depends on the rotation of crops and the restoration to the soil of elements taken from it by plants harvested or eaten by stock. Since these animals provide the best manure their density bears directly on productivity where stock-keeping is integrated with arable farming, as is the case in most of 'temperate' Europe ; this is the mark of 'high farming' in the north-west, where, however, there is also the greatest use of artificial manures. Possession of sources of these minerals or ability to buy and to prepare them are factors which bear upon this question, and these matters are referred to elsewhere.

There is an aspect of stock-keeping on rough pasture concerning the soil that is often overlooked : the minerals constantly removed from it, those that are contained in the plants consumed, are only very partially restored to the soil as manure. The bodies of the animals are used elsewhere as meat, bone, horn, leather, hair, wool and glue. In the long run the soil is depleted of elements essential to good herbage. A fact of more recent discovery is the need in animals for various elements, such as cobalt or copper, in minute amounts if they are to be healthy. Where these ' trace-elements ' are deficient they can easily be supplied artificially ; but the restoration to hill pastures of elements such as phosphorus often needed in large quantity calls for more ambitious operations.

High farming comes more and more to depend upon mechanisation, and in the U.S.S.R. the agricultural revolution of the past three decades has been planned to make the fullest use of the tractor, combined harvester and other machines. In western Europe their use is affected by economic questions as in the case of fertilisers, but in addition the nature of the farm-pattern and the size of holding exert a strong influence. These subjects remain to be discussed, but mechanisation is related above all to the supply of farm labour. Britain, as already mentioned, has the lowest farming manpower, and the great output of crops is possible only because of machines. In the decade ended with 1948 tractors alone were increased nearly five-fold ; by 1951 there was one tractor for 52 acres of arable land, which is a world record. The other countries with less than 100 acres arable per tractor in that year were Switzerland, Iceland, New Zealand and the Netherlands.

In districts with low yields it is often difficult to distinguish physical from other causes because land that is naturally marginal tends to be cultivated by relatively primitive methods. These in turn are related to poverty, insecurity of tenure and the like, and so to the social background that is rooted in history. The lowest general standards prevail where feudal systems have lasted longest and where the peasantry has been without incentive, adequate means or reward ; and such broadly is the rural history of eastern Europe, which in this respect differs little from the southern lands. But with the foundation or enlargement of the national states as successors of the empires, vast numbers of peasants became owners of land. Yet while the incentive to better cultivation was thus attained the average holding was too small to allow of any great improvement, save with the help of widespread co-operation ; and progress to this end was interrupted by the Second War. The period of recovery from this, everywhere from Estonia to Bulgaria, has been marked by absorption into the social and economic system of the U.S.S.R., so the countries of east-central Europe are in various stages of transition, while the effects of the change upon their agricultural welfare cannot yet be seen clearly from the west. In the Soviet Union itself a very low average production was increased greatly by means of revolutionary changes involving the creation of large collective and state farms, mechanisation (that had the additional advantage of freeing workers for industry), and great attention to plant-breeding and other applications of science to agriculture.

Over wide tracts of western and central Europe, where there has been no such break with the past, progress in farming remains gravely hampered by the character of land holdings, the plan of the fields and the laws on inheritance. The motley pattern of strip fields was described at the beginning of Chapter 13 as the mark of the open champain and a heritage of the Middle Ages. The detail and variation of this pattern has been the subject of much research and controversy, particularly in Germany, and many questions remain unresolved, but the systems of long narrow strips are probably the oldest. These are slightly curved like an 'S', and some of them exceed 600 yards (550 metres) in length, although generally now split into shorter patches. There are also systems of shorter and straight strips laid out along or across a slope, as well as isolated blocks irregular in shape and contrasting with the strip systems. And whatever the original holdings most of them have been subdivided by inheritance since they were planned. The full modern significance of the pattern, however, appears only when several scattered strips are identified as belonging to a given farmer. These are often so widely scattered that the owner must walk several miles to visit them all. Moreover, where, as in many countries, property has been shared equally among the heirs and the fields themselves repeatedly divided, the latter may be minute and without access by road. Such is the fragmentation that is only too characteristic of European peasant agriculture, except where property is kept intact as in Britain by its system of primogeniture, or where, as in Denmark, state intervention has had the same effect. In parts of France it is now the custom for inheriting families to agree that one member shall hold the land. Elsewhere, governments have tried to remedy the evil by forbidding further fragmentation of small farms and instituting means for assembling strips to make larger fields. This process of consolidation has been successful in some parts of Germany but much less so in France; equitable exchanges of land become very involved in view of the individualism of the farmers and their attachment to ancestral holdings.

There is therefore a possibility that the complete eradication of old land tenures in eastern Europe may have endowed the rural economy there with a definite advantage by eliminating this impediment to agricultural efficiency.

The question remains : if a large proportion of the countryside of the west were reformed piecemeal in the near future would this allow its people to retain their social character while securing the full economic results as skilled farmers ? The answer seems to depend upon the speed with which a wide spread co-operative spirit can be combined with the traditional individualism of agricultural working.

CHAPTER 16

AGRICULTURAL TYPES AND REGIONS

AMONG the criteria which serve in the recognition of types of agriculture, and so agricultural regions, the relative importance of crop-growing and stock-keeping seems on the whole to be the most helpful; but in any classification it is obvious that many others must be considered. The scale of farming operations may be judged by the size of holdings, but this may give no clue to efficiency. A group of voluntary co-operators, each on his own small farm, as in Denmark, may represent the most productive way of working the land. At the opposite end of the scale is the huge collective farm of the U.S.S.R., perhaps entirely mechanised. This is in an entirely different social category, yet the production per unit area might be the same in the two cases. Again, there is the differing status of the proprietor working his own land, the tenant paying rent, and the share-tenant with the reward for his labour varying according to regional custom. Finally, it is desirable to compare the degree in which the aim of farming has passed from simple subsistence toward one that is governed by a money economy, and which, whatever the scale or the amount of capital involved, may be said to serve a national or an international market. Under prevailing conditions all such dealings are closely affected by the dictates of governments, and in many countries almost everything the farmer does is regulated by this. Evidently, then, the subject is most complex, and all that can be attempted here is to indicate how some of these elements combine in different parts of Europe to give character to agriculture as an industry and a way of life.

MIXED FARMING

North of the Mediterranean lands mixed farming prevails nearly everywhere, the keeping of animals is universal, and this is in some measure integrated with the growing of crops; but except in the maritime countries bordering the Atlantic and in the mountainous zones of the centre the crops are of greater economic importance than the stock. This is the case throughout the inland parts of the great lowland from the Pyrenees to the Urals and the intermont basins drained by the Rhine and the Danube. It is also generally true that in the more southerly lowlands peasant farming still predominates, and that, hampered by lack of capital and the smallness of the holdings, its productivity is low in spite of very great effort ; also the work-animal is usually the cow or bullock and not the horse. Although peasant farming is generally backward, it would be wrong to assume that this economic type might be easily replaced by another, among the hills and mountains ; where there has been emigration from the less favoured sites the land usually reverts to nature. Throughout such a large expanse as Europe there is, of course, considerable variation in the quality of this small-scale husbandry, as there is also in the crops that are grown and the systems of their rotation. Moreover, there are areas of notable fertility, to be mentioned below, where high production by small farmers justifies their inclusion in a higher category of farming. Finally, eastern Europe now stands apart owing to the agricultural revolution which has eliminated the independent farmer, at least from the U.S.S.R., and created a new agricultural type, that of the collective and the state farms.

The Garonne Basin

The character of the peasant-farming type with emphasis on crops is well exemplified in the basin of the Garonne, which is worked by small owners with some share-tenants. It is a region whose climate and soils favour a wide range of crops and tree fruits, and which, along with much wheat, raises most of the French maize, largely used to feed poultry and pigs. But in spite of this there has been much emigration, that has not been offset by immigration from Brittany and especially from Italy ; the peasants in general have not been able to break the bonds of tradition, and in places the old two-course rotation is still in use. There are exceptions to this inability to comply with changing conditions, as along the Garonne itself where market gardening prevails, and above all around the Gironde with its famous commercial vineyards, which were greatly developed in medieval times under English rule to serve the English market and have been skilfully improved throughout the centuries.

Lorraine

Another good example is that of Lorraine, where in a harder climate than that of Aquitaine the much divided strips around old linear villages are still worked on a three-course rotation aiming at little more than local subsistence. Wheat is the main crop, with oats second, for here the heavy soils are ploughed by horses, and with green fodder and potatoes to complete the shift. But there are orchards round the villages, and communal rights in the woodland as in former times. The rural population of Lorraine has declined, no doubt to the advantage of neighbouring industrial districts.

Central European Hill and Scarplands

Almost the same account may be given of most of the hilly country of central Germany, the eastern part of the German scarplands and southern Bohemia. Naturally there is some variety : areas in which barley and spelt vie with wheat among the crops, and conditions for cultivation becoming less favourable eastward. But in general there is the same minute subdivision of the lands of the large villages, reliance on the three-course rotation, subsistence farming or little better, and stagnation or decline of population. It seems unnecessary to follow these examples by others from the Danubian and Balkan lands, where in too many parts the subsistence offered by the peasants' soil has been far more meagre than in the west. This has been sufficiently indicated already. Moreover, these countries are at various stages in social transition.

The more advanced Mixed Farming regions

In western Europe all the lands that have the best soils and climate for crops are worked under farming systems of a high order, using much animal and artificial manure in the rotations that are best suited to their respective conditions. These are the marks of husbandry in north-eastern France, the Low Countries, the Rhine valley and its branches, the southern belt of the great plain to the Moravian Gate, together with inner Bohemia. Nearly all these have the fine loam soils of loessic type, and similarly, on the extension of these in eastern Europe, agriculture is relatively most productive. Again, in the north it is the glacial deposits with rich deep soils that are marked by the most advanced arable farming in eastern Britain and the larger area centred on the Danish islands. The northern plain of Italy forms a similar outlier in the south. All of these produce high yields of most varied crops. These always include wheat, but the most significant single distribution in relation to them is probably that of sugar-beet (Fig. 29). While these areas are pre-eminent for their crops they are all bound up with the economy of adjoining regions where stock-rearing is the chief aim, and there are many districts within their borders which specialise in animal husbandry.

From the Loire to the Rhine

Farming of a high order now marks the country almost continuously from the bend of the Loire to both sides of the lower Rhine. The greater part of this tract is floored by chalk or limestone overlaid by deep loams, but in Flanders and the Netherlands heavy clay has been drained and worked to fertility since the Middle Ages. On these latter heavy soils where the climate is also more maritime there is a much greater density of animals ; the coastal polders form the cradle of the Flemish cattle whose progeny yield milk and beef in northern France. Flanders, then, is distinguished by enclosed fields of small to medium farms mainly worked by tenants in disseminated steadings ; and they raise an immense variety of crops and stock. Other districts with retentive soils suitable for grass in summer now specialise in cattle and dairy produce : Herveland in Belgium and those of the Thiérach, the Brie and Bray in France. Throughout the main area upon the loams there is much stock-feeding, but the beasts are generally indoors so this land is the typical open champain extending from the Beauce in the south through the Ile de France, Picardy and Hesbaye to the Meuse and thence to the embayment of Köln, and devoted mostly to wheat, oats, beet and fodder crops in varying proportions, with orchards around the large villages. It has been converted to modern systems only in the nineteenth century and the greater part, except in Germany, is worked by skilled tenant farmers who know how to feed the soil. In France and Belgium the land is often owned by townspeople, and thus the town-country relationship of medieval Flanders has been extended and brought much capital into farming enterprise. Without this productive tract the many cities and towns between Paris and Köln could scarcely have grown to their present size.

Eastern Britain

Arable farming is seen at its best in the eastern counties of England, including Yorkshire, an area of low rainfall and the most continental variety of the British climate ; the deep soils lie mainly upon till or the silts and peats of reclaimed fens. There are smaller similar areas in south-eastern England, and in Scotland from Lothian to Angus and around the inner Moray Firth, while south Lancashire forms an exceptional patch in the west. Knowledge of reformed agriculture radiated to these and other districts in the eighteenth century from East Anglia ; but much of the knowledge came from the Low Countries. These then are the principal croplands of Britain, but they are emphatically devoted to mixed farming ; the country everywhere is enclosed and numerous and valuable stock contribute to the great output of the farms which are operated in large measure by tenants. Capital investment is high, and many prosperous farmers are ready to buy or extend their land as opportunity offers, and to adopt innovations. Although all is lowland there is much more difference in relief than in the region just described, and also local variation in aims which defies brief generalisation. Many comparisons might be made with the neighbouring continental types, but perhaps the most notable is that between the Low Countries and the English Fens, where over three-quarters of the farmland is cultivated with great specialisation and the small farm predominates.

The Loess Belt

In the northern plain of Germany the area of dark soil on the loess broadens out eastward to form the Börde extending from the Weser to the Elbe ; this fertile land then sweeps round the Harz Mountains into the Thuringian bay. The tract has a long agricultural history, and it has been of first importance in feeding the industrial population in modern times. In the western part it is worked in rather small properties, where there is an old established grading of the rural population according to the size and tenure of their land ; here the cereals tend to give place to market gardens. Farther east where rainfall is less the farms are larger and are mechanised, strips are replaced by square fields mostly under grain, sugar-beet and fodder crops ; yields are the highest in Germany, and animals drawn from other regions are fed in byres. Then in Thuringia, if the aspect is less modern, the production is almost as great, and it includes that of the vine in places. The whole arable tract has the advantage of being near the sources of fertilisers—potash and the nitrogen factories. This type of intensive agriculture on similar land is repeated on smaller areas in Silesia (south of the Oder) and in Moravia and the inner basin of Bohemia (which constitute the twin agricultural cores of Czechoslovakia).

South-western Germany

Mention has been made earlier of exceptionally productive peasant farming, and the most outstanding example must serve to illustrate this : the valleys of south-western Germany. These have been tilled in part since Neolithic times, and now most of the land is worked in very small farms, each with minute and usually scattered fields. Yet a cash economy is well developed and the standard of living is surprisingly high ; this, however, is influenced by the opportunity for supplementary employment in a region where many manufactures are disposed in the large villages as well as the towns. From the attention given to special crops and to the feeding of poultry and pigs this valley system partakes in a market as distinct from a subsistence economy. The upper plain of the Rhine and the lower valleys of the Main and Neckar may well stand comparison both with the irrigated parts of the Mediterranean lands and with Flanders. A long growing season and a hot summer coupled with sufficient rain ensure success with maize, vines, hops, tree fruits and tobacco, and the quick growth of green fodder. The variety, the care and the intensity of the husbandry match those seen in the small farms of Flanders.

It will be seen that these tracts where arable farming is most highly developed, together with extensions in Britain and in Lombardy still to be mentioned in relation to their animal industries, coincide with the two zones of highest density of population in Europe, which intersect in the Low Countries (cf. pp. 234-5).

Western Baltic Lands

In the western Baltic lands, famous for their stock-rearing, over half of the area is under crops destined in large measure to feed the animals. The region includes, in Denmark the islands and the neighbouring fringe of Jutland, in Sweden the adjoining district of Malmö, together with the Baltic slope of Slesvig, Holstein and Mecklenburg, in which loamy soils among the moraines have been largely cleared of beechwoods. Throughout the whole region old systems of cultivation have given place to extended rotations and the old landscapes to enclosed fields as in England. But while small or medium-sized farms prevail in the west and north, modern progress was effected in Mecklenburg under large estates. The dominant crops of these Baltic lands are wheat, barley, oats, sugar-beet, green fodder and roots in varying proportions and with very high yields. This, then, is a region of fully integrated mixed farming, where the co-operation of smallholders has spread from Denmark to the adjoining countries.

The Atlantic Fringe

Rural economy throughout the Atlantic margin and the central and southern mountains is distinguished by the relatively great importance of domestic animals. Yet it is not easy to state precisely the areas where stock and their products are of greater value than crops, whether in subsistence farming or in one with a cash economy ; there is often a gradual transition in this respect. Again we have seen that a large proportion of the animals born in these zones pass most of their lives in the principal regions of arable farming as an essential feature of that system. However, the inherent advantage of the seaboard in the almost natural pastures is no less important today than in the past ; the zone contains the chief nurseries of cattle and the largest dairying industries. The chain of massifs composed of ancient rocks, from Spanish Galicia to Norway, does not as a whole possess wide areas of rich soil ; prolonged soaking by rain has leached valuable elements from it. Nevertheless, innumerable pockets of the better soils are worked, characteristically, by small farmers who possess rights on poorer rough pastures or, as in Norway or Asturias, high summer grazings. Galicians and Bretons take advantage of the rapid growth of gorse (*Ulex*) to cut great quantities for winter fodder, while in Britain and Ireland the growth of heather is managed by periodic burning to make it nutritious for sheep. Galicia cannot fully support its dense population despite its fisheries ; Ireland has been seriously over-populated ; and so with Brittany too, but there on the northern coast, as in southern Cornwall, the mild climate has been exploited by intensive market gardening for export. These are some of the features of the outer parts of the Atlantic fringe. The inner parts have many great advantages, notably much better soils developed upon younger sediments, including limestones in France and the British Isles, and on glacial and alluvial deposits. This inner zone, extending northward from the Gironde to the Clyde and eastward to the Elbe and Jutland, impinges on, or overlaps, areas of fine arable farming, and it includes many tracts of first-class land devoted mainly to stock and managed generally in medium-sized farms or by smallholders in co-operation.

In France this belt is continuous northwards from the Charente, where reclaimed salt-marsh gives perennial pasture, and the good soils inland, once largely under vines, have been devoted to dairy farming. Thence to the English Channel lies the typical *bocage* of the Vendee, Anjou, Maine and Normandy. It is broadest where it thrusts eastward, prolonging the Armorican axis far over the younger rocks of the Paris Basin to embrace the Perche that is famous for its heavy horses ; and it ends in the Cotentin Peninsula, the greenest landscape in France and containing over fifty cows to the hectare.

Cattle-feeding and Dairying in Britain and Ireland

The great cattle-feeding land of Britain lies in the English Midlands, a triangle formed by the estuaries of the Mersey, Severn and Wash, together with outliers in the western peninsulas of Wales and Cornwall and the several northern lowlands, including those of Scotland. Before World War II permanent grass occupied many of the fields in those parts of England, but this has now been replaced largely by ploughing at intervals (ley-farming), or by green crops. The corresponding feeding area of Ireland lies in the eastern part of the plain. Although hardly any of these lands are without dairy industries, there are two quite remarkable concentrations of these in England, and two in Ireland. The latter lie north and south of the mountains of Kerry and Cork, the former are the till-plain of Cheshire and the alluvial Vale of Somerset. In Scotland the main dairies are in the south-west between the Clyde and the Solway Firth.

The North Sea Lowland

The greatest area, in numbers both of cattle and pigs, is the lowland bordering the North Sea from Flanders to Denmark. As already noted, this great density of animals is in part due to very efficient cultivation of fine soils inland and of the plain of Flanders nearer the coast, but it must be added that in the German part north of the loessic soils at least a third of the land is under grass and, above all, that the whole region has a coastal rim of empoldered land. In parts of Holland where there have been lakes there is valuable peaty soil ; but otherwise deep loams rest upon heavy silt or marine clay which when drained is extremely fertile and gives high returns with wheat and other crops. Grass, however, dominates in many parts, and always where the water-table is near the surface. It is on these meadow polders in Holland that cows give phenomenal amounts of milk, over 1,050 gallons (about 4,500 litres) annually. From the Ijssel Lake eastwards this land abuts on the sands of the geest which are comparatively poor, but the two zones are economically interdependent. In southern Jutland the polders end, and the sands and heaths have been improved so much that the co-operative dairies are thickly spread over the mainland, although less so than on the better arable land of the eastern margin and the islands.

The Central and Southern Mountains

The mountains of the centre and south of Europe obviously are at a disadvantage in soil and climate as compared with the maritime lands, so the raising of stock, especially cattle, is much more dependent upon storage of winter fodder. Animal industries are much less organised except in Switzerland and the adjoining parts of France ; Czechoslovakia probably comes next in order, since Bohemia was the chief source of cattle products in the Habsburg Empire. The importance of cattle to the Swiss is great : there is about one head of cattle for every three people, but in Denmark the ratio is always three to four. Some two-thirds of the cattle are on the plateau and the Jura, where agricultural systems, except in war-time, are directed chiefly to production of grass and other fodder.

Western Lombardy

The great density of cattle throughout the northern plain of Italy is due largely to the numbers needed to maintain the high intensity of cultivation that prevails, since tractors are little used and horses mainly about Cremona. But the occurrence of summer rainfall and the natural abundance of water from rivers and springs explain the existence of cattle in the region, which is in so many ways exceptional among the Mediterranean lands. It is, however, the ingenious management of irrigation in certain parts, and above all in western Lombardy, that brings this outlying area into the category of intensive stock-farming and makes it unique in southern Europe. The system in central Lombardy makes use of water from the chain of springs which have a uniform and relatively high temperature throughout the winter and also that derived from the latitudinal canals—the Grande and Martesana—to irrigate permanent meadows. These are mostly of clover or other legumes, and they are cut from six to nine times a year. This practice, believed to have begun in the Middle Ages, includes the use of sewage from Milan, which may raise the cuts to fourteen: a detail that suggests comparison with Flanders. It is chiefly with this hay that the milch cows are fed, and so the largest dairy industry of southern Europe, directed mainly to cheese-making, is a direct development of the medieval progressiveness on this unique plain.

AGRICULTURE IN THE U.S.S.R.

The U.S.S.R., and probably some of its satellite countries as well, stand apart because of the recent reformation of their agriculture. The old backward cultivation of the Russian peasantry was changed by state action, which took effect after 1927 with the inauguration of the first five-year plan. The peasants, who had taken over practically all the farmland at the Revolution, had continued to work it on the strip system and with inefficient methods and implements. They would never have pulled their weight in building up a state such as that planned by the leaders. The Soviet government had already established a number of very large state farms (*sovkhozy*), each devoted to some special type of production, but the great change was the creation, in vastly greater number, of collective farms (*kolkhozy*) after 1927. These in theory are voluntary organisations; but their introduction at first met with stubborn opposition, which was overcome by propaganda—in which the motor tractor was a potent element—and other means, including the ' liquidation ' of the richer peasants or *kulaks*. Mechanisation is an essential feature of the new system, and mainly for this reason fields are very large. Innumerable peasant properties were replaced by the collectives which at first had an average size of over 1,000 hectares, if on wheat land, depending on the work of over 100 households. They were planned in relation to existing villages, and to this extent the new rural Russia is related to the old; moreover, each household is allowed its small garden of one-quarter or one-half hectare and a few animals. Except for this small fraction the use of the land is in effect determined from above with the aim of raising production of the crops and stock that are most needed by the state. In 1950 the average size of the *kolkhozy* in the U.S.S.R. was more than doubled by merging; but in the north-western quadrant of the European part the average increase was greater than this, since the number of farms was reduced to less than one-third, or about 6,500 in all. The collectives had previously been relatively small in this region that is broken up by moraines, bogs and lakes. The ostensible reason for the increase in size is economic, but it may well be that there are others, to be classed as social. Here, then, is an entirely new phenomenon in agriculture, a system designed to suit a totalitarian form of national government aiming at uniformity coupled with efficiency. It is impossible to state whether the latter has been attained in the expected measure; but it seems likely that the output is still comparatively small in relation to the labour force, despite the great use of machines. On the other hand the yield of most crops has been raised, although still subject to large fluctuation according to the weather ; but the increase is most marked with industrial plants like sugar-beet and flax, and there seems to be much room for improvement over most of the land. However, Russian agriculture is now under scientific guidance such as is purposely prominent in the state farms and it has most of the tools, the products of plant-breeding stations and the like. The system apparently now provides for maintenance of fertility by rotation of crops, although doubtless there is still widespread deficiency in animal manure and also lime, which is needed by the northern soils, as well as some of the artificials. In any comparison with the west the question of transport must be borne in mind : the great distances in Russia and the relatively small extent of the metalled roads. And, again, in regard to the farms themselves, it must surely be doubtful if the best husbandry can be attained in such immense units. Nevertheless the role of the machine is of the greatest importance in relation to the climate. By speeding the plough immediately after the spring thaw it gives the spring-sown crops enough time to mature before the dryness of late summer, especially in the south. Again speed in ploughing and sowing is of great advantage to the main crops over most of Russia. Thus mechanical cultivation is vital not only in saving man-power, as in Britain, but also in saving the food supply from the seasonal disasters that have been all too common. The machines are kept not on the farms but in machine tractor stations (M.T.S.), each of which serves a large number of collectives and forms a key to agriculture and a new element in the geography.

Emphasis in Russian agriculture has always been upon crops rather than stock, this mainly because of the climate ; nomadic stock-rearing has receded in the south as agriculture progressed to its present limits. Animals have played the same part in the rural economy as among the peasantry farther west, but with special reliance upon the horse. Now the integration of stock-keeping with the new agriculture has been unduly delayed largely because the numbers of animals have been inadequate and their condition, on the whole, poor. The decimation of stock in two world wars was very serious, but another cause of loss was the inauguration of the collective farm. The wealthier peasants slaughtered their beasts when their land was taken, and then the others seem to have found it harder to co-operate over animals than over land ; subsequent increases in animals have not been matched evenly by expansion in fodder growing, and so on. In time, however, a scheme of mixed farming suited to the collective system and to the workers and the animals will no doubt emerge.

CHAPTER 17

MANUFACTURING INDUSTRIES

COMPREHENSION of the vast and complex pattern of modern industry in Europe is not easy, and perhaps the chief reason for the difficulty lies in the political division of the continent. If the Industrial Revolution could have arisen in a Europe without such divisions, it would seem that the pattern might have developed in a simpler way ; but this is mere speculation. Governments by various means have favoured the growth within their territories of as many kinds of industry as they considered necessary for their national economies and their strategic defence. Hence the establishment of certain manufactures in many districts which geographically are not ideal locations, but may yet be the best that exist for the purpose within a particular country. In short, then, political considerations have had great weight in determining the distribution of industry. Again, behind this modern growth of manufacture using steam or electric power, whether thermal or hydro, lies a long history of the crafts aided by primitive water-power on a small scale, during which the material needs of the people were met by production of goods much smaller in range than is now the case ; and these crafts were carried on in towns or villages widespread in all countries, each serving a small district. Regional specialisms such as that of woollen textiles in Flanders were uncommon. Nevertheless these old-established crafts are often seen to be the ancestors of modern factories in districts where geographical conditions have been relatively good and traditional skill well rooted. In many cases this continuity can be discerned in the huddled core of a manufacturing town where factories are outgrown workshops hugging the banks of streams still that give them some of their power. But where the need for economic efficiency has pressed, more spacious sites have been sought, and the fact of continuity can be established only by historical record. Another reason for complexity lies in the fact that since the Industrial Revolution changes have occurred in the source of power and at the same time, with improvement in means of transport and with other technical inventions, an ever widening area has yielded supplies of raw materials for the factories. For a long time machinery was driven by steam raised by burning coal, supplementing, of course, the older water-wheels ; and this naturally led to the location of manufactures on or near the coalfields, including those with quite small resources which have since been used up. So even where direct coal burning is no longer the main source of power, many industries remain tethered to the coalfields, and in others the use of coal or coke is still indispensable. Indeed, there has been much expansion of these where the reserves of fuel are great. The generation of electricity and the ever-increasing distance of its transmission in recent times have led to the reduction of this geographical bondage even where the current is generated in thermal stations. Moreover, where it comes from water-power, new industries have been created at or near the source of power, largely in mountains where formerly only small crafts existed. Hydro-electricity is also responsible for much expansion of old manufactures located at a distance in countries, like Italy, which previously had to import coal. Another change has been due to the exploitation of lignite, especially in Germany, and more recently of peat, in Russia, to feed thermal power-stations. The progressive transformation of industry in respect of motive power has not been accomplished equally throughout Europe, and the stages reached form essential characteristics of the various manufacturing regions.

The expansion in the choice of raw materials with its effects upon the economic geography of the continent does not lend itself to brief treatment in general terms, but this subject will be referred to in the description which follows ; as already indicated, it is closely related to the character of routes by land and by sea. Similarly the questions of suitable labour and of markets, which are bound up with the distribution of population, will be treated in this way as well. A general reference, however, must be made at this point to the direct consequence of the two European wars within three decades, and this for two reasons ; first, because nearly all the great industries twice had to be diverted to the production of the innumerable materials of war, and, secondly, because destruction of factories and communications was a principal aim of all the belligerents.

COALFIELDS AND THEIR INDUSTRIES

The principal resources of coal, as depicted on Fig. 3, lie in the several groups of deposits from Great Britain in the west to the Donets basin in Russia. The working of coal on a large scale began in Britain and then developed in the coalfields just beyond the Strait of Dover, in France, Belgium and Germany as well as in the smaller fields of France and Saxony. But the process was delayed in eastern Europe ; indeed, British coal had been driving machinery for more than a century before the systematic working of the Donets basin began about 1880. Thus the older industrial districts of the west are marked specially by the untidy traces of early mining at numerous small pits and by factories erected when competition was slight and planned location unthought of.

The Ruhr

By far the most productive of the continental coalfields has been that of the Ruhr in Westphalia, which lies north of the lower course of the River Ruhr for sixty miles from the Rhine. Here within an area of some 4,500 square miles (11,700 sq. km.) about seven million people live, mostly in a score of industrial cities and towns. This marks the greatest concentration of mining and manufacturing in Europe with a notable degree of economic integration, and the Ruhr offers the best example of the attraction exerted by vast resources of coal where they include various qualities of the mineral and where communications by water and rail are well suited to bulky transport. Because of the great part it played in the production of German armament, the Ruhr suffered from immense destruction during the Second War and from dismantling of factories thereafter. Nevertheless the inherent qualities of this district for the location of heavy industry must again be utilised fully, so the essential facts about the unique concentration of manufactures should now be noted as they were for the most part prior to devastation.

Like many other industrial districts the Ruhr had manufactures before the coal age. From its southern edge the Rhine Highlands rise, in the Sauerland where there were pockets of iron ore that for long was smelted with charcoal from the forests and worked by water-driven hammers ; and this power was used also for textile mills. The people and the factories of the Ruhr now depend for their water supply upon reservoirs built in these rainy Sauerland hills. The association of iron ore bedded with the coal then led, as in Britain, to the growth of a modern iron industry where the smelting was by coke ; but again, as in Britain and Belgium, the ores of good quality were used up. Yet the iron and steel industry, once established with good local coke, has been maintained by the import of other necessary raw materials.

This German coalfield stands out on account of the assembly of inter-related manufacturing processes that are carried out on and around it. But many of the raw materials came from a distance, and the products in turn serve widespread markets. So the means of transport by the Rhine and the canals as well as by railways have been as important as the coal itself. Thus, for example, the Ruhr in 1937 used nearly half of the coal mined ; the rest was moved to other parts of Germany and to foreign markets in equal proportions. About half of the iron-ore used came from Sweden and only one-fourth from German sources, and there were other bulky commodities as well. The traffic of the Rhine port Duisburg-Ruhrort, therefore, is the greatest of all Europe's inland ports. The coal for power is used either for raising steam or generating electricity, and surplus current serves a wide area. But in addition the Ruhr was the greatest manufacturer of products derived from coal.

From the making of metallurgical coke there came ammonia, benzene and tar, each of which in turn yields other compounds of great importance and most varied uses. Moreover, coke-oven gas remains to be distributed as domestic and industrial fuel. Finally, synthetic petroleum and diesel oil are made by the liquefaction of coal. The sites of these and other industries were chosen to eliminate waste of energy, with coke-ovens and electric stations near the mines of suitable coal and similarly the blast-furnaces and the steel-plants where these are worked by the same owners, and there is a special concentration near the Rhine. Farther from the coal there is a zone of steel works which do not make their own pig-iron, and with these are placed many factories that use steel for various purposes, as well as chemical works. The sound geographic relationships of these heavy industries of the Ruhr reflect the high degree of their economic integration, the accomplishment of vast combines which produced this remarkable industrial organism. Less closely bound to all this by function is an outer zone of towns devoted to making textiles of nearly all kinds as well as to dyeing them. The Ruhr is not matched in compactness by any other region. Certainly the coalfields of Britain may be regarded as at least equivalent in resources of coal attainable by present mining methods, and their greatest output of coal has reached a much greater amount. But they lie scattered, and so do the industries that depend on them. So while the aggregate British production of iron and steel and all that is made of these, as well as that of heavy chemicals and textiles, exceeds in quantity the manufactures of the Ruhr, these British industries are not united geographically to the same degree.

Northern England

The Yorks-Notts-Derby coalfield is most nearly comparable to the Ruhr in extent, industrial character and population, including vast metallurgical and textile manufactures. It is difficult to describe succinctly the wide industrial relations of this coalfield. On the other hand, northern England offers a unique example of vast and balanced economic development astride the Pennines; and the essential features of this may be simply and usefully stated here.

The coalfields of Yorkshire and Lancashire are the twin nuclei of manufacturing districts, each of which is characteristic of British industrial development, involving abundant coal for power and easy access to the sea (Fig. 32). Moreover, equally typical is the evolution from industries formerly dependent upon water power, for the hammers of the Sheffield ironworks and the widespread woollen and cotton mills which still need large supplies of pure water. The plateaus of the southern Pennines separate the two districts, the high rainfall provides the water and, since it flows from the silicious Millstone Grit, it is suitably soft for scouring, bleaching and dyeing the textile fibres and fabrics—woollen in the east, cotton in the west. Thus the two greatest British concentrations of these industries are near the hill-foot and in the valleys of the Pennines, and each industry has a large commercial centre, Leeds and Manchester respectively. The seaways are the Humber and the Mersey, with Hull and Liverpool as seaports, the latter linked also to Manchester by ship

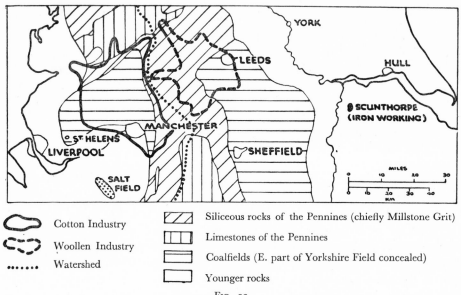

Cotton Industry	Siliceous rocks of the Pennines (chiefly Millstone Grit)
Woollen Industry	Limestones of the Pennines
Watershed	Coalfields (E. part of Yorkshire Field concealed)
	Younger rocks

Fig. 32

Part of Northern England—Manufactures as related to Rocks

canal. Therefore both estuaries, as main gateways for the entry of bulky imports, have furnished the sites of many other manufactures. But it is not only for this reason that the two textile districts have important industries on their southern edges. Sheffield, as already mentioned, typifies the highly developed steel-making and steel-working, while beyond it is a series of towns engaged in varied steel-using manufactures. Corresponding to this, west of the Pennines lies the salt field of Cheshire, in an otherwise rural area, and this, along with the facility for import of other raw materials, forms the basis of many of the heavy-chemical manufactures of Merseyside, and the glass industry of St Helens.

France and Belgium

Industrial districts of similar order are centred upon the northern coalfields of France and those in the adjoining strip of Belgium along the Rivers Sambre and Meuse. But while Artois is the greatest producer in France of coal, coke and its by-products and glass, metallurgy is comparatively unimportant ; on the other hand the large textile industry of French Flanders is associated. The main Belgian iron and steel plants, however, are placed upon the coal, between Mons and Liége, as is the glass-making in which Belgium excels, while the textiles lie at a distance, in Flanders. All these heavy industries are favoured, as in the German case, by means of transport : those in Britain lie at or near seaports, while the Franco-Belgian region is served by sea, through Dunkirk and Antwerp, and internally they are linked by railways and water-ways, notably with Lorraine, its main supplier of phosphoric iron-ore.

It may be noted in passing that the greatest concentration of heavy metal-lurgy in France is found upon the Lorraine iron field, but that the rich coalfield of the Moselle and Saar, some 25 miles to the east, has no really great industries located on it, as might be expected. Among the reasons for this is the nature of the coal ; little of it is suited for coke-making by itself, so coal, as well as coke, is sent from the Ruhr both to Lorraine and the Saar, and as there is a large movement of ore in return these three mineral fields are linked by an economic bond.

Upper Silesia

The great coalfield of Upper Silesia, situated just north of the Moravian Gate and favoured by easy communications probably contains more coal than any other basin in Europe ; but most of it is of relatively poor quality. Political subdivision has hampered its exploitation, although the former Prussian section came to resemble the Ruhr in aspect and functions, and likewise on a smaller scale, the Austrian part. These areas possess the coking coal, and they now contain the chief heavy metal industries of Poland and Czechoslovakia re-spectively. The nearest source of iron ore is in Slovakia, but adequate supplies call for long haulage from Styria or Sweden. Besides the iron and steel industries there are on the Polish side the notable manufactures of zinc and lead derived from nearby mines, and that of glass across the frontier.

The U.S.S.R.

The last example of the phenomenon under review is provided by the Donbas, the basin lying south of the River Donets, which contains great reserves of coal of all types, from gas- and coking-coal in the broader western part to anthracite—more than in any other field—in the narrow eastern end. Although relatively recent in its development under the former regime, the Donbas quickly became the 'Ruhr' of Russia, with a remarkable impetus in the decade before the Second War. By this it was widely devastated, but has probably now more than recovered. It is slightly less compact than the Ruhr, but the industries are similarly integrated, and they employ at least as many workers. The chief source of iron-ore is the Krivoi-Rog district, some 300 miles (480 km.) to the west, doubtless soon to be supplemented from Kursk on the north-west, and it receives manganese from Nikopol on the Dnepr. Hence exchange of ore and coke, but with more smelting in the coal-field, and it is there in the Donbas that are found the steel-making and steel-working industries of most kinds, as well as the chemical processes based on coal, and those using the salt that is mined on the northern fringe of the basin. Moreover, the leading potteries of the Soviet Union are located there.

The new metallurgical district of Magnitogorsk in the southern Ural Mountains is the analogue of Lorraine, and it represents one of the more spectacular of Russian enterprises. The Urals are rich in metals but very poor in coal, so this immense mass of fine iron ore was originally worked for smelting with coke from the Kuznetsk coalfield 1,140 miles (2,250 km.) away ; but while this interchange has been replaced by that with Karaganda the coal and the ore are still separated by 600 miles. (1,000 km.)

Changes in sources of ore and fuel

The geography of raw material sources has altered considerably on account of the varied chemical composition of iron ore throughout Europe. The iron content must be high to justify long transportation ; moreover, during the nineteenth century many ores were unsuited to the making of steel owing to the presence of phosphorus, until the discovery in 1878 by Thomas and Gilchrist in England that this impurity could be absorbed by adding man-ganese ore and lining the furnace with the ' basic ' mineral dolomite. The effect of the subsequent use of this ' basic ' process of making steel was the mining of great untapped reserves of ore. In Britain, where the rich haematite of Cumbria had been developed for making ' acid ' steel and other ores had been imported from the Basque districts of Spain and from central Sweden, the widespread deposits of the Jurassic rocks of eastern England were now worked. So also in Germany : to the ores of the Siegerland and other districts and imports similar to those of Britain the ' minette ' of Lorraine was added. Moreover, all steel makers were able to draw from Sweden not only more material from the old central mining district, but by 1887 the richest, although phosphoric, ores from the far north ; while further sources were found in Andalusia and the Atlas lands to supply both the processes of steel making. Again, as metallurgy progressed, minerals other than iron were required in greater variety for making special kinds of steel, in which Sheffield was the leading centre ; so the net was cast even beyond Europe for supplies of man-ganese, chromium, molybdenum, nickel, tungsten and titanium.

Because of the fortunate situation of the great coalfields the iron and steel industries of Britain, northern France, Belgium and Germany that developed on the coal have generally persisted in, or very near, their original location, with separation in some cases of the smelting from other branches of the industry. But in other cases the furnaces have been placed at the source of the ore from the start, with the coke as well as the limestone flux, where needed, transported to the ironfield. This applies to the Furness and Northampton-shire districts of England and to Lorraine, which receives some of its coke from the Ruhr.

The geography of the metallurgical industries has been subject to great changes in the past, due to inventions particularly connected with smelting. For many years now this has depended upon supplies of hard coke, but coal for this is absent from many coalfields. It is possible, however, that in the near future it will be economic to pass oxygen into the smelting furnace instead of air, and so to dispense with the use of special coke as the fuel ; such a change might have considerable effect upon location.

The fuels other than bituminous coal, i.e. wood, peat, lignite, petroleum and natural gas, are all of course potential sources of energy that may be used to drive machinery ; but with few exceptions none of them has led to a geo-graphical concentration of manufacturing industries on the modern scale, and the reasons are easy to understand. Wood when reduced to charcoal for smelting determined the situation of iron-making, and charcoal still plays a large part in Swedish smelting ; but wood in general is more valuable for other purposes. Peat, which covers a huge aggregate area in northern Russia, is now used there as fuel for generating electricity. Lignite or brown coal is the only form of coal in most parts of southern Europe, but its fullest exploita-tion has taken place in Germany and in Russia to supplement their great resources of bituminous coal. While it is cheaply extracted, its chief use in the form of briquettes for long was domestic, but the Tula coalfield, with a mineral somewhat better than lignite, served largely to maintain the power for the manufactures of the Moscow region. Between the two wars Germany developed her lignite fields to the full.

Industries outside the Coalfields

Northern Italy

At this point it is well to consider notable examples of the clustering of industries which are not related to coalfields, and especially those of northern Italy and central Sweden. The manufacturing industries of northern Italy present an example of location that resembles that of Yorkshire and Lanark-shire in some respects ; textiles are prominent, and their manufacture has again been dependent upon an assured water supply, in this case from the

Alps. Hence, as in northern England, the hill-foot location is characteristic; and again the mills are found lining the banks of rivers, not however the great ones which are shunned as unruly. But as coalfields are absent it is the development of the great hydro-electric power in the Alps that has promoted the growth and diversification of industrial enterprise both upon the plain and in the valleys of the Alps, so that Lombardy and Piedmont contain one of the major assemblies of factories in Europe; and these include the leading group in Italy devoted to heavy metallurgy and engineering, although the materials have to be imported.

Throughout the plain the northern or upper zone is the part favoured by industry, and for this there is an additional reason, that it is vastly inferior to the lower part as agricultural land and in places still remains uncultivated; the zone coincides largely with the high plain of permeable gravel and sand and the great moraines of the Quaternary glaciers.

The modern pattern of industry may be illustrated by a transverse section between the Simplon Tunnel and Milan, which is both the largest industrial city of Lombardy and the commercial focus of the north. Industry avoids the terraced valley of the Ticino and is clustered on the level and dry gravelly surface of the plain, and to a lesser extent among the moraines that rise from it. The smaller valley of the Olona is marked first by the textiles, especially cotton, silk and rayon, by the making of paper and chemicals, and in the lower towns by metallurgy and engineering. Elsewhere in the district textiles are associated with metal-working to serve this industry, or with cycle works as at Varese. In Milan there is a very wide range of manufactures, textile, metallurgical and mechanical, electrical, chemical and printing, while Sesto San Giovanni nearby has the iron and steel works and the heavy engineering. This section of the plain, like Milan itself, has the advantage of direct access to central Europe by the Simplon route, which along with the water power influences the location of industry in the Alps. Thus the two large sources of power in the Toce valley serve the electro-chemical and the aluminium industries, the latter in turn linked with aircraft construction; at Pallanza and Gozzano rayon is made, and Omegna deals with iron founding and engineering.

Analogous Sections

This is a distribution typical of many valleys throughout the Alps, but in some, notably those of the Arc and Isère in France, the works concerned with electro-chemistry and metallurgy are much more numerous. Again the sample of the industrial location on the plain of Western Lombardy might be repeated, with some variations, in Piedmont, in the eastern part of the Swiss plateau, centred on Zürich, on the Rhône valley about Lyon, albeit the latter lies alongside the coalfield of St Etienne, or on a smaller scale, the basin of Vienna.

The Jura Mountains in the 'French' part of Switzerland and adjoining area in France have seen the growth, organisation and perfection of the manufacture of watches, and thus offer the most striking example of high specialisation for a world market without any geographical advantages except a good position in western Europe. The industry, originally a seasonal occupation and subsidiary to a pastoral economy, arose from skill in other fine handwork. It requires little power, and its raw material is of fine quality but small bulk. The industry is housed in many small and a few large works, so its economic importance is much greater than appearance would indicate in a countryside where fir woods and dairy cattle are much more obvious.

Central Sweden

In central Sweden there is an industrial belt that is comparable in several respects with that of Lombardy and Piedmont. It is similar in extent and in its position, just north of the most fertile plains of the country; it lacks coal but abounds in waterfalls and, moreover, in wood to burn. But its origin is entirely different, since it is primarily one of the great metal-mining districts of Europe, and it still makes use of its own iron and some other metals, and further has in the neighbouring forests abundant raw material for varied industries.

The belt crosses Sweden from south-west, about the northern shore of Lake Väner, to north-east, reaching the coast around the Gulf of Gävle, and is bisected by the sixtieth parallel. The core is named the Bergslag, a word originally denoting an organised and privileged mining community and applied later to territory where mining was active. Its fortunes have been determined by the quantity and variety of the ores, and these are associated with the rock leptite which lies in belts that fan out from the centre northward and eastward through the lower basin of the Dal Elf. Most of the eastern mines, famous from the Middle Ages are worked out; the huge quarry at Falun is a monument to four centuries of mining copper (c. 1300–1700), and it still yields some other products. There are examples, too, of somewhat shorter records at Sala for silver and at Dannemora, which once dominated the iron trade of Europe. These leptite rocks contain the sulphide ores of copper, zinc and lead, some gold, silver and manganese, and the large bodies of iron ore which have led to the pre-eminence of Swedish metallurgy as it is now developed in this central part of the industrial belt with its heart about Grängesberg. With local ores of high grade, supplemented by others from Lapland, with processes adapted to suit the character of the ore and the smelting done with charcoal supplemented now by the electric furnace, great

purity of steel is attained.   The industry has a roughly concentric distribution
—mining, smelting and steel-making, with the steel-working factories located
on the railways or on the rivers which flow south-eastward before diverging ;
hence the frequent termination -*fors* (waterfall) in place-names famous for
their steel products.   Thus machinery and component parts, most varied in
type and known through the world, emanate from the banks of many rivers
from Jädra-ån and the Dal-elf in the east to the Klar-elf in the west.   Lake
Väner and the canalised Göta have encouraged great development of wood-
working along the Klar and rivers farther west, and thus the industrial belt is
prolonged almost to the frontier.

Similarly near the Baltic coast the wood industries are added to those
of metal working.   This eastern part of the belt indeed, although now without
large metal resources, contains some of the leading steel works, the greatest
saw-mills and pulp and paper mills, and, along the lower Dal, generating
stations of the first order.   These vigorous and efficient industries are therefore
situated along rivers and transverse railways.   The meshes of the lattice in
the northern part are largely forest growing on the thin soils of ice-scoured
rock and with many lakes ; but this merges irregularly into the farmland on
lacustrine silts.   The belt has three marginal commercial centres, Gävle,
Kristinehamn and Västerås, and has obvious close relations with Stockholm
and Göteborg, as well as with Oxelösund, the port through which the surplus
ore is sent.

FOREST INDUSTRIES

Among the industries whose location is determined by the sources of raw
material, that of wood-working is the most outstanding, because of the bulk
of the lumber.   The clearing or degradation of the European forests, outlined
in Chapter 8, may be linked also with the growth of modern industry and
of population, since this has led to great acceleration in the process of deforestation.   Not only has the demand for sawn timber and pit props risen,
but wood-pulp has become the raw material of paper in ever-increasing
measure ; moreover, artificial silk or rayon, and to a lesser extent artificial
wool, both derived in part from cellulose and so from wood, have been placed
upon a growing market for substitute fibres.   With these and other new uses
for wood, the overwhelming need is for coniferous timber, chiefly pine for
construction and spruce for pulping.   About nine-tenths of the wood required
by the industrial nations is softwood.   Now there is only one great expanse of
such forest, in Fennoscandia and northern Russia, and the rest of the Continent
has relied upon this in great part to meet its growing needs, but even these
resources together with timber grown, in varying amounts, within the borders

of the consuming countries have been insufficient ; so substantial supplies have been imported from North America, notably by Great Britain. It must be noted, however, that the U.S.A., with its enormous appetite for paper, has obtained some of its raw material from the European source.

The Second World War has altered considerably the international trade in wood and its products ; it has led to a partial interruption in the movement from the northern forest to other parts of Europe. Nevertheless the geographical conditions for such a flow of products are singularly favourable, and in the case of Scandinavia and Finland they also serve the economic interest of the producers, since they are able increasingly to export manufactured wood instead of raw timber. The forests of Norway cover roughly a quarter of its area, those of Sweden over a half, and those of Finland nearly three-quarters, and their annual growth is estimated respectively as 10, 48 and 44 million cubic metres, but the wood taken from them in the years before the Second War somewhat exceeded this amount. Hence these nations evidently must make the most of their timber resources which play such a large part in their economy.

Apart from the trees themselves the first asset lies in the ease of inland transport by water. This is at its best in Scandinavia, where the numerous rivers have steep gradients and large volume during and after the spring thaw ; and the channels become clear of ice progressively upstream, so that the driving of logs takes place rapidly and evenly. Again many of the Swedish rivers traverse lakes which serve for the sorting of the logs, while there is ample space for this on the Baltic coast sheltered by many islets. In all three countries, as in Russia, the cover of snow assures easy haulage of trunks to the rivers. Throughout Finland and Russian Karelia the rivers have much lower gradients and they link vast numbers of lakes ; moreover, in the northern parts the seasonal flow lasts for only a short period, so the transport is slower and requires more towing of rafts ; it often takes more than one year for logs to reach the coast, and so many of the mills and factories are situated inland upon the lakes. East of the White Sea there are no lakes, but the rivers are sluggish and the towing of rafts is the usual method of transport. The former glaciation is responsible for many of the features mentioned, and also for the waterfalls and rapids that mark the rivers of Fennoscandia ; and these form the second great asset of the timber industry, abundant water power in countries where coal is absent. While the sawmills formerly were placed at the falls, they and other factories now depend upon electricity, and so are situated on the coast or at points convenient for transport by sea, rail and road. Motor transport of logs is on the increase since their value is about one-third greater if they have not been soaked in water. The freezing of the Baltic and White Seas in winter, of course, places the industry at some disadvantage except in Norway, but this is partly offset by the railway outlets of central Sweden to Trondheim and Göteborg, and that of Russia to Murmansk ; Leningrad and Archangel, however, remain the chief ports of the Russian timber industry, which now benefits by the opening of the Baltic-White Sea canal.

The large forests in the basins of the northern Dvina, the Mezen and the Pechora form the principal reserves of the north, since the exploited areas near the waterways are comparatively small. This may presumably be regarded as the chief future source of timber for building and mining, but it is uncertain how much will be available for Europe in view of the needs of the U.S.S.R. In the meantime exploitation seems to be much more vigorous among the forests of the Ural, which are more accessible from the regions under rapid industrial development. Moreover, it must be realised that the rate of growth of trees becomes less in the northern latitudes. In no other part of Europe is there any concentration of the wood-working industries to compare with those near the main source of timber.

INDUSTRIES OF CAPITAL CITIES AND SEAPORTS

Manufacturing industries in great variety are located throughout Europe in cities and towns of all sizes which are not primarily industrial in function ; but while these have great significance in the national economies of the individual countries, they may be disregarded here. On the other hand, the really great clustering of factories in and around the capitals and other major cities, especially those on the coast or on leading waterways, is a typically European phenomenon, at least in origin. The most outstanding examples of capitals as industrial magnets are London, Paris, Berlin and Moscow. Each of these is marked by the signs of rapid outward growth, a principal cause of which has been the building of factories near the successive perimeters of the city, with provision for the necessary quarters of the workers. These vast aggregations include a great variety of manufactures, but they are distinguished by the large proportion of establishments producing finished goods of high value. The three continental capitals are served by navigable rivers and canals ; but London has the additional industrial attributes of a great seaport. These it shares with Liverpool, Antwerp and Rotterdam, Hamburg, Bremen and Marseille, and a number of other cities with smaller concentrations. The special advantage of the seaports is, of course, in dealing with raw materials from overseas which, owing to their bulk cannot easily bear railway freight charges, but which will do so if manufactured wholly or partially. Examples among the minerals are bauxite for refining to alumina, crude phosphates for fertilisers, or iron ore for reduction to metal where it is economic to bring coke to the seaport. Again, timber, wood-pulp and oilseeds may all leave the coastal factory for the interior as products of enhanced value and smaller bulk. At many seaports grain elevators and oil-storage tanks are striking features that indicate not merely distribution of wheat and petroleum, but frequently also flour-milling and the preparation of numerous oil products. All are more or less concerned with repair of ships, and a smaller number with their construction, while in a few great ports shipbuilding and marine engineering are the dominant industries. Naturally the particular assemblage of industries at a seaport depends upon the character of its hinterland and upon national needs, and both of these subjects call for treatment in another chapter.

CHAPTER 18

MODERN TRANSPORT AND COMMUNICATIONS

IT is wellnigh impossible to grasp the full significance of communication for the fifth of the human race that lives in Europe and its Borderlands, and the difficulty of doing so grows with the increasing opportunity of movement for man and his products and the almost instantaneous transmission of information and ideas. Nevertheless it is helpful first to recognise that the peoples of Europe and the Borderlands are not yet equally affected by the acceleration, and, secondly, to make a geographical analysis of the several means of communication, while considering the degree in which these are integrated to the economic advantage of the various states. 'States' is here the key word, because the great development in transportation coincided with that of the modern state. Hence the pattern of new or improved routes and the organisation of traffic have differed in adjoining countries, and the frontiers of the later nineteenth century, often established for military reasons, have a notable influence on the geography of transport. Owing to political division no organised system of land-routes could develop, comparable in extent with the road-net of the Roman Empire, except in Russia ; and there uneven conditions of population and economy delayed its growth. On the other hand, intercourse across national frontiers has been favoured by the adoption of a standard gauge throughout most of the continental railways, save in Spain, Portugal and Russia, and, more locally, by the international character of certain rivers. Yet the so-called 'iron curtain' of the years following World War II is in many ways the most effective barrier ever erected by man.

But for the making of canals and the improvement of rivers and especially the building of railways the revolution in manufacture could not have taken place ; moreover, the same progress in transportation made possible the commercial development of agriculture and the increased production of food. The concurrent maritime expansion likewise played an essential part. Improvement in roads was less spectacular, except in France which, with a School of Bridges and Roads established in 1747, had by the end of the century a national network of reliable roads measuring 40,000 kilometres (25,000 miles), many sections coinciding with Roman roads ; and this length by 1900 had been extended only by one-quarter. The great work of the characteristically British bodies, the turnpike road trusts, came later when the railways were already in competition ; so Britain had to wait until 1937 for a small proportion of its system, the ' trunk roads ', to become ' national '. However, the British contribution, and especially that of McAdam, to road-making everywhere has been important, and the roads of Britain are excellent although mostly too sinuous for very fast traffic. Their average density, about 200 miles per 100 square miles (125 km. per 100 sq. km.), is exceeded in France by about a quarter, but is twice the density for Germany. The German Empire, in fact, developed its economic and military strength with the help of railways and waterways rather than roads, but before World War II an entirely new type of trunk road for fast motor traffic was introduced. Except among the high mountains and in plateaus intersected by gorges the construction of roads has not been seriously hampered by physical conditions. Consequently their relative abundance is roughly proportional first to that of population and secondly to the degree of industrialisation, these two being closely related in western and central Europe. On the other hand, gradients are of first importance to railways, which can surmount obstacles only by extended mileage and by tunnelling ; and it is, of course, not capital investment alone that is involved. Thus, for example, a steam locomotive which can pull a train weighing 2,800 tons on the level at 10 miles (16 km.) per hour can haul only 1,400 tons up a slope of 1 in 50, and only 400 tons on a gradient of 1 in 100, such as often occurs in hilly lowlands. With still steeper slopes common in the mountains, electric traction is specially efficient ; and this is fortunate in Europe, with the abundance of electricity now generated in or near the ranges. Waterways are still more sensitive to gradients, both on rivers, where the current must be reckoned with, and on canals with their need for locks and water supply. Navigation upstream on rivers usually ceases where the slope exceeds 1 in 1,000 ; beyond such places a canal must be built along the valley.

WATERWAYS

The rivers of the European Plain constitute a great asset, actual or potential, as providing a series of natural transverse courses which are, or could be, linked by latitudinal canals. Moreover, such links extend the system to embrace the Seine and to connect the Rhine with the Saône by the Burgundian Gate ; the small canal joining the Main to the Danube could be enlarged, while at any time the Oder may be connected with the Danube through the Moravian Gate. Hitherto, the greatest use has been made of this asset in the west, in France, Belgium, Netherlands and Germany. In the east the government of Soviet Russia is engaged in similar full exploitation of the river system.

The U.S.S.R.

During the imperial régime small canals had been built joining the Volga to the Gulf of Finland and the Dnepr to the western Dvina, the Neman and the western Bug. The construction now in progress is on a vastly greater scale. New canals of the greatest capacity already connect the White Sea by Lake Onega with Leningrad, and the upper Volga by Moscow with the Oka ; the lower Dnepr has been regularised and the elbow bends of the lower Volga and Don have been joined. These works are parts of a grandiose plan which will allow ships from five seas to reach Moscow. In the north-east the Kama, the Pechora and Vichegda will be linked together ; vast amounts of electric power will be generated at the various dams, and the regulated Volga will serve to irrigate a huge tract on its left bank below Kuibishev. Some of these rivers were the arteries of medieval Muscovy ; its history has been marked by outward expansion to the ' five seas ', and now, by remarkable feats of hydraulic engineering, Soviet Russia is accomplishing the triple aim of joining distant economic centres, adding to the power supply, and irrigating semi-arid land. In doing so it is exploiting the natural advantages of low average slope and majestic rivers ; but it cannot alter the period during which the waterways are frozen, save by partial ice-breaking, and this amounts to over two months in the south-west and seven in the north-east. The task is still incomplete ; and the old canals where still in use are fitted only for smaller shipping. Again, apart from the districts of Moscow and Leningrad, waterways scarcely serve the major industrial areas, or they only touch their fringes, and these depend mainly upon the railways.

The Central Section of the Plain

In the central section of the European Plain the rivers suffer from the defect, in common with those of northern Russia, that water is released by the spring thaw in the upper parts of the basins first, which results in flooding throughout their lower northern valleys. For this and other physical reasons maintenance of banks and channels is costly. Moreover, during the nineteenth century, when the rivers were shared by three empires, only those within German territory, the Elbe, Oder and lower Vistula, were regularised and adequately cared for ; the Germans, too, connected them by canals following marginal valleys of the Ice Age, and such links were not made in Russian and Austrian territory. The effects of two destructive wars upon the waterways were serious, and the change of frontiers has twice shifted responsibility. First, the Vistula became a Polish river with the international Free State of Danzig at its mouth, while the Elbe was subjected to international administration since it is vital to Czechoslovakia, which acquired a free port

in Hamburg.   Then in 1946 the Vistula became wholly Polish, but the Oder
in part formed the frontier with Germany, and the Elbe remained divided
between the East and West Zones of Germany, with Czechoslovakia retaining its free port in Hamburg.   The Elbe is the essential waterway for Saxony
and Thuringia, a region not only most productive agriculturally but including
the principal German sources of lignite, salt and potash together with a coalfield ;   hence a great assemblage of manufactures, especially those of textiles,
chemicals and leather.   The river also serves the varied industries of Bohemia
despite the strong current in the defile at the frontier where chain-haulage
may be used by vessels moving upstream.   The lower Elbe, again, and the
canalised Havel are essential to the economy of Berlin.   The political situation
has reduced the importance of the main rivers and their connecting canals ;
but there can be no question of the economic value of these routes to all the
riparian states, particularly perhaps in relation to the coalfields of Silesia and
the industrial development of Poland.   It would seem certain that the Moravian
Gate eventually will be penetrated by a canal.

The Western Section of the Plain

Engineering skill and constant attention have been lavished upon the
western rivers, and many canals have been built to connect them.   This has
been fully justified on economic grounds, since these are the waterways of the
most densely populated and highly industrialised part of the Continent.   Moreover, physical advantages are considerable.   In the first place, the hills and
plateaus between the plain and the Alps are deeply dissected by the Rhine
and its tributaries, the Mosel and the Meuse, while the relief of the Paris
Basin, a concentric series of scarped plateaus and vales with transverse and
longitudinal rivers, favours the construction of waterways.   Throughout the
whole tract water is plentiful and its flow, on the whole, is equable.   Again,
interruption to shipping from freezing is not serious ;   the average period
decreases from 60 days for the Vistula to 18 days in the Rhine gorge, and
its length varies greatly with the years.   In Flanders water transport has
been bound up with industry from the Middle Ages ;   the commercial prowess
of the Dutch, and indeed the very existence of their country, have depended
on inland waterways ;   Paris owed its growth in no small measure to its location
between two important confluences ;   and the Rhine carries greater traffic
than any other river in Europe.

The Weser is far inferior to the Elbe as a waterway, and its traffic is
surpassed by that of the Mittelland canal (built 1905–38), which crosses it,
following the southern edge of the plain to join the Elbe to the Dortmund-Ems
Canal and so to the Rhine.   The latter canal, lying along the valley of the
Ems which prolongs it to the sea, runs parallel to the Dutch frontier and so

reflects the German purpose to divert some of the Rhine traffic from the mouths of the river in the Netherlands. Beyond the Rhine delta the Belgians, whose waterways converge upon Antwerp and the estuary of the Schelde, hope to share more directly in the trade of the great river. But any canal built between Antwerp and the lower Rhine must cross a part of the Netherlands and, since a diversion of shipping from Rotterdam would result, there is Dutch opposition. On their own ground the Belgians have a finely developed system, which includes two important links between Antwerp, the Meuse and the heavy industries of the coalfields ; these are the new Albert Canal to Liége and the improved canal through Brussels to Charleroi.

The Netherlands

In the Netherlands the maze of rivers and canals is hard to unravel on a map since they lie largely either on the delta or on land reclaimed from the sea ; thus they are partly essential for drainage, but they carry most of the heavy commercial goods. Of the three distributaries of the Rhine the smallest, the Ijssel, flows north to the lake of that name, formerly the Zuider Zee. The Lek and the still larger Waal flow more directly to the sea, and the latter once mingled its water with that of the Meuse. It was mainly towards the end of the nineteenth century that the Dutch equalled the German efforts upstream in making these branches into first-class modern routes ; also by the bold cutting of the New Waterway they ensured the greatness of Rotterdam as the chief seaport, while improving the access to Dordrecht, its nearby rival, as well as to Amsterdam with its own ship canal to Ijmuiden. Constant vigilance is needed during spates on these lower rivers and on both sides of the frontier, and especially when ice-jamming is likely to damage the banks and cause dangerous floods. Along the Rhine, and all rivers to east of it, shipping must be provided with harbours of refuge from ice, whether firm or moving during the thaw.

The Rhine

The Rhine always possessed special advantages in its generally low gradient, its regular flow and large volume, which in the lower course averages c. 2,000 m.[3] per second. But even now after great works have been performed on its course there are still rocks that become dangerous, at low water in the gorge below Bingen. Again from Basel to Strasbourg the current is so strong as to be a serious hindrance ; but from Rotterdam to Strasbourg trains of barges of up to 2,500 tons, or still bigger in lower reaches, are to be seen, towed by strong tugs. They carry ore for the Ruhr, raw material for the chemical industries there, and in the cities near the confluences of the Main and the Neckar, oil and, above all, coal in both directions from Duisburg-Ruhrort.

They fly the flags of Germany, Netherlands, France, Switzerland and Belgium, for this is a truly international river. Beyond Strasbourg in addition to the old canal to the Saône the large Alsace Canal is under construction, with two sections completed and power-stations at the dams of Kembs and Ottmarsheim.

France

The waterways of northern France and Belgium are intimately related and adapted on the larger canals to barges of 300 tons. Traffic passes by six links from the Rivers Lys, Schelde, Sambre and Meuse to be gathered into the lower Oise, and so to the Seine and Paris; the system also reaches the sea at Dunkirk and Calais and connects with the upper Marne at Condé. The waterway from Paris to Strasbourg is a remarkable achievement; from the Marne it crosses the Meuse, Moselle and Sarre and, with branches, serves most of the industries of eastern France. South of this again the high divide is crossed by canals following valleys including that of the Loire, which converge upon the middle Saône. Thus the waterways west of the Rhine radiate from three foci—Antwerp, Paris and Chalon-sur-Saône.

The three largest rivers of France, the Rhône, Loire and Garonne, are not important waterways because of their liability to severe and sudden spates and the prevalence of sandbanks that change rapidly. In the past much labour has been spent on the two western rivers, to make and keep them fit for navigation; but in view of the physical defects they have languished commercially under competition from the railways. On the Garonne navigation ceased in 1856 with the construction of a lateral canal that is linked with the bold *Canal du Midi* of 1681 through the Gap of Carcassonne; but its use suffered after acquisition by the Southern Railway. Nevertheless, with further improvement of the connection between Toulouse and Beaucaire on the Rhône, by Sète and the coastal lagoons there is still a steady flow of goods across this isthmus of Europe. It is proposed to divide the swiftly-flowing Rhône, which has a volume three times that of the Seine, into navigable sections, to generate electricity at each of the dams, and to provide additional water for irrigation in Provence. Connection with the port of Marseille has been ensured by the tunnelled canal to the lagoon of Berre, and at the head of the Rhône valley the installation of the hydro-electric station of Genissiat is regarded as a prelude to the vast operation.

The British Isles

In the British Isles inland waterways now play a small part in transport. In the eighteenth century canals were made and rivers improved with a feverish activity like that of the railway builders in the nineteenth. But since these undertakings, like the railways later, represented numerous private enterprises there was little system in the effort and, unlike the railways, the canals have never become co-ordinated. Hence, with competition from railways and from coasting vessels many waterways are virtually extinct. Those whose usefulness has led to repeated improvements are notably the ones that radiate from the Humber, the lower Thames, the Severn and, chiefly for drainage purposes, the Wash ; while the only ship canal is that from the Mersey to Manchester. Although Ireland, with a central plain, an important river and large lakes, is physically better adapted for water transport than England, the history of its canals is much the same and their present status unimportant.

Sweden and Italy

Isolated areas with water transport that should be borne in mind include the various lakes north and south of the Alps and the greater lakes of Sweden, which are connected by canal from Göteborg to Stockholm through the most populous part of the country. The northern plain of Italy, again, is in this respect more comparable with the Low Countries, since canals are numerous and are needed for drainage, although the higher ones were built mainly for irrigation. But navigation originally was the primary purpose of most of them, as is clear from the name *naviglio* retained in many cases ; but here again competition from the railways has reduced their use. The Po, which resembles the Rhône in volume, is similarly unruly ; yet it is navigable to Torino, and with it there are in all some 1,200 miles (1,900 km.) of rivers and 450 miles (720 km.) of canals that are used to some extent.

The Danube

Apart from the Volga the Danube is the greatest European river ; it is *c.* 1,800 miles (2,900 km.) long, and in volume 5,830 m.^{3} per sec. near its mouth, it is nearly three times greater than the Rhine. Yet its commercial use falls very far short of its capacity. Its basin has never been a political unit, and the curse of the frontier has lain heavily. In this respect the modern position was simplest at the beginning of this century, with five riparian states, and at the end of the period the tonnage carried in the part most used, from Budapest downwards, was about 7 per cent of that carried on the Rhine. From 1920 there were seven states on its banks and, after World War II, with Russia at the delta, there were eight. But apart from politics, the Danube has the disadvantage of flowing away from the highly industrialised part of Europe, and so its more obvious functions have been the carriage upstream of agricultural produce and Romanian oil, with bauxite from Hungary and other ores from Yugoslavia in recent decades ; downstream the cargoes included manufactured goods in great variety. In 1936 when German requirements were great the tonnage on the Danube was still only 10 per cent of that on the Rhine. This powerful river needs constant supervision from the engineers almost throughout its course, but especially in the delta. Moreover, there is great expenditure of fuel during the spates due to the Alpine contributions to its flow ; shelter from ice must be provided and skilful pilotage in many sections. Two natural hazards stand out above all others, where the current is concentrated in the gorges through the Transylvanian mountains. In places the passage is too narrow to allow passing, and at the exit of the canyon is the Iron Gate, where the water when low is broken by rocks. An artificial channel cut on the right bank must then be used, and this is a severe impediment.

Egypt and Iraq

It remains to note the importance of the Nile, Euphrates and Tigris as waterways under modern conditions in so far as it is relevant to the main theme. The points of physical likeness and difference of these rivers will be recalled ; because of these the age-old manner of using them for transport is contrasted. The prevailing northerly winds in Egypt favour upstream sailing and the current brings the boats back ; except in the delta depth suffices and there are locks at the barrages. Neither of the Nile mouths is navigable near the coast, but the Mahmudiya Canal, from the Rosetta branch, reaches Alexandria, which deals with nine-tenths of the foreign trade of Egypt. The aggregate register tonnage of all craft passing the locks in Lower Egypt, still in majority sailing boats, is about one million, and in Upper Egypt one-third of this. But since Egypt is well supplied with railways only about one-quarter of the goods is now carried by water.

On the rivers of Iraq sailing craft are restricted to the deltaic plain and steamers to the Tigris. The upper courses of both rivers are suited only to the ancient practice of transport downstream by rafts of brushwood and inflated skins, the latter being returned later by land to serve again. However, the total amount of goods transported in Iraq is very much less than in Egypt, since the oil leaves by pipe-line.

RAILWAYS

The varying degree in which Europe is equipped with rails is not easy to appreciate from atlas maps which usually omit many lines, and maps showing all of them are uncommon and barely legible on small scales. The attempt to represent the relative density of railways given here (Fig. 33) has been made from study of such maps, with the grading effected by eye. Laborious measurement would no doubt give a result somewhat different in detail, but the sketch brings out certain facts reasonably well. The influence of relief is not very striking except in the Alps and in southern Europe. On the other hand the effect of industrialisation is very evident, though this does not explain the abundance of railways near the west Baltic coasts or in parts of France and England, where it is related rather to highly developed agriculture.

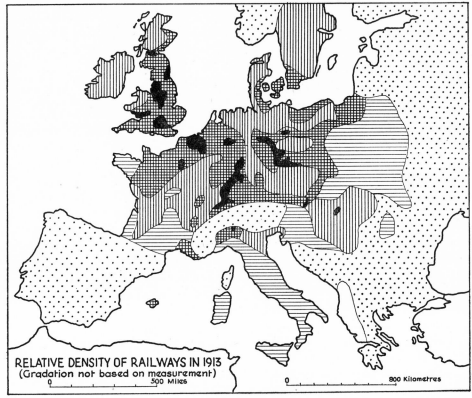

RELATIVE DENSITY OF RAILWAYS IN 1913
(Gradation not based on measurement)
0   500 Miles
0   800 Kilometres

FIG. 33

Again, the effect of imperial strategy is plain in the east, with intensely developed railways up to the German frontier of 1913, contrasting with deliberate sparseness in what was then Russian Poland. Strategy, too, partly explains the higher densities in Hungary, but on this alluvial plain it was found more economic to build railways than good roads. Since 1913 notable building of railways has taken place only in Russsia, Poland and Scandinavia in Europe, but there has been much more in the Borderlands.

Density of Traffic

The study of density is of limited value since the maps upon which it is based cannot distinguish single from double tracks. Thus in Britain and Germany, as in 1939, over half the mileage is double, and in Belgium and France the proportion is only slightly less ; moreover, in Britain parts of many routes carry more than two lines. It follows, then, that a conspectus of railway use is desirable, such as might be based upon numbers, for each route, of trains per day or year, or of passengers or, again, the tonnage of goods carried. The relationship between numbers of trains on a route and their speed must not be passed over. Where the total use of railways is slight the speed of freight trains may be very much slower than that of passenger trains ; but unless the two classes are kept on different lines, which is unusual, this ceases to be possible unless freight trains are to be side-tracked at short intervals. Hence in Britain and other areas with great dependence on railways for all kinds of traffic freight-trains are run at greater speeds. Similarly because of the intense use of British railways for coal and other heavy freight and the great numbers of trains, the routes available for expresses are limited, and mainly for this reason Britain has not introduced the light but very fast trains, hauled by diesel engines, which appeared on German and Italian lines between the wars. NO !

International Routes

Further reference may now be made to the international functions of the railways. The importance of the standard gauge of permanent way has been mentioned. This width, 4 ft. 8½ inches (1·435 m.), was adopted because all locomotives were imported from Britain when the earlier railways were built, so while there are many lines of narrower gauge for local purposes, rolling stock and its load may pass throughout much of Europe over uniform lines. Transhipment is obligatory only at the frontiers of Spain and Russia, where the gauges are respectively 1·656 and 1·524 metres. The interchange of rolling stock throughout the countries with standard gauge was under a well-organised international supervision, but after the Second War this had more limited scope ; moreover, certain routes stand out as those that are, or have been, followed by the international expresses distinguished by their names. In several cases the continental route has been extended by train-ferries, thus eliminating the breaks between German and Danish and Swedish sections and also the interruption of the Strait of Dover on the route London-Paris. There is a striking radiation of these trains from Paris, and because of the links with England the Low Countries form a crossroads.

Development of National Patterns

The present railway map of Europe acquires special interest when it is compared with earlier versions, since the origin of parts of the net at once becomes clear. For example, the network in France is essentially a spider's web centred on Paris, while the English railways have a similar although more lop-sided pattern dominated by London. But the origins differed. In England the cradle of the railway was County Durham, and nets were woven simultaneously between the Mersey and Humber, around Birmingham and around London. The existing pattern grew up for economic reasons and largely unco-ordinated ; the gauge of 7 ft. on the Great Western was converted to standard only in 1892. But in France the system was devised with a political aim, to join Paris to the peripheral cities—Bordeaux, Brest, Le Havre, Lille, Strasbourg and Marseille. Hence the transverse routes came later, those in the east and other radials to the frontier having a strategic as well as commercial significance. The greatest traffic is carried by the radials, especially their inner sections, by the route linking industries along the frontier and by the southern line, through Toulouse and Marseille to Italy. The spider's web pattern reappears in relation to the political and strategic units of the later nineteenth centuries, especially those of Hungary, centred on Budapest, in pre-1914 Russian Poland, with much opener mesh centred on Warsaw and in the much larger but flimsy web of Moscow. From Vienna, again, nine main lines radiate, but five of these are now in Czechoslovakia ; of those still in Austria the one to Trieste has a nodal point at Villach on the Drave ; its five lines mark the chief convergence within the Alps. The railway node at Lvov (Lemberg), now in the Soviet Union, marks an Austrian strategic concentration beyond the Carpathians.

Political disunity of Germany before 1871, along with the physical features, accounts for the general lack of a uniform pattern of railways. But the eastern plain has its web like the others mentioned, and the radii from Berlin are remarkably straight. The other notable centres are Leipzig, Hanover, Köln, Frankfurt a/M, Nürnberg and Munich. The Spanish railways present an open net conforming roughly to the trends of the coasts, but with a deliberate gathering of lines at the central capital ; those of Italy, apart from the plain, are aligned with the relief with minor concentrations at Pisa, Rome, Naples and Foggia.

Routes across the Alps and Pyrenees

Construction of railways across the Alps has amply repaid the effort. Thanks to the relatively low height of the main passes and depth of the connecting glens the main and subsidiary tunnels were possible and the gradients surmountable at economic rates. These routes and that of the Brenner Pass, without a main tunnel, have been of great benefit to Switzerland and the neighbouring countries, especially Italy. They surmount the formidable barrier with remarkably small deviations : between Verona and Munich by the Brenner Pass (4,495 ft., or 1,370 m.) and Innsbruck ; between Milan and Zürich by the St Gotthard Tunnel (3,786 ft. or 1,154 m.). From Milan the main route to Paris by the Simplon Tunnel (2,313 ft. or 705 m.) bends down the Rhône to Lausanne, but the Vallorbe Tunnel in the Jura gives a very straight course to Dijon ; while from the Simplon the direct line to Basel traverses the Lötschberg Tunnel (4,078 ft. or 1,243 m.). The so-called Mt Cenis Tunnel (4,230 ft. or 1,289 m.) offers a slightly more devious way from Turin to Dijon. At the western end of Austria the Arlberg Tunnel (4,301 ft. or 1,311 m.) under the Rhine-Inn watershed has a special international function by allowing traffic from the west to reach Vienna without touching Germany.

The Pyrenees are penetrated by two tunnels, those of Somport (3,973 ft. or 1,211 m.) leading from Pau to Saragossa, and Puymorens (5,141 ft. or 1,566 m.) between Toulouse and Barcelona. Neither of these routes, which were opened respectively in 1928 and 1929, carries traffic equivalent to that of the older lines along the two coasts.

Effects of two World Wars

In the wholesale creation of new frontiers in 1919–20 the economic viability of the succession states was held to depend in many areas upon an adequate railway system. Partitioning the Austro-Hungarian Empire involved inter-ference with the networks centred upon Vienna and Budapest ; the Hungarian system was cut in such a way as to allow the new Czechoslovakia and the expanded Romania to include almost continuous railways just within their frontiers with Hungary. In Romania this meant unbroken connection between Satul Mare on the upper Tisa to Timişoara in the south, but left Slovakia with gaps to fill in amounting to nearly a third of the whole ; and this task is still incomplete. The delimitation of these boundaries, not on ethnic, but on economic and strategic grounds left large Hungarian minorities in the neighbouring states.

Such are some of the results of the First World War in upsetting railway systems established when aims were different. Changes of this kind have not followed the Second War except those due to the westward shift of the frontiers of Poland and the U.S.S.R. on the northern plain. On the other hand, this war caused destruction of railways on an unprecedented scale throughout all Europe except the neutral countries, and, in particular, the permanent restora-tion of bridges and the replacement of rolling stock absorbed much effort and expenditure and added special impediments to economic recovery. In one direction, however, the period was marked by progress upon the railways by the extension of electrification, especially where coal is not available and much hydro-electric power developed. Thus in Switzerland practically all the state railways are now electric, and the proportions of mileage converted is about a third in Sweden, a quarter in Italy, a sixth in the Netherlands and a tenth in France.

Integration of Means of Transport

The integration of routes involves two ideas. The first of these is topographic and the other economic. On the one hand, if rail, road and waterways run more or less parallel without touching they cannot be physically integrated, but with numerous exchange points they can feed one another with passengers and goods. Whether they do this or not is on the other hand an economic question involving costs of fare, freight and transhipment, and of course the time element as well. Physical integration in some parts of Europe has been planned at an early stage, while in others it has been effected only partially and under economic pressure. The co-ordination of traffic likewise varies in degree and in date of origin ; but in many countries well provided with roads it has been an important question ever since motor transport has offered serious competition with railways. The special advantages of the three modes of modern transport are well known, so it must suffice here to refer briefly to their respective functions and status in some of the countries. While the comparison to be made refers primarily to inland transport, in maritime countries this has to compete with carriage of goods in coasting vessels, particularly in Norway, Denmark, Britain and the Mediterranean countries. The relative importance of inland waterways and railways for goods traffic may be stated thus : in the Netherlands as 9 to 1 ; in Belgium as 1 to 2 ; in Germany and in France (both as in 1938) as 1 to 3, and in Britain (1950) as 1 to 25. From the preceding description of waterways it will be obvious that these countries, except the Netherlands, are not evenly served by the waterways and the degree in which railways in turn contribute to them will be located partly in relation to the seaports. Road haulage again is a real competitor with railways in the same countries, particularly in Britain, and least in the Netherlands. To get a fair comparison of the general function of the railway we may turn to the national statistics of an inter-war period, averages for 1935–7, comparing tonnage with passengers per kilometre. In five states the passenger traffic was more important ; in Britain, Denmark and the Netherlands, with coastal and inland shipping in competition for goods, in Portugal and in Switzerland with its great tourist traffic. In six countries goods traffic predominated : in Finland, Sweden and Germany, together with three where relatively few people had acquired the habit of travel—Poland, Spain and Yugoslavia.

The Middle East

Throughout the Borderlands modern communications are in an elementary stage compared with those of Europe. For example, in Turkey there was, in 1949, 1 mile of railway for 60 square miles (1 km. for 96 sq. km.) of territory compared with 1 for 17 (27 sq. km.) in the Iberian Peninsula, while the corresponding road densities were 1 for 25 (40 sq. km.) and 1 for 2·3 square miles (3·7 sq. km.). A large proportion of Turkish roads and railways are works of the last thirty years, although they often follow the trail of ancient Persian and Roman routes, as is also the case with many recent constructions all along the Mediterranean coastlands. In Turkey itself the railways of the Ottoman Empire represented concessions to foreign companies, and, in the case of the line from the Bosporus opposite Istanbul to Nisibin well on the way to Baghdad, also German ambitions in the Nearer East. By extension since 1923 the railways may now be described as a very open network, mainly of standard gauge, with two continuous longitudinal routes and three transverse links ; but the relief of Armenia does not encourage the making of such a route near the eastern frontier. The road-net may be said generally to fill in the meshes and to feed the railways. Since the coastal zones of Anatolia and the Levant are the more populous there is much reliance upon coasting vessels. The land routes of Syria, Lebanon, Israel and Jordan are made up of long parallel lines from north to south and short transverse ones ; the latter connect with desert trails notably at Damascus. This has always been the case, but modernisation of the routes has followed no uniform plan. The most remarkable event was perhaps the construction of the narrow-gauge railway in Arabia. Its main purpose was to make pilgrimages easier and safer, but it was no doubt also of pan-Islamic as well as Turkish imperial significance. Because of the latter the Arabian section was largely destroyed in the First War by T. E. Lawrence and his Badawin. On the other hand, British intervention in the two World Wars was largely responsible for links or replacements of railway between Aleppo and Cairo, built on the standard gauge ; so a continuous train journey from the Bosporus to the Nile is now a physical possibility. Similarly, the Baghdad Railway is complete, and Iraq has another railway system, on the metre gauge, leading from Baghdad southward to Basra and sharing goods traffic with vessels on the Tigris, and northward to the oilfields of Kirkuk. From Kirkuk oil is led by pipe south-westward across the Tigris and Euphrates, and then by alternative pipes which end at Haifa in Israel and Tripoli in Lebanon. Saïda, the ancient Sidon, receives oil from a much longer pipe-line from Qatif on the Gulf coast of Arabia. Export of oil from Kuwait, however, is by sea ; similarly that from Persia, since Abadan on the Shatt el Arab is the terminus of the pipe from the Persian fields. Persia is badly off for roads and railways, but since 1938 there has been a continuous railway from the Persian Gulf at Bandar Shahpur by Teheran to Bandar Shah on the Caspian Sea, this piercing both the Zagros and the Elburz Mountains. From the capital, too, a line runs toward the north-west, but this link with Soviet Armenia remains incomplete.

Creation of routes in Africa by the French Government and in much smaller degree by those of Italy and Spain, bears all the marks of colonial development. These are the result of progressive expansion inland from a number of points on the coast, followed by efforts to link up the various systems of routes. This stage has barely been reached even in the Atlas lands, although it is now theoretically possible to run a train from Gabes to Marrakesh, a distance of some 1,800 miles (2,900 km.). In Tunisia, where relief is least obstructive, the network of rail and road is comparable with that of the Roman roads in their heyday, but the main interior plateau is crossed only by isolated branch lines such as penetrate other parts of Africa. In Morocco railways serve the phosphate mines and there is a connection to Tangier.

It seems likely that the building of new railways throughout the Borderlands will be undertaken chiefly with the purpose of linking existing routes to make them more efficient, and that roads will be multiplied more rapidly. But the road systems will for long include elements differing greatly in quality, since while more stretches are made to rival European standards for motor traffic animal transport will remain alongside most of them. Although it takes at least 20 camels or 40 mules to carry the load of a 4-ton lorry and at slow speed, these animals are valuable assets in most of the lands, and presumably they will always bring their loads to the motor road, to the railway station, or as in Egypt and Iraq to the river bank.

SEAPORTS AND SHIPPING

Very few of the seaports most famous in history now stand high in the published lists of daily sailings and arrivals. Some of them, like Ostia the port of Rome, and all but one of the Cinque Ports of England, now lie inland ; Dover flourishes because it has been built to serve its modern function as a ferry-port. This also applies to Marseille, and the Phoenician Akka has been replaced artificially by Haifa across the bay. While ports in general have flourished or declined with the economy of the state to which they belong, the number of the fortunate in each country has decreased. The fittest have survived and grown. They are usually the ones which are most easily accessible to the area which they serve, while at the same time having a harbour that can be extended to take larger and more numerous ships and also a site that is not cramped. Ports are commonly said to compete with one another, and this implies of course human initiative on the part of authorities and merchants. In the leading European seaports there is in fact a long mercantile tradition. The measure of commercial importance is the record of the number of ships using a port, their aggregate tonnage, number of passengers arriving and departing, and the amount of the cargoes loaded and unloaded ; the latter may be measured either by weight or by value, but the former is more obviously related to the physical size of the port. It will be seen, however, that statistics alone may be misleading. For example, Dover and Southampton both have large quotas of passengers, but these are using the two ports for very different voyages, while the aggregate tonnage at the former is swollen by the daily record of a few small vessels while at the latter it represents large ships using the port at much longer intervals. Evidently, then, the differing functions of European seaports cannot be fully revealed merely from general statistics.

The English Channel

At a given moment the English Channel and an equal area of the North Sea just east of it will be found to contain a notable proportion of the world's shipping varying in type from tramps and tugs to liners and tankers, since this is the most used part of the European seas ; these waters carry the concentrated commerce of the largest industrial tract of Europe with world-wide connections. From the Channel these ships are found to 'fan out' along well-defined routes in the Atlantic Ocean. Most of them are seeking or leaving the seaports of the Channel and southern part of the North Sea ; and smaller volumes of trade are evident along the western seaboards of Britain and France. Most of these north-western ports occupy the estuaries of rivers, which owe their origin to the post-glacial submergence and their continued existence to large tidal range, which at springs exceeds 12 feet (3.7 m.), except in the Netherlands which lie near the tidal node of the North Sea. The outward scour helps to keep the channels open, but dredging and other devices are usually necessary. Moreover, enclosed docks, or at least floating quays, are required with such ranges of water-level. In some cases, too, outports have been created to avoid loss of time and some dredging : Cuxhaven for Hamburg, Bremerhaven for Bremen, St Nazaire for Nantes, Verdon for Bordeaux, Avonmouth for Bristol, and, for some purposes, Tilbury for London. Antwerp cannot have an outport since the estuary lies in Dutch territory, while Rotterdam and Amsterdam have ship canals to the sea. These estuarine ports have a first advantage in the natural sheltered roadstead where ships may anchor when not alongside a quay ; Cherbourg, not on an estuary, has its roadstead enclosed by an outer breakwater. Again, land on the banks being low allows for the building of warehouses and railways ; there are 500 miles of track within the port of Antwerp. While none of the north-western seaports is hampered by natural barriers behind it, those with great inland waterways have a special advantage, and at Hamburg, and especially Rotterdam, much trans-shipment takes place in the roadstead.

Hinterlands and Entrepôts

Competition between commercial ports has been mentioned, and this involves the idea of the hinterland, the area tributary to the port. To define the extent of this is in no case easy, since it pays to send some commodities much farther than others, but hitherto European governments have certainly encouraged preferential rates and improvement of routes, so as to direct traffic to their own seaports. Nevertheless, even if national barriers of this kind were eliminated the flow of trade to the different ports would still vary with the kind of commodity as it does in Britain. Moreover, special equipment is required for the handling of such things as coal, oil, grain, timber and fish. But with due allowance for all this, it is clear that the whole area of Europe that is drained to the Atlantic must be divisible into segments each tributary to a seaport or to a small group of these ; also that these will overlap mutually. Similarly there are undoubted overlaps of hinterland between Atlantic and Mediterranean ports, e.g. Bilbao with Barcelona, Le Havre with Marseille, Rotterdam with Genoa. Measured by the register tonnage between the two wars, there was no great difference between the trade of Rotterdam, Antwerp and Hamburg ; but that of London exceeded them by about one-third owing largely to its pre-eminence as an entrepôt, i.e. by collecting goods from distant sources for re-export. Liverpool, Southampton, le Havre, Tyne ports, Bremen, Copenhagen and Cherbourg followed, usually in that order, by ship tonnage, but differently arranged by weight and by value of cargoes. Southampton and Cherbourg now share the distinction of chief passenger ports in their respective countries, first because of the additional time used between London or even Le Havre and the ocean, but also from their fitness to receive the largest liners which furthermore may visit both ports in succession. Copenhagen like London benefits from its position as an entrepôt for the Scandinavian lands. On a sheltered strait, it has the advantages of an estuarine site, while with little range of tide it needs no docks ; but for the packet service to Harwich it is replaced by Esbjerg on the west coast of Denmark.

The Baltic

The defects of the Baltic ports from freezing increase northward ; from Stockholm round to the Gulf of Riga ice prevails for over three months, so where goods cannot easily be held up the southern ports derive advantage. Sweden's greatest port is Göteborg for this reason, and from its other advantage of location, and similarly the U.S.S.R. may be expected to develop the facilities at its southern group of ports of Libava (Liepeja), Klaipeda (Memel) and Baltiyisk (Pillau). Poland is now in sole possession of the Vistula mouth, and so with the twin ports of Gdansk (Danzig) and Gdynia while she is in occupation of Szczecin (Stettin). The fact that the ship tonnage of all those in Germany during the period before the Second War was less than half that of Hamburg is a measure of the disadvantages of the Baltic. To reduce this chiefly from a naval point of view the Kiel Canal was cut from the Elbe estuary to the Firth of Kiel, 61 miles (98 km.) long, with one very large lock at each end. While it has carried mercantile tonnage in an average year before or since the war that is about equal to that on either the Suez or the Panama Canal, the number of vessels has been about ten times as great.

Specialised Ports

Most of the north-western ports so far mentioned have a large general trade in both directions, although exports rarely equal imports in their bulk, so many ships must sail without full cargoes. In this respect the coal ports are exceptional, and indeed many British harbours are specially designed to export coal in large quantities, e.g. Cardiff, Sunderland and Methil, and to import wood, at least for pit-props, or, again, in Spain Gijon is adapted for coal and Bilbao for iron ore. Others are adapted to receive fresh fish, and often have difficulty in procuring other trade to offset the fluctuations of fishing ; this applies even to Grimsby, the greatest fishing port of Europe. But the most specialised of all seaports are those created solely for naval use, like Brest and Portsmouth.

Natural Harbours

It may be said of all the north-western coasts so far discussed, with the exception of those of Iberia north of the Douro, Armorica, western Britain and Ireland, that few natural harbours are without a port. But this is very far from the case along the outer coast of Europe, north of Glasgow, Aberdeen and Göteborg, where deep water reaches far inland on innumerable fiords, although some are shallow at the entrance. Indeed, there may well be more good natural harbours than people. In Scotland two have been used for naval purposes, Cromarty Firth and Scapa Flow.

Norway; U.S.S.R.

In Norway there are many small ports, but only Oslo and Bergen have much general trade, the former being the chief importer for Norway, while

Bergen has the fast passenger connection with Newcastle. But the size of Norwegian ports gives little indication of the great part played by the country in the ocean transport of the world, a matter for discussion later, or of its share in the whaling industry of the Southern Ocean. On the other hand, the concentration upon fishing is more obvious in the various ports, as has been pointed out in Chapter 4. Wherever there are minerals in the far north the presence of open sea in winter is a valuable asset, as is seen in the development of Narvik for the export of iron ore from Swedish Lapland. But it is the U.S.S.R. which may be expected to exploit the ' gulf of warmth ' to the fullest, and especially by means of shipping at Murmansk ; this not only if the minerals of the Kola Peninsula were to be exported but also because of the closing of the inner seaport of Archangel for six months.

The Southwest

From the Douro southwards to the limit of Morocco and throughout the Mediterranean and Black Sea good natural harbours for moderately large ships are generally far apart. The notable exceptions to this are the coasts of the Aegean Sea and eastern Adriatic, and in smaller measure those of the Tyrrhenian Sea, with Provence and the Barbary coast. These tracts coincide largely with deeply dissected or greatly fractured masses of stronger rocks that have been partially submerged. Elsewhere weaker rocks prevail, and emergence has produced smooth and shelving shores where longshore drift tends to emphasise the smoothness. Moreover, the virtual lack of tides favours the formation of deltas. The latter, however, does not apply on the Atlantic side, but even there Lisbon is unique first for physical reasons. The rock structure and submergence account for its deep narrow entrance and wide harbour, the tide-range is slight and occasional floods of the Tagus are the only defect. Lisbon, again from the Age of Discovery, has had world-wide connections evident in its function as an inter-port ; but it is fit to have a much greater hinterland which, but for the frontier, would be the larger part of the Peninsula. Seville, far inland on the tidal Guadalquiver, has still some value as a port to Spain, but it shares the trade of the south-west with Cadiz and nearby havens. To balance Lisbon on the south, the French have built the modern port of Casablanca, with full protection from the ocean and well placed to develop the hinterland of Morocco.

The Mediterranean and the Black Sea

Within the Mediterranean there are certain obvious general locations for commercial seaports of note : first are those near the heads of the northern gulfs, hence Sète and Marseille, Genoa, Venice, Trieste and Rijeka (Fiume), Salonika and, with additional reason, Istanbul, while Iskanderun (Alexandretta) is potentially important ; and secondly, those in forward positions because of their special connections with the opposite coasts such as Naples, Palermo and Tunis, Brindisi, Patras and Piraeus ; but these possess additional functions. In a different category are the naval ports : Toulon and Spezia, strategically placed in the north-west, but especially those established to control the narrows —Gibraltar, Bizerta, Malta and Taranto. The other seaports in distribution and relative importance reflect the commercial development of the various countries and most of them have restricted hinterlands.

Few of the greater ports are favoured by a large and deep inlet like the Golden Horn of Istanbul or Sevastopol on the Crimea, and most have break-waters on at least one side often prolonging a headland. Marseille is an example of expansion along the coast from the original harbour with quays sheltered by a long breakwater ; Genoa and Algiers have similar points, and Alexandria as in ancient times has twin harbours facing east and west. The lagoons, so typical of Mediterranean shores, have been used to make large inner harbours at Tunis, Taranto and Venice and others on lesser scales. The relation between ports and deltas is significant ; they are naturally associated because of agricultural output and inland routes, but the harbour stands apart and not on the side of predominant silting. Valencia is an exception, with its new port built on the delta of the Turia, but Malaga, Marseille, Salonika and Alexandria are typical, and on the Black Sea Samsun, between two deltas, Batum and Constanta. Among the Russian ports Sevastopol's forward position is specially valuable in view of the freezing of Odessa and Nicolaiev, and especially places on the Sea, of Azov. Of the ports along the Caucasian shore only Novorossiysk has any real natural protection.

The greater seaports, as in the north-west, conduct a general trade with imports and exports not seriously disproportionate, but they vary with the national economies and with the capacity of their hinderlands. Marseille and Genoa are great industrial ports, and, like their northern counterparts, are ' world ports ' with regular sailings to other continents, and both are ports of call for liners of other countries on the oriental voyages. Marseille is the leading French port, yet its hinterland is more restricted than those of its rivals in most respects, since the great bulk of its imports are manufactured in its vicinity. Genoa and its industries suffer from lack of space, but it is the port of the northern plain to a much greater extent than Venice, and is also a commercial outlet for Switzerland. Trieste is potentially the port of a large area in the Danubian basin, and under the Habsburg Empire it served this purpose, but it became a political victim. Salonika similarly has suffered from Balkan politics, but can scarcely fail ultimately to benefit from industrialisation in the north. Istanbul sees many more ships pass through the Bosporus than enter its harbour, and like Salonika lies too near the frontier ;

but it is the chief port of Turkey, and is the centre of a vigorous coasting trade. The Black Sea carries about half of Russian sea-borne commerce, and the ports west of the Caucasus have considerable hinterlands.   Naples, despite its central situation, cannot compete with Genoa commercially, such is the economic contrast of north and south.   Yet with a fine harbour it is the chief centre of passenger traffic, including the now depleted flow of emigrants, and is the link through Palermo with Sicily.   Brindisi serves this function in the east with sailings for Greece, the Levant and Egypt.   On the African side the four leading ports are Algiers and Oran and Tunis with well-marked hinterlands, the lesser places being chiefly exporters of minerals, and Alexandria serving all the Nile valley in Egypt.

The Suez Canal

Many of the cities mentioned owe their prosperity in some measure to oriental trade by the Suez Canal, whose opening in 1869 caused a real renascence in some, notably Marseille.   The importance of this canal from its position need scarcely be discussed ;   as an engineering work it is admirably fitted for the transit of the shipping that serves the oriental trade—c. 6,000 transits in 1929 and 1938, nearly 9,000 in 1948, about one-half being British. In length it is about 100 miles (160 km.) between Port Said and Suez, 34 feet (10 m.) deep—soon to be 36 (11 m.)—and there are no locks.   Here then is another node of sea traffic, added by man to those already noted at Dover, the Irish and the Danish channels, Gibraltar, Malta and the Hellespont. Elsewhere in European waters ships have more choice.   But it is as well to remember the pack-ice crowding in the far north-east and limiting harshly the passage of the Kara Strait to the Siberian coasts.   Nothing that man can do in the north will ease the passage to the Orient as de Lesseps did at the Isthmus of Suez.

AIRWAYS

Conquest of the air has given freedom from control by the irregularities of land and sea, of mountain and plain.   With technical improvements of aircraft and with ever increasing meteorological information available to pilots, variations of the atmosphere come to have less and less influence upon navigation, although such air qualities will continue to affect speed of flight and expenditure of energy.   But there will always be the question of contacts with the land or the water.   At present airfields are relatively few compared to towns or railway stations, since their area and cost are great ;   and for this reason they are inconveniently far from the centres of the large cities which they serve, a serious defect where short flights are concerned.   Civil and military airfields, too, have taken much valuable land from agriculture, so a great saving will be made if invention provides means for aircraft to alight in a given direction, whatever the wind. Still more would be gained by provision for landing at slow speeds and for nearly vertical ascents and descents, since presumably small airfields might then be as well distributed as railway stations.

The status of civil aviation in Europe and the Borderlands is determined largely by economic conditions, and there are important limitations arising from international relations. But by means of aviation Europe has acquired a new relationship with the rest of the world ; personal visits may be made by people living at great distances within a lapse of days instead of weeks or months. The Sahara desert and the frozen northern seas are not the barriers they were. Gradually this air-mindedness is dispelling the common misconception of the earth that is due to over-familiarity with the Mercator map.

It remains to be seen to what extent aviation will discourage future building of railways or even of roads ; this will depend upon the ability of aircraft to carry freight at economic rates, perhaps with towing of gliders. But it is at least clear that life in outlying and thinly peopled regions will be altered considerably by extension of air services. This applies particularly to the northern forest, the islands of the north-western coasts, the highlands of Armenia and Persia, and to oases of the desert, and the first two of these would seem to call especially for the greater use of hydroplanes and helicopters. Whatever types of freight aircraft may carry in the future, their use as the principal vehicles for letters throughout Europe must already be recognised as effecting a minor revolution in the speed of intercourse. More obviously aircraft compete for passengers with the railways and shipping services, and there is every indication that they will be increasingly successful.

CHAPTER 19

POPULATION

THE most outstanding fact about the distribution of population in Europe is the vast concentration in a tract that widens south-eastward from Britain to enclose the mouths of the Seine, Rhône and Po, the upper Oder and the whole of the Elbe basin (Fig. 34). In this tract, together with Great Britain south of the Scottish Highlands, about half the population of Europe is found, a number not differing greatly from that of the entire U.S.S.R. It is over one-third of the population of Europe, including the European part of the U.S.S.R., just under one-third of that of Europe and the Borderlands, and 8 per cent of the world's population. The reason for this phenomenon is, of course, the intensity of industry and commerce that prevails throughout most of the tract. Only a quarter or less of the ' active ' population are engaged in agriculture, while one-third are manufacturing for a living. Of the rest some are miners and builders, but the majority have commercial or administrative occupations. It is, of course, impossible to appreciate this mass of population, by no means evenly distributed over the land, and to give an arithmetical value to their average density would be misleading ; although such mean densities of population may be quoted usefully in other connections.

At this point some of the implications of density may be considered, beginning with the self-sufficient agricultural communities that prevailed in medieval Europe, and presuming the people had been counted. The number in a given village in relation to the area of the farmland and common would be a real measure of the productivity of the land as used by the methods of the period ; it really indicates maintenance of population by the local produce. Further, since there was then little variation over considerable areas, either of methods or of standard of life, a figure of average density for such an area would have similar explanatory value. While these self-sufficient conditions prevailed until the nineteenth century in many parts of Russia, for example, they are now very uncommon in Europe, and in general the population cannot be regarded as supported by the land it lives on. Two examples showing different degrees of local dependence may be compared. Figs. 35 and 36 are population maps of mountainous districts, western Arcadia in southern Greece and the Vosges in France ; they are comparable in height and relief, but not in climate.

Arcadia in ancient Greece was the typical remote pastoral district, and it still remains purely rural in its life, growing its own food but exporting animals and cheese. Villages are most numerous on the higher less dissected land with more soil and richer pasture, and there the mean density, in 1928, was 44 per square kilometre (114 per sq. mile), but it falls to half of this at lower altitudes except where, in the south, there are several very large and more accessible villages. The fact is that not even in Arcadia are the people fully supported by their land. In winter shepherds go down to the lowlands with their flocks, and others travel far as skilled artisans, and return periodically or to retire.

The Vosges are still largely under forests, but neither forestry nor agriculture and stock-keeping in the clearings would serve to maintain the population whose varying densities were mapped by Lablache, from the census of 1910. The people have seized the opportunity to make use of another natural resource, the abundant rivers of pure water, for the manufacture of textiles. This has increased since the valleys are reached by railways with coal and materials and now also by electricity. The industry also had a special fillip from immigration of Alsatian workers after the loss of Alsace to Germany in 1871. In contrast with Arcadia, there are several real towns in addition to many industrialised villages.

These examples must serve to indicate the varied degree and manner in which population may be held to depend upon the area in which it lives and works. Moreover, under modern urban conditions the large towns have their dormitories at some distance from the places of work. With such things in mind it is obvious that generalised maps showing the distribution of population on small scales have limited value ; but the value is real if causes are not too readily deduced from them. The more obvious reasons for concentration of people are the location of manufacturing industries and the development of commerce, both being characteristic of towns. The former has been discussed already, and the latter is geographically related to the routes of transportation. But even where population density is high for these reasons a proportion of it must generally be assigned to direct use of the land for agriculture, which is specially intensive in such areas. It must, however, be remembered that the population map of mainly rural areas by itself gives no information about the productivity of agriculture, and still less about the standard of life of the people ; furthermore, among a purely rural population there are elements not directly dependent upon agriculture, especially where the standard of life is relatively high. These elements as a rule may be assumed to serve the needs of the agricultural majority, but, as in Britain, they may include people dependent upon extraneous incomes.

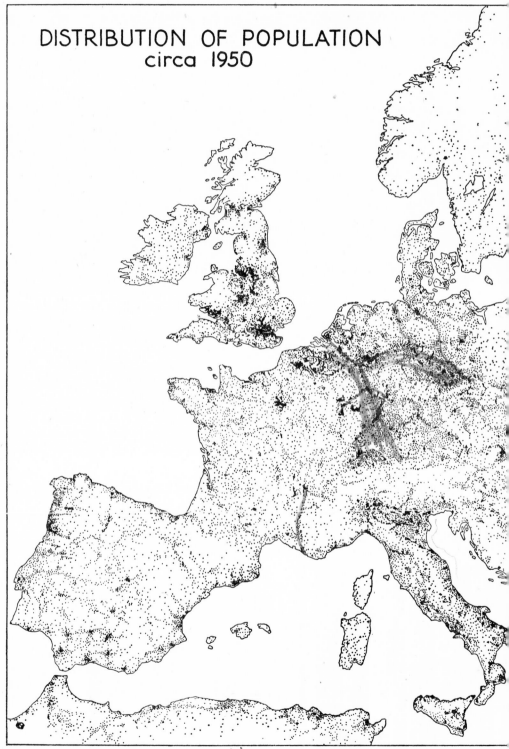

DISTRIBUTION OF POPULATION
circa 1950

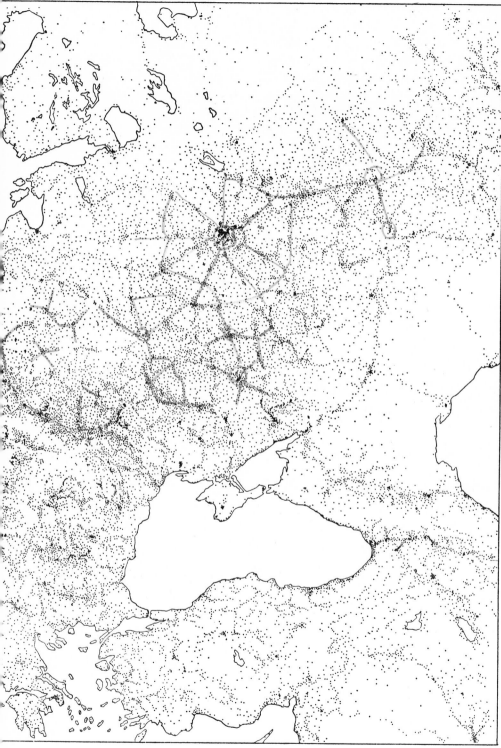

Zones of dense Population

Now to return to the most populous part of Europe to examine the general distribution within it. The agglomeration in northern Italy stands apart, except on the Mediterranean coast, since the Alps, with relatively low densities, intervene. But elsewhere there are no physical features to reduce the population in this way. Moreover, the Alps have influenced indirectly the specially favoured lowlands near their foot on all sides ; east of the Bodensee, however,

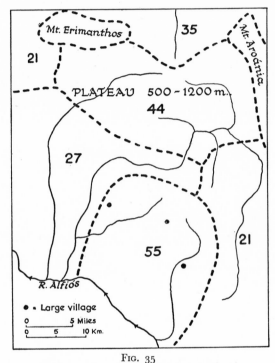

FIG. 35

Density of Population in western Arcadia.
The figures represent mean density per sq. km. in 1928.

only the Danube valley itself is so favoured. In southern Germany agricultural productivity is reflected by a zoning of population that corresponds with the scarplands, and so also in the Czech lands the soil and relief have notable effects ; but in all of these lands industries have penetrated more or less.

The dominant feature, however, is the convergence upon the lower Rhine of two belts of great population. The one follows that river continuously from the Swiss plateau, but has extensions in the basin of the Neckar, along the valley of the Main and also north through Hesse to the Fulda and Weser valleys. Most of this, it will be recalled, has a numerous agricultural population working small farms intensively, as well as many and varied industries and a close network of communications and important nodal centres. The other may be designated the hill-foot zone all the way from the valleys of the Sambre and Meuse in the west to the foot of the central Carpathians in the east, and it crosses the Rhine zone at the Ruhr coalfield. From very early times it has supported relatively dense population because it is largely floored by the best loamy soils on the plain, the adjoining hills saw the rise of metal mining in Europe, industries grew with water power, and trade developed at every

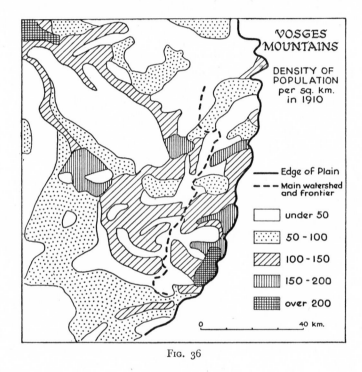

VOSGES MOUNTAINS

DENSITY OF POPULATION per sq. km. in 1910

——— Edge of Plain
— — — Main watershed and frontier

under 50
50 - 100
100 - 150
150 - 200
over 200

0   40 km.

Fig. 36

point of exchange between hill and plain. With these earlier advantages there are the resources of coal, lignite and the salts, exploited in modern times. The zone varies generally in breadth and in population, with the distribution of all these as they are or were, for 'geographical momentum' has had its effect ; moreover, 'hill-foot' must be freely interpreted since the zone includes the inner part of Bohemia and it embraces the Harz Mountains as an island. Between the Moravian Gate and the Rhine the largest areas with very great population are the Leipzig embayment and the vicinity of the Ruhr. The latter block extends west and north to merge in the great nexus of the Low Countries where there is still a slight interruption with lower density on the sandy plain of the Campine or Kempenland ; but taken together this block, enclosing Westphalia, most of Netherlands and Belgium together with the northern corner of France is the most populous part of Europe.

In France the ' Rhine zone ' is fairly well defined on the west by a more sparsely peopled belt, and the ' hill-foot zone' is delimited on the plain by the more purely agricultural but less fertile land of the fluvio-glacial deposits, where large properties till recently emphasised the reduction in farming population. But Berlin and its satellites stand out amid this rural zone, and so does the strip along the Elbe, to link with Hamburg and Bremen and the intensively used coastal reclamations. Since 1946 there has been a marked difference in density on similar land on the two sides of the boundary of occupation owing to the settlement of refugees on the west, and particularly north of the Elbe in Schleswig-Holstein.

In Britain high densities of population mark the English lowland except the south-west and an area centred on the Wash, while the most urbanised tract lies across the country from the Humber to Lancastria and narrows southward in the Midlands ; it is still just separate from the outer satel-lites of London. This London area covers some 1,200 square miles (over 3,000 sq. km.), and is larger than the three outlying districts situated on the coalfields of South Wales, Northumbria and mid-Scotland.

The central block of European population is flanked on the east and north by a larger block of more dispersed population and, on the west and south, from Ireland to the Aegean Sea, by another and much smaller ; these two will now be described in turn.

Northern and Eastern Europe

Northern and eastern Europe beyond the limit of the central block consists of plains, except for the Carpathians, the Scandinavian highlands and the Ural and Caucasus Mountains ; therefore variations in the density of population, like those of soil, climate and vegetation, are more gradual than in the rest of the continent. The rapid growth of industries in the U.S.S.R., with greatly expanded towns in some parts, tends to alter the simplicity of the pattern ; but this may still be described as a wedge of greater population, broadest between the Baltic Sea and the Danube and narrowing across European Russia. The axis trends about east-north-east from the upper basin of the Prut to the central Urals, passing through the belt of rich soils. The chief interruptions in the wedge are the Carpathians and the marshes of the Pripet ; by far the greater mass of the Russian people still live west of the Volga within the wedge, but this now has an extension south-eastward to embrace the Caucasus. The presence of the Baltic Sea, again, is clearly favourable and population is dense near its western entrances. Moreover, as a result of the ancient geological structure of Fennoscandia and its post-glacial history, there is a populous zone along the sixtieth parallel which includes three capital cities and Leningrad ; the bodies of water reduce the rigours of winter and give access, while central Sweden has good soils derived from silts of the former lake. Apart from this zone settled population is concentrated mainly on the coasts, in Norway largely from the fishing, and on the Gulf of Bothnia from lumbering. For the latter reason, too, thin filaments extend up the rivers, or in northern Russia down the rivers. Thus, north of latitude 60°—but in Norway, the Arctic Circle—there are lands of modern and sparse colonisation along the coasts and rivers. But there are also mining settlements exceptionally placed and served by railways, such as the two sources of iron in Swedish Lapland, those of iron and copper pyrites at Meldalen in Norway and Outokumpu in Finland, and of apatite (phosphate) near Kirovsk in the Kola Peninsula. Colonies again, though not modern, are found as European outposts overseas and beyond 60° : the Zetland Isles, the Faroe Isles and Iceland, all dependent on fishing and their sheep, with Iceland acquiring new importance from its position on the Atlantic air route. Finally Spitsbergen has a small modern colony of coalminers in latitude 78°.

The southern flank of the main wedge of population also bears many traces of its history of colonisation, and beyond the lower courses of the Don and Volga there is still a pioneer fringe ; but from the Sea of Azov, as already mentioned, continuous agricultural settlement now links with the ancient communities of the Caucasus. With the completion of the irrigation works on the lower Volga population will soon spread eastward of the river. Finally, the pattern of settlement on the plains of the middle and lower Danube has been alluded to in an earlier chapter as due to colonisation in the last two centuries.

The greater part of the area, in which the main body of population in eastern Europe was found, was devastated in the years that followed the census of January 1939 in the U.S.S.R. Moreover, although the reproduction rate in Russia before 1939 was higher than in any other part of Europe, authorities on demography believe the vast losses in the war are likely to have been replaced only about 1952. This fact might seem to be convenient for the present purpose, but there must have been considerable changes in the distribution of the people since the last census. The wholesale removal of factories and their workers to places in or beyond the Urals is well known, and so, too, is the progressive collectivisation of agriculture ; the latter process freed manpower for industry, but not necessarily in the same region.

Between the south Baltic coast and the Rivers Sava and Danube over half the population is made up by the Poles and Germans not already counted in the central block, together with the populations of Slovakia, Hungary,

Romania and Yugoslavia north of the rivers. Beyond this mosaic of peoples lies the population of the present Soviet territory in Europe. Throughout the plains within and around the Carpathians and thence within the wedge across Russia to the middle Volga, tracts that have for long been devoted to agriculture, there is a fairly evenly spread rural population which with that of the 'country towns' shows densities between 125 and 250 per square mile, but above this in southern Poland and the best parts of Ukraine. To the north of the main wedge, whose limit may be taken as a line joining Gorki to Tarnopol, the density is much lower, and it becomes also irregular according to conditions of the soil and its drainage. Owing, however, to the presence of large towns some areas are much more populous. The central industrial region of Russia stands out in this respect, and most of it lies outside the wedge of high rural population, being embraced by the Oka and the upper Volga. It contains Moscow, with over 4 millions by 1939 and a score of big towns holding as many more between them. Yet this region is nearly as large as England, and the towns are generally at least 50 miles (80 km.) apart. Like all Russian towns they grew rapidly before the war, especially those on the Volga which trebled or more. But the greatest collections of towns are the two groups in the Ukraine and south of the zone of high rural density ; they lie within the lower bends of the Dneper and the Donets-Don respectively. By 1939 three of these towns were five times larger than in 1926, and many more had doubled or trebled. Two similar but outlying groups of towns are those of the Urals and of the Caucasus, while the other notable series are the four lying along the main axis of population : Kiev, Kharkov, Voronezh and Kazan on the Volga, from which another string follows the river downstream. Since the German invasion reached a front extending from Leningrad and west of Moscow to Stalingrad and the central Caucasus, all the towns of Ukraine and many others in the west had to be repopulated, if not virtually refounded.

Western and Southern Europe

And now to consider how the population of western and southern Europe is distributed. Western France, as here excluded from the central block, comprises about three-fifths of the country but less than half the population. This is least dense in the western part of the Paris Basin, the northern flanks and the highest parts of the Central Plateau, the Landes and the Pyrenees. The higher densities occur on the Armorican coasts, where there is dependence on the sea as well as intensive agriculture ; the valley of the Loire up to Orleans ; a string of local concentrations from La Rochelle eastwards in the plateau ; and the wine districts of Gironde and Languedoc. On the whole this distribution corresponds to agricultural conditions.

The Iberian Peninsula has the great bulk of its population near the coasts, the exceptions being that of Madrid and the valleys of the Guadalquivir and the Ebro ; and so the dependence upon water for agriculture is plain—rainfall on the Atlantic sides, in the east rainfall greatly supplemented by irrigation. Both sides have examples of very high agricultural densities, but in Catalonia and the Basque Provinces manufactures are a partial cause, as is fishing in the north-west. Both Portugal and Spain have high reproduction rates, and Galicia and northern Portugal are over-populated ; these, along with the Biscayan lands, have long furnished the majority of the emigrants who have peopled the Americas.

The part of Italy included in the central block amounts to nearly a third of the area with over a third of the inhabitants. Hence the Peninsula, here regarded as including Emilia but not Liguria, and the islands are nearly as populous as the north. Yet except in central Italy industry is not an important cause of the high densities ; this is a mainly agricultural people, working intensively where this is possible and elsewhere living at a low standard. The Iberian densities are exceeded in Sicily and several coastal parts of the mainland, as well as in the British islands of Malta and Gozo. In Italy, and especially the south, the large family continues to be the ideal, and it was encouraged by the government until 1945. In consequence of this and the economic conditions the south suffers from over-population, and unfortunately the outlet of emigration which was very large at the beginning of this century is no longer available.

The Balkan Peninsula, south of the Danube and Sava, is roughly equal to Spain in area and exceeds it in population. Because of the relief the distribution is patchy, and owing partly to the effect of former Turkish rule many rugged areas are surprisingly populous ; moreover, on the mainland the coastal strips are often thinly peopled. But the three large cities, Athens-Piraeus, Istanbul and Belgrade, are on the periphery, and in Greece many islands and coastal towns depend upon commerce. Intensive fruit and tobacco growing accounts for concentrations on small plains that match those in Italy, but the three marginal lowlands that compare in area with the plain of northern Italy are not nearly as populous ; these are eastern Thrace with the basin of the Maritsa, the Bulgarian tableland, and the fringe of Serbia and Bosnia. Nevertheless these lowlands have too many people dependent on agriculture, and, in view of the high rate of reproduction prevailing among Balkan peoples, further industrial development is badly needed. The distribution of population changed materially with the retreat of the Turkish rulers from the accessible plains, and this was accentuated in Greece by the exchange of population after 1923, which added over a million who were settled mainly on the plains of Macedonia but also served to increase the size of certain towns, especially Athens.

The Borderlands

To complete this survey of population it remains to review the Borderlands. Anatolia resembles the Iberian Peninsula in the arrangement of its population which is strikingly coastal, except for the southern coast which in its sparseness has no Iberian counterpart. One-third of the population of Asian Turkey live in the fifteen provinces that line the north and west coasts as a narrow fringe; the remainder is rather evenly but thinly peopled, but exceptionally sparsely in the Armenian highlands. This distribution obviously reflects agricultural opportunity, but also the relative backwardness of regions not naturally favoured. Much less is known about the population of Iran, but it is probably smaller than that of Turkey. Iran includes a large area occupied by nomads, and the bulk of the settled farmers are found in the north-west, notably on the slope to the Caspian Sea which resembles the nearest coast of Anatolia both physically and in its agriculture. But Azerbaidzhan is also well peopled, with a density greater than that of Soviet Armenia to the north and much greater than in the neighbouring part of Turkey. Adjoining these highlands on the south is the Assyrian part of Iraq, among the foothills of the Zagros; as the rainfall here exceeds 15 inches (380 mm.), this is the most populous part of the kingdom, with over a third of the total in less than a sixth of the area. Most of the remainder are either in Baghdad or are widely distributed near the rivers of the lower plain.

The settled part of the Levant now included in the four states, Syria, Lebanon, Israel and Jordan, supports a population of whom nearly a third live in twelve large towns, thus indicating the persistence of ancient commercial tradition, since their origin like that of other smaller places is prehistoric. The rural population varies greatly in density with soil and water, and this applies also to the half million inhabitants of Cyprus. In Israel immigrant Jews are crowded on the best land, while one-third of the Arabs of Jordan are refugees from the former state of Palestine.

The delta and valley of the Nile in Egypt, about 13,000 square miles (34,000 sq. km.) of precious cultivated land have practically the entire agricultural population, together with other 3 millions in Cairo and Alexandria; except along the Suez Canal the remaining population of Egypt is negligible. This teeming peasantry has no parallel for concentration and is hard to match for its dangerous fecundity; their density in the southern part of the delta and along the valley is from 1,500 to 2,000 per square mile (580 to 770 per sq. km.).

The future of the peoples of those Bridgelands of Asia is closely bound up with their economic and social status, including conditions of health and their attitude to their predominantly Muslim religion. They are more prolific than the Europeans. While vital statistics are unsatisfactory, it would appear that the birth rate increases generally eastward and southward from about 37 in the Aegean coastlands to 60 or more per 1,000 in Arabia, and that the natural increase lies between 12 and 17 despite the low standards of nutrition, hygiene and literacy and the toll taken by epidemics. Egypt is a special case that is better known. Its population of 6·8 millions in 1882 had doubled by 1917, and more than trebled by 1952. The probable birth and death rates in 1937 were 57 and 44, and the demographers expect an increase of over 40 per cent with each generation ; and this despite the ravages of the parasitic diseases hookworm and bilharzia associated with the irrigated fields. Here then the term population-pressure has exceptional meaning ; the fertility of the fields is insufficient to cope with that of the people.

From the Nile to the Gulf of Gabès the desert with its nomads prevails except for the upland of Cyrenaica and the coastal oasis of Tripoli, where Italian colonial effort before 1940 extended the opportunity of settled life. But relatively this is a void. Thus the Atlas lands represent a substantial outpost not only of Islam and the Arabic language of which this is the extreme domain, but also of France. The total population is comparable with that of Egypt or of Turkey. The European minority, mostly French, has been very important in the economic development. For climatic reasons the density of population declines inward from the coasts, but, while the settled areas are broad at the two ends, in Tunisia and eastern Algeria and in Morocco west of the Middle Atlas Mountains the central part is narrow, with nomadic life prevailing upon the interior plateau. The distribution is most uniform in Morocco with its relatively monotonous relief apart from the mountains ; elsewhere, and for similar reasons, it is patchy as in the Balkan Peninsula, fruit-growing leading to the greatest concentrations.

Thus the Borderlands are seen to sustain population broadly in proportion to the water that is available for agriculture, a question of rainfall and evaporation except in Egypt and southern Iraq which are watered by alien rivers. Because of this physical factor the film of humanity is discontinuous and takes the form of zones and narrower strips. Agricultural and pastoral surplus, coupled here and there with mineral production leads to commerce, which is seated in the towns. Manufactures are but slightly developed, but from the rate at which these peoples multiply it is evident that the creation of industries is most desirable.

The distribution of population has been described, with but little reference to the processes of migration and accelerated reproduction that lie behind it. We may reasonably adopt the assumption of a gradual spread and increase of mankind, following more or less the directions taken by the progress of civilisation westwards, northwards and then eastwards, but the occurrence of setbacks must also be recognised, to be ascribed generally to disease, famine and war.   Outstanding examples are the epidemics of plague, the Hundred Years War in France, the Thirty Years War in Germany and the two World Wars.   Moreover, periods of insecurity have had specially dire effects in parts of the Mediterranean lands and their borders, where ability to make the most of restricted water supply depends upon powerful organisation, as notably in Mesopotamia.

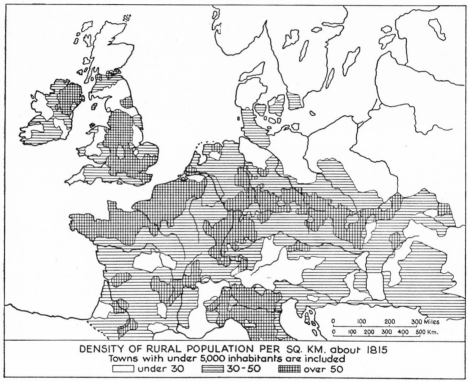

DENSITY OF RURAL POPULATION PER SQ. KM. about 1815
Towns with under 5,000 inhabitants are included
☐ under 30   ☰ 30-50   ▥ over 50

FIG. 37

Population Changes since 1815

An attempt must be made to examine the changes that have taken place during the past century or more, in so far as these are recorded statistically, since these have obvious bearing upon the present regional characteristics. Data are limited to western and central Europe, and these have been analysed for the period 1815 to 1925 by H. Haufe,[1] whose maps have been simplified

[1] H. Haufe, *Die Bevölkerung Europas, Stadt und Land, in den 19ten und 20ten Jahrhunderten,* Berlin, 1936

here as Figs. 37, 38, 39, in order to present the more outstanding facts clearly.
Fig. 37 shows in three grades the density of population in 1815 after elimination of towns with over 5,000 inhabitants, i.e. essentially rural population.
Incidentally this has some general value for the appreciation of conditions
prevailing during the two previous centuries, except in the case of Britain
where the Industrial Revolution wrought great changes in the eighteenth
century. But in France and Flanders this general distribution had probably

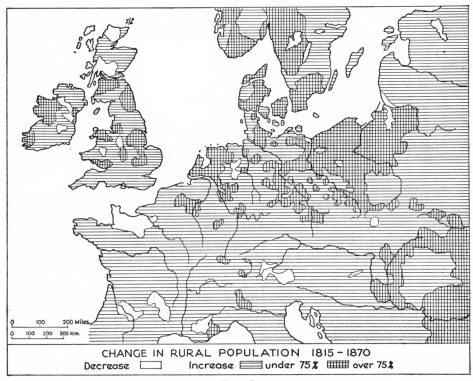

CHANGE IN RURAL POPULATION 1815 – 1870
Decrease ☐   Increase ☰ under 75% ▦ over 75%

Fig. 38

been established since the end of the Middle Ages, while throughout central
Europe the devastation of the Thirty Years War had retarded the growth
of population ; at this date France was still the greatest power, with about
one-fifth of the population of Europe, less Russia. In studying this and the
following figures it must be realised that they are cartograms with political
boundaries limiting the shadings, so that the influence of physical features is
often blurred. But this does not apply to Fig. 40, showing the towns by size,
which, of course, completes the picture for 1815. There were already two
axes of great population, the one from northern Ireland by the Rhinelands

to northern Italy, the other from Brittany to the upper Vistula, and these intersect in Flanders, and both belts included areas with over 100 per square kilometre (260 per sq. mile). Of the marked concentrations of towns two were old, in Italy and Flanders, and one new, in England; the sparseness of towns in the east is notable. Moderate rural densities appear around the Danish islands, then a corn-growing district; in France the less populated

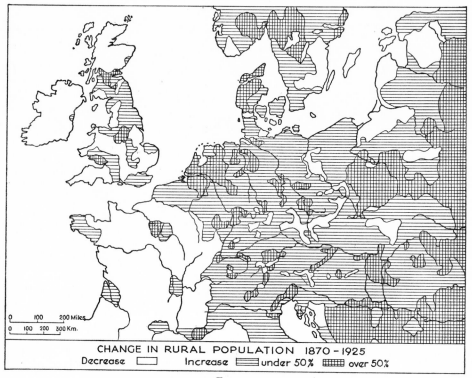

CHANGE IN RURAL POPULATION 1870 – 1925
Decrease ☐   Increase ☷ under 50% ☷ over 50%

Fig. 39

central belt with few towns coincides with the ancient cultural division between the north and the south. On the whole the rural densities reflect the status of agriculture and, as in Brittany and Cornwall, dependence on the sea, but sparseness in some areas like the Danubian plains tells also of delay in colonisation of fertile land, and in England effects of industrialisation are traceable on both maps.

In Fig. 38 certain facts about the movement of rural population in the fifty-five years following are represented, the population of towns with less than 10,000 inhabitants in 1870 being counted as rural; the distributions are shown of areas that suffered absolute decline in population, and on the

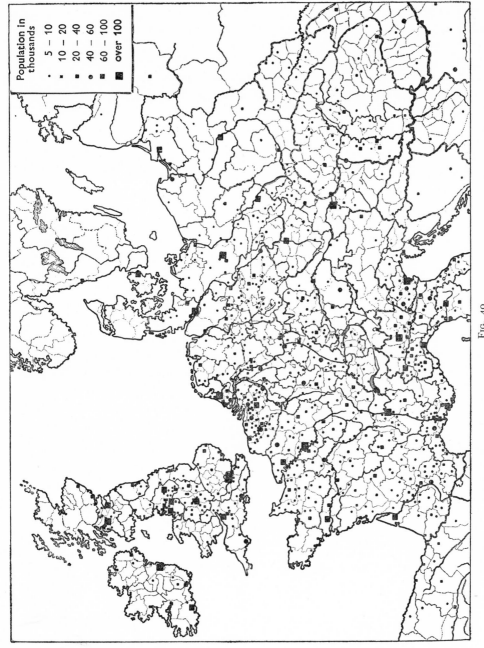

Population in
thousands
•   5 – 10
✕   10 – 20
▪   20 – 40
●   40 – 60
◉   60 – 100
▦   over 100

FIG. 40
Distribution of towns *circa* 1815

other hand those which gained by more than three-quarters. Thus only the more outstanding changes appear. The remaining tracts are marked either by virtual stagnation or less pronounced growth, and such are found both upon the poorer lands and on those that already had nearly as large a quota as they could support. The spectacular changes were evidently those of colonisation backed by high birth rates in the eastern parts of central Europe. This is notable first on the plain between the Elbe and the Neman, where the development of large estates was accompanied by the growth of efficient agriculture on poor as well as on good land, and it concerned mainly German territory ; stagnation in Russia is probably attributable to conditions of land tenure. Next, there is the colonisation of forest in Sweden, Norway and the Ardennes, while in Denmark, north-western Germany, the Netherlands and eastern England reclamation and intensification of farming are reflected in the rapid increase of population. Again, on the plains beyond the Carpathians the black earth was progressively occupied and similarly the eastern part of the Hungarian plain. In western Germany, already marked by long-developed peasant farming, there was little opportunity for increase save in the towns, but the effect of industrial development is none the less apparent in Thuringia, Saxony and the Rhineland. In Britain the pull of the cities and the coalfields can be traced. Ireland experienced famine and emigration with a general decline following, but the changes indicate increasing congestion in the west and decline in some of the previously over-populated counties. While most of France continued to show very slow rural advance along with migration to the towns there was absolute decline in Normandy which lost much of its rural textile industry, and on some of the poorer lands of the south. In the Alps there is indication of the onset of depopulation, beginning in the driest parts or the most remote glens.

It is unfortunately impossible to show the growth of towns on a map of small scale, but the process of urbanisation is revealed in a general way by the two graphs (Figs. 41 and 42) showing the growth of total population by countries or groups of countries and the proportions of these living in towns. The period 1815-1925 is divided at 1870 to correspond to the two cartograms of rural population movement. It is obvious that Europe as a whole was filling up more rapidly after 1870 ; the rate of total increase became greater in all countries except France, Spain and Portugal, vastly greater in Russia following the emancipation of the serfs in 1861, and predominantly rural, as rapid urbanisation was still delayed. But in nearly all other countries this process was accelerated, and especially in Germany after the formation of the Empire. In Britain, on the other hand, it was slowing up. All this must be kept in mind in studying the changes in rural density from 1870 to 1925 (Fig. 39) ; in this case, however, towns with less than 15,000 inhabitants in

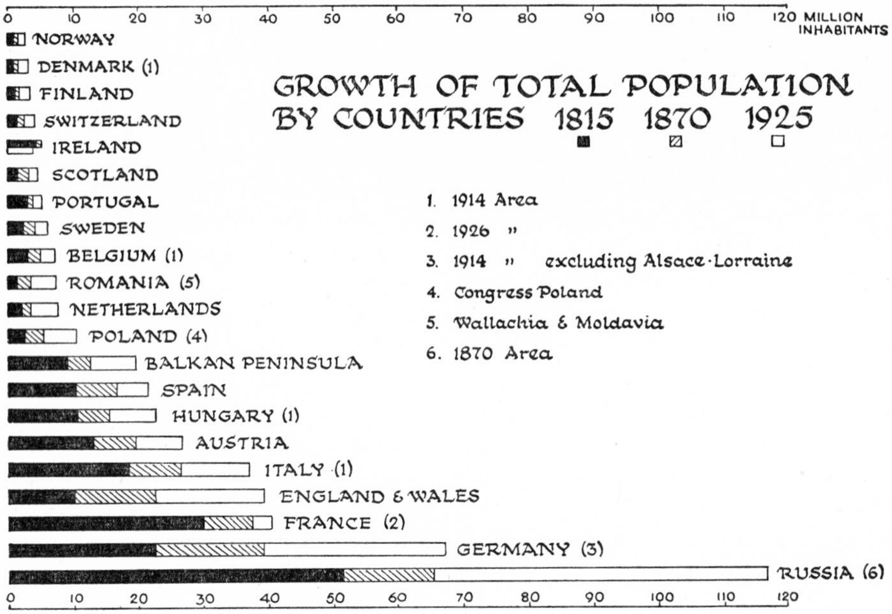

0   10   20   30   40   50   60   70   80   90   100   110   120 MILLION INHABITANTS

◼️ NORWAY
◼️ DENMARK (1)
◼️ FINLAND
◼️ SWITZERLAND
◼️ IRELAND
◼️ SCOTLAND
◼️ PORTUGAL
◼️ SWEDEN
◼️ BELGIUM (1)
◼️ ROMANIA (5)
◼️ NETHERLANDS
◼️ POLAND (4)
◼️ BALKAN PENINSULA
◼️ SPAIN
◼️ HUNGARY (1)
◼️ AUSTRIA
◼️ ITALY (1)
◼️ ENGLAND & WALES
◼️ FRANCE (2)
◼️ GERMANY (3)
◼️ RUSSIA (6)

GROWTH OF TOTAL POPULATION BY COUNTRIES 1815 1870 1925

◼️   ▨   ☐

1. 1914 Area
2. 1926 "
3. 1914 " excluding Alsace·Lorraine
4. Congress Poland
5. Wallachia & Moldavia
6. 1870 Area

0   10   20   30   40   50   60   70   80   90   100   110   120

FIG. 41

0   10   20   30   40   50   60   70   80   90   100 PERCENTAGE

◼️ RUSSIA (6)
◼️ GALICIA
◼️ ROMANIA (5)
◼️ FINLAND
◼️ HUNGARY (1)
◼️ PORTUGAL
◼️ NORWAY
◼️ AUSTRIA
◼️ POLAND (4)
◼️ SWEDEN
◼️ IRELAND
◼️ SWITZERLAND
◼️ SPAIN
◼️ DENMARK (1)
◼️ ITALY (1)
◼️ FRANCE (2)
◼️ BELGIUM (1)
◼️ NETHERLANDS
◼️ GERMANY (3)
◼️ SCOTLAND
◼️ ENGLAND & WALES

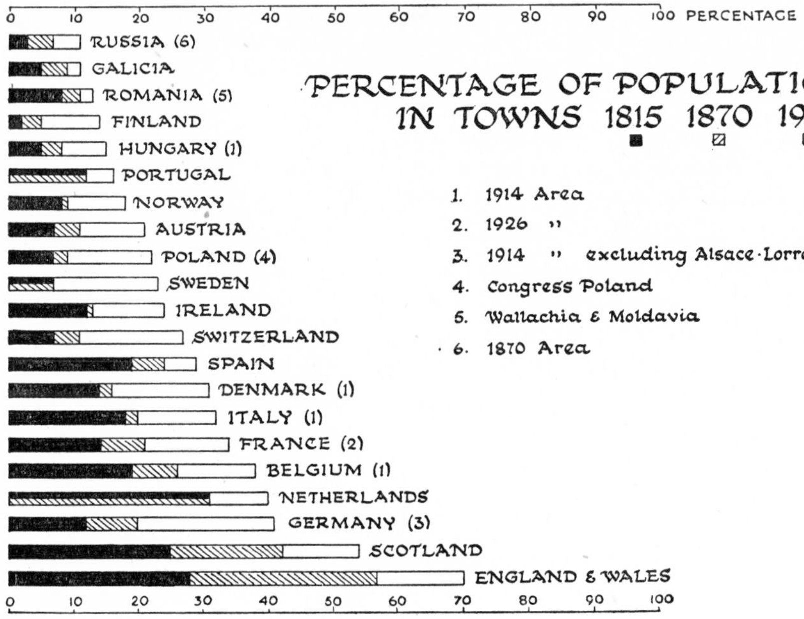

PERCENTAGE OF POPULATION IN TOWNS 1815 1870 1925

◼️   ▨   ☐

1. 1914 Area
2. 1926 "
3. 1914 " excluding Alsace·Lorraine
4. Congress Poland
5. Wallachia & Moldavia
6. 1870 Area

0   10   20   30   40   50   60   70   80   90   100

FIG. 42

1925 are included with the rural population. The shadings indicate absolute decline and also increase, this time by more than 50 per cent. The great contrast is that between west and east. Decrease prevails in Ireland, much of Britain and most of France, the causes being urbanisation and falling birth-rate, along with emigration from Ireland and Scotland. In contrast to this, high natural increase is an important cause of growth in the parts of Russia and the Balkan Peninsula included in the cartogram. The continued colonisa-tion of the Hungarian plain is evident, this time most marked on the central more sandy part ; while the effect of the improvement of land along with the growth of industry in small towns is seen in the Netherlands and eastern Belgium, and of further reclamation in Jutland. Agricultural improvements, too, had similar effects in Venetia and Emilia. In Germany the changes shown are doubtless in the main due to the spread of manufactures, leading to rural decline in parts of the plain, notably in East Prussia and along the Oder and to increases near the industries. Depopulation of the mountains and lower plateaus has set in among the Alps and western Carpathians, in Bohemia and Franconia, but is balanced by growth in many of the adjoin-ing lowlands.

Russia did not keep pace with the rest of Europe during the first period under review, but by 1897, when the first reliable imperial census was taken, the population of the European part was 87 millions, and the peasants from about 1880 had been freer to move to new land. The cartogram of total population (Fig. 42), therefore, shows, if somewhat crudely, the existing wedge of density well developed, although the eastern fringes were not yet as well peopled as were the poorer parts of France in 1815 ; but this spread of rural population had been accomplished before the census of 1926. The following period was marked in the U.S.S.R. by the agricultural reformation which while increasing the cultivated land led to an absolute decrease in rural popula-tion, most marked where mechanisation was most highly developed. Thus large numbers of people became available for manufacturing and for public works, and so a vast increase of urban population ensued. It seems likely that some 25 millions settled in the towns of the Soviet Union, and the growth of many of these places was indeed spectacular. Forty-eight towns with over 50,000 at the second census had trebled in size by 1939, thirty-one of them being in the European part of the Union, and of these seventeen had quad-rupled. While there was great expansion of Moscow, Leningrad, Kiev and many administrative centres, the urbanisation is the result of the planned impulses of the mining, metallurgical and engineering industries as compared with those making consumer goods. Hence the process was most marked in the Ukraine, the Urals and the newer oil districts of the south-east.

In the period 1820–1939 Europe lost about 70 million inhabitants by emigration overseas, nearly half of them to build up the population of the U.S.A. The greater part of these emigrants came from the outer countries, 18 millions from Great Britain, 7 millions from Germany, 6 millions from Italy, and most striking are the losses of the small nations ; Ireland sent 5 millions or the equivalent of the present population, Norway and Sweden 2 millions, while 1·5 million went from Portugal to Brazil. The effect of such emigration, mainly of younger people, is of course to be seen in the structure of the population left behind, a matter to be treated below, while a less measurable consequence is the loss of a proportion of the adventurous types. Throughout the century the sources of this westward current moved gradually inwards to reach the Slavonic groups, including the Russian ; but the greater emigration from Russia ultimately flowed eastward. The main stream originated in White Russia and with gathering volume in the central provinces populated Siberia, and a lesser stream from the Ukraine reached central Asia. Down to the Russian Revolution these had taken perhaps 5 millions into Asia, or 9 millions if those settling in Caucasian districts be counted.

This emigration represents long-continued movements of people. But the two World Wars were to set up displacements of a different order, and the lasting effects of these can scarcely be foreseen. This is hardly the place to relate the story of upheaval and eviction, movement and counter-movement which affected the people of many countries and led to years of mass misery. It has been estimated that from 1939 to the beginning of 1943 more than 30 million people had to leave their homes in Europe for longer or shorter periods, apart of course from the fighting forces ; and these waves of migration continued on a great scale to the end of the war, and on a smaller scale in the years following. No doubt it was largely the same unfortunate 30 millions who were involved in the later waves. These are important events in European history which happily concluded for many of those involved when with international aid they were repatriated ; and this chapter on the geography of population must be concerned only with the considerable minority who have been unable or unwilling to return.

The chief permanent migrations dating from the aftermath of the First War were those of Greeks and Turks referred to earlier, and that of the Russians who emigrated at the Revolution, chiefly to France. In 1937 there were 356,000 of these still unassimilated in western Europe. Between the wars there were about 500,000 emigrants from Germany, Italy, Spain and Portugal who left for political or religious reasons. By 1950 all of these still classed as refugees were reckoned as under half a million. However, by that year there were about a million of various groups other than German who had been displaced for political reasons after the Second War, together with 600,000 Greeks homeless in their own country as a result of the civil war. Vastly greater than these movements is the new concentration of the German people, and it presents a serious problem for Europe. Within a decade the results of a millenium of German expansion have been annulled. The descendants of the miners, craftsmen, peasants and merchants who were the pioneers of the western world from the Middle Ages have been forced back to the land of their ancestors. Thus before the war there were about a million Germans in Russia, including the 600,000 of the (German) Soviet Republic of the Volga, half a a million in Yugoslavia and a quarter-million in Transylvania. But the main body lived more or less in contact with Germany in Czechoslovakia, Poland and the Baltic States ; moreover, the number is increased by the westward shift of Polish territory. The result in 1950 was the addition of 11·8 million Germans from beyond the frontiers and only 4 millions of these were in the Soviet Zone ; furthermore, movements from this zone had added 1·3 millions more or 9·1 millions in all to the population of western Germany, and this infiltration had not ceased. The absorption and employment of this mass of people, to say nothing of their housing, presented an immense problem to the Republic.

Age Groups

So far all the matters discussed have referred to the total numbers of people enumerated in censuses ; but there remains the important question of the structure of the population in regard to age. Until 1914 the peoples of Europe multiplied at more or less steady rates, although countries were far from equal in the rates of growth, and this resulted in populations in which the proportions declined regularly from that of the infants to that of the oldest.

Fig. 43, plotted from computations made for the League of Nations,[1] shows the age and sex structures of nine selected nations in 1940 with the percentages of total population, male and female, falling in each age-group of five years. The countries evidently belong to three distinct categories. Italy, Spain and Netherlands come near to the regular structure of population, although with some recent decline in the proportion of the youngest groups. These pyramids may be compared with the broken lines inserted for nations of the next category, Belgium, the British Isles and Sweden ; these lines represent more generally the structure prevailing from 1871 to 1880. But by 1940 the effect of decline in both birth and death rates in these countries and in France had produced the top-heavy structures of relatively old peoples, and the graphs resemble haystacks in shape. This change had taken place in France before 1880. Romania and the U.S.S.R. are examples of the third category, and stand out with the large proportion of the young, owing to maintenance of the

---

[1] *The Future Population of Europe and the Soviet Union : Population Projections, 1940–70.* League of Nations, Geneva 1944.

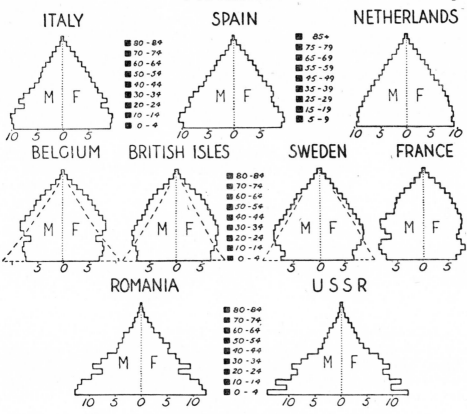

FIG. 43

Population Structure, Age and Sex, in 1940
Refers to period 1871–80

high birth rates characteristic of eastern Europe. The graphs for nations which participated in the First World War have irregularities due to war losses and reductions in births during the war, and this gives notably small populations between the ages 20 to 24 in 1940. The Russian population also shows the effect of famine and other post-war vicissitudes, while the Spanish Civil War doubtless reduced the lowest age group in Spain. If graphs were drawn for the populations in 1946 or a later year, they would reveal similarly the effects of the Second War.

CHAPTER 20

THE WHOLE AND THE PARTS

THIS book has been concerned with the study of phenomena as they are distributed over land and sea ; notice has been taken of the tendency of distributions to coincide, and there has often been some attempt at correlation or even causation. Thus geological causes have been invoked, however vaguely, to explain the distribution of land and sea, the varying depth of sea and height of land, the different types of relief and the occurrence of accessible minerals. The interpenetration of sea and land, again, has been shown to account for certain qualities and movements of the sea water and of the air, such as to modify the theoretical planetary circulation of these fluid elements. The turbulent air-masses moving over the land have certain average qualities, summed up as climate, which in turn are obviously related to the growth of plants and animals, and so to the distributions of vegetation and fauna ; but the exact bearings of these organic phenomena are somewhat obscure. This uncertainty is due partly to insufficient knowledge and partly to the fact that since the last Ice Age the advances and retreats of species, at least of plants, have been slower than the changes of climate ; moreover, man has interrupted the course of nature in various ways. The mantle rock, the skin of detritus that largely conceals the bedrock, owes its nature to lithologic and climatic causes together, while its composition and that of the vegetation past or present determine the qualities of its upper layer, the soil. It follows, then, that study and comparison of the geographic distribution of these clearly related natural phenomena lead to better understanding not only of the processes involved but also, when taken together, of the environment of man.

With phenomena concerned with mankind the matter is infinitely more complex, for at all stages human beings have been able to exercise some choice in the response to conditions imposed by nature. For the ruling groups or castes in ancient times the choice was widened by the universal practice of slavery. The oldest monuments of civilisation around the Mediterranean and in the Bridgelands of Asia were built by this forced labour, and the erection of those monuments in the kingdoms of the rivers was favoured by the existence of slack seasons in agriculture imposed by the rivers themselves, from April to October in Egypt and probably September to January in Mesopotamia.

In the Middle Ages the choice was restricted by feudalism which prevailed while the attractive parts of Europe were becoming fully settled and devoted to agriculture, yet this period gave to posterity fine churches and cathedrals built as a labour of faith. It is because Europe changed so little until the Industrial Revolution that the man-made part of the landscape still derives many of its distinguishing traits from the Middle Ages or even from earlier times. Nevertheless, all parts were subject to external human influences, whose effects are still stamped upon town and countryside, the degree varying with that of accessibility. Hence it has seemed valuable to discuss some of these elements of progress, however cursorily, in order to appraise their effect on the present. It is often possible to perceive generally the order in which the various marks of man were imposed, and likewise to realise that, perhaps because evolution was slow, there is a certain harmony between the natural and the cultural elements of the scene, the result of the process of learning to make the best use of different kinds of land by means of simple techniques. Much research by the methods of historical geography is needed before the various elements of the rural landscape can be clearly distinguished according to their relative ages. But the modern features are usually clearly imposed upon old patterns ; in many areas they partly conform although functionally hampered by them, while in others they either obliterate or show harsh disregard for the earlier marks of settlement and traffic. Most prominent are the numerous industrial and commercial towns that have grown with manufactures, commerce and administration, and with them the intricate nets of their communications. But between the meshes of the latter the countryside may also present a new appearance in response to the need of the towns for foodstuffs, and it has to be noted that in the exceptional cases of Flanders and northern Italy this was a medieval conversion. The Agricultural Revolution of the eighteenth and nineteenth centuries greatly increased the contrast in rural economy and productivity between the north-west and the Mediterranean lands. Thus the aspect of country and town alike came to reflect the rapid growth of population, the acceleration in all human activities induced by inventions, and the new power to break down isolating barriers. Local self-sufficiency has given place to interdependence of districts, countries and continents ; but this has not happened equally throughout Europe and the Borderlands. The modern changes originating in Britain and the adjoining parts of the mainland have spread towards the south and the east, and with less effect in those directions until the recent rise of Soviet Russia.

THE MAJOR REGIONS

At this point we may turn from the method of pursuing phenomena, natural or human, simple or complex, over the whole territory and give attention to the salient features in the geography of the several large parts or regions that compose it. In this way it is easier to grasp the effect of integration. This involves the problem of dividing the territory in a way which will bring out well-marked regional differences and at the same time correspond to real unity within the region in respect of the leading aspects of its geography.

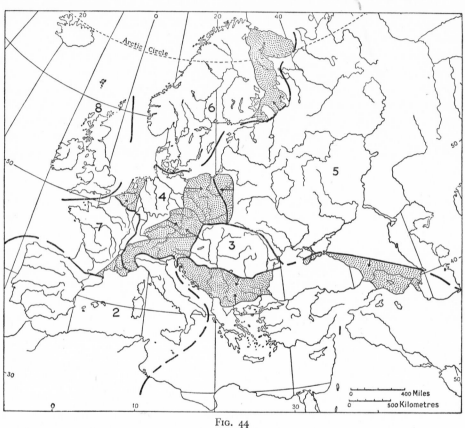

FIG. 44
The Major Regions

1 Eastern Bridgelands	4 Central Europe	7 France
2 Western Mediterranean Lands	5 Eastern Plain	8 British Isles and
3 Danubian Lands	6 Scandinavian Lands	the Northern Isles

Nature offers no well-marked boundaries except the shoreline, but there are many zones in which the natural phenomena change in their intensity within a narrow space. This applies also to many 'human' distributions, such as density of population, while linguistic areas are often marked by linear boundaries, whether these are also political frontiers or not. In the present phase of human relations nationality has great importance, so the boundaries of sovereign states must be respected in determining the extent of the various major regions we seek to delimit. But since the purpose is to recognise only the salient characteristics of each region and not to describe it systematically, no detailed discussion of the boundaries will be attempted ; it will be shown indeed that it is more realistic to stress the importance of transitional zones. The entire territory will be treated broadly as divided into the eight major regions shown on Fig. 44 and the transitions and overlaps will be dealt with in the discussion of these. The Mediterranean lands and the Borderlands must first be treated as a whole and then as two regions, viz : (1) the Eastern Bridgelands and (2) the Western Mediterranean Lands. The others are : (3) the Danubian Lands ; (4) Central Europe ; (5) the Eastern Plain ; (6) the Scandinavian Lands ; (7) France ; (8) British Isles and the Northern Isles.

Each of these regions comprises the territory of one or more of the European nations, whose regard for their history is a leading factor in their national life. The place where each nation was formed, its core or nuclear area, has been plotted on Fig. 45 for reference in the sequel. It will be noted from the key to this map that the picture presented is historically a highly composite one, since the areas plotted achieved their national importance at very different periods, from the early centuries of our era, as in Scandinavia, to the nineteenth century, as in Italy and the Balkan Peninsula.

As a further prelude to the task of regional characterisation it will be useful to restate in briefest form some of the facts discussed in the earlier chapters. Europe has three sides, and is flanked on the east by the lowlands of Siberia and on the south overseas by habitable Borderlands. Its relief presents a threefold division : high near the Atlantic side, low in the centre and east, highest in the south as well as in two-thirds of the Borderlands. There are three main types of climate, of which the 'Mediterranean' alone has its limits well marked ; the physical and biological consequences of this climatic division need not be restated. European languages fall into three main groups : the Romance in the south but reaching to the English Channel ; the Teutonic in the north and centre, and the Slavonic in the east. Arabic, Berber, Turkish and Persian dominate the Borderlands. In the latter Islam is the chief religion, while European Christianity has been divided east from west, and in the west, again split by the Reformation. The centres of higher civilisation have developed progressively westward in the Mediterranean lands, and France has been a region of fusion for southern and northern cultures. Thence the progress was northward and eastward ; the independent cultural branch which reached Russia directly from the Greek world was affected repeatedly by influences from inner Asia. Medieval and Renaissance civilisation has left imprints that vary according to the region. The leading geographical factor in the growth of modern industry has been the sources of power from coal

and water. Hence its development was first directed along the zone of Carboniferous outcrops, from Britain through central Europe south of the plain ;
then, with hydro-electricity in turn, to the zone of high glaciated mountains
first in the south, next in Scandinavia, but finally to make use of great rivers
even where relief is slight, from France to Russia. The same period has seen

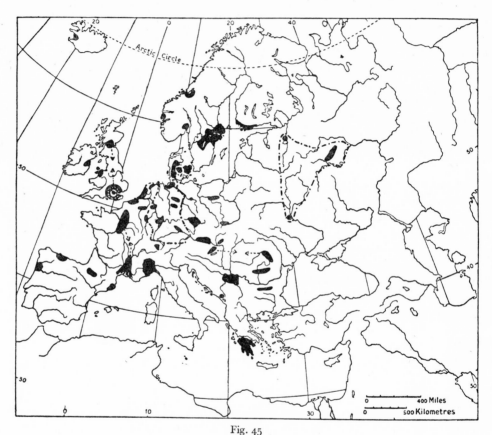

Fig. 45
Cores or Nuclear Areas of the Nations

the revolution in northern agriculture, vast increase in urban population,
growth of international trade and of the most favoured seaports, and the rise
of very large cities with world-wide commercial relations. But all this has
been repeatedly interrupted by wars which retarded harmonious economic
and social progress, intensified national mistrust and hatred and, in the case
of the two World Wars, caused immense destruction as well as forced migrations
that have greatly altered the composition of several nations and the ethnic
pattern of Europe and the Borderlands.

Explanation of Fig. 45

Iceland : Principal Norse settlement of tenth century ; independent 1918

Scotland : Nation formed in eleventh century ; union with England, 1707

England : United under Normans in eleventh century ; Wales : area of last resistance, thirteenth century

Ireland : Area containing seats of ' high kings ' till conquest by England, twelfth to sixteenth centuries. Eire independent 1937 (now Republic of Ireland)

Norway : Successive capitals Trondheim, Bergen, Oslo, eleventh to seventeenth centuries

Sweden : Svealand, extended by westward conquest of Gothland by fifth century

Finland : Part most affected by Swedish influence, fourteenth to eighteenth centuries

Denmark : Organised to control the straits by eighth century

Russia : Fluvial domain of Varangians or Rus, Novgorod and Kiev, ninth century, then Muscovy, twelfth century

Poland : Great Poland (in north), tenth century, Little Poland (in south), eleventh century

Netherlands : Holland and Zeeland, successful resistance to Spain, sixteenth century

Belgium : Flemish towns (County of Flanders, thirteenth century) and Walloon towns along Roman route ; united, 1830

Germany : The western part as under Charlemagne (814), with seven nuclei shown ; one, the Grand Duchy of Luxembourg independent, 1815. Berlin also as capital of Prussia and, from 1871, of Germany

Switzerland : The original Three Cantons and Luzern, 1332

Austria : The Ostmark of tenth century

Czechoslovakia : Core of Czech Kingdom of Bohemia, tenth century

France : The northern core lands of French crown in the ' Ile de France ', eleventh century ; and the southern core, not wholly in France until sixteenth century

Spain : Refuges from Moors in Asturias and Aragon ; these with Catalonia became sources of Crusading Reconquest from seventh century

Portugal : County of Portugal independent of León (Spain), eleventh century

Italy : Kingdom of Piedmont, which effected liberation of all Italy, 1859–71

The following relate to liberation from the Ottoman Empire :

Hungary : Refuges of Magyars in north-west and in Transilvania (now in Romania) leading to liberation, 1699

Yugoslavia : Montenegro unconquered, and Shumadiya, reconquered by Serbs, 1829

Romania : Southern foothills of Carpathians as refuge, pending liberation of Walachia 1829

Bulgaria : Northern foothills of Balkans as refuge, pending liberation, 1878

Greece : Peloponnese—war of liberation, 1821

Europe North of the Mediterranean

It is with considerations such as these in mind that Europe north of the Mediterranean must be divided for discussion on a regional basis. The most difficult tract to divide reasonably is the great plain. From its physical geography it seems to be divisible in two ways on account of two sets of distributions that intersect almost perpendicularly on the map. On the one hand there are those which depend ultimately upon the climates of the Ice Ages, moraines, marshes, sand-spreads and loess, all of which lie concentrically upon the Baltic, the great lakes and the White Sea. Furthermore, in harmony with the present climate of the south-east, and chiefly its aridity in summer, these same trends are paramount in the southern half of Russia. On the other hand, the main rivers flow transversely to these zones, although conforming to them in parts of their courses. Moreover, the northern winter becomes progressively colder from west to east, and then north-east. The responses of mankind to these composite natural patterns have not been simple, yet it is possible to recognise some of them clearly. The distributions of the chief agricultural crops may be correlated broadly with those of the climatic elements in the growing season and with the mantle rock and the soils ; thus with the roughly concentric zones. But the various peoples throughout their history have tended to be grouped along or near the rivers : Germans on the Rhine, Weser and Elbe ; Poles on the Warta, Vistula and Oder ; Lithuanians on the Neman ; Letts on the Daugava (Dvina) ; and Russians first on the Volkhov and Dnepr, and then on the Volga and Oka. Hence in the ethnic grouping of mankind the transverse divisions have prevailed, as is seen from the present frontiers ; nevertheless the former eastward colonisation by the Germans along the concentric zones already described and especially the Baltic coast has left many marks.

These relationships are simplest in Russia, and indeed east of the line between the mouths of the Vistula and Danube, which also marks the most rapid increase of continentality in climate ; while Poland, astride the Vistula, is in many respects transitional. West of this they are complicated, first because as the plain narrows the intricate system of hills and basins thrusts north and the latter invite deep penetration from the plain, and secondly because the North Sea and English Channel offer wide maritime contacts ; even more important are the land-gates from which western civilisation has permeated this part of the plain. For many reasons then hills and plain must be reviewed together as the essential central Europe, and this must include the Alps as a whole which, despite their height, have not prevented regular intercourse with Italy. The main basin of the Danube east of the Alps forms a striking geographical unit, and it will be treated as such, with due regard to the overlaps into regions already mentioned. Each of the three remaining parts of Europe has strong individuality : the Scandinavian lands and Finland ; France as the principal isthmus of Europe ; and finally the British and the northern Isles in their various degrees of isolation from the Continent. And division of this kind involves difficulties : transitions and mutual relations must never be forgotten.

THE MEDITERRANEAN AND THE BORDERLANDS

Despite notable diversity among the lands surrounding it the Mediterranean Sea is the element that unites southern Europe and most of the Borderlands. Its influence is both direct, as a medium for intercourse by sea, and indirect, through the climate associated with it, and with the Atlantic Ocean immediately to the west. The annual sequence of winter rain and summer drought is common to all the lands, and so, consequently, is the dependence upon tree fruits along with annual crops. Prolonged effort was needed to evolve Mediterranean agriculture and extend its practice to the limits of the climatic region from Iran to Portugal and Morocco. The spread of knowledge of agriculture as of the other features of the Mediterranean mode of life was no doubt encouraged by sea trading and of course by colonisation. The agricultural effort has been repaid amply where water has been adequate and soil retained, but throughout history the devastation of woodland has proceeded, soil has been lost at an increasing rate, and the ground-waters have receded from the surface. Consequently the resources in soil and water now vary considerably even over short distances, and it is mainly for this reason that the present distribution of population is so uneven, the ultimate cause thus being the ruggedness of relief.

Proximity of mountains to the coast, again, is almost as important as the presence of the sea ; the mountains have a cooler and wetter climate and, at least on the European side, a summer-green vegetation. Hence they offer a habitat complementary to the lowland, providing timber now sadly depleted, and herbage for flocks. The Mediterranean climate in its drier types prevails in the belt that fades into the desert—in the Atlas lands except where they face the sea or ocean abruptly, in Cyrenaica, and again along the Syrian saddle to Iran. In Europe the peninsulas are drier on their eastern sides, while Iberia and Anatolia have interior plateaus and basins with higher rims, and so with low rainfall and relatively great ranges of temperature. The plateau of Shotts amid the Atlas ranges is similar, while the much larger interior basins of Iran belong mainly to the saline desert.

At intervals in the past ' barbarian ' invaders have come over the northern mountains, Celts to Iberia, Lombards to Italy, Greeks and Slavs to the Balkan Peninsula. Others again have entered from the deserts to east and south, and so by renewal of the human stock they have surely contributed to the virility of peoples who were already subject to the stimuli of a seasonal climate and maritime intercourse. But all newcomers seem eventually to have adopted most of the ways of the older inhabitants, and the culture which, with its roots in the banks of the great rivers, absorbed much in turn from the Hittites, Hebrews and Phoenicians, Persians, Greeks and Romans. Christianity brought a new life-giving stream which, like the older elements, spread westward. But this religion was replaced throughout the Borderlands, with few exceptions, by the expansion of Islam six centuries later. The present state of large tracts of these southern lands in many respects may be attributed to the fact that they formed parts of great empires over long periods—Roman and Byzantine, Persian, Arabo-Berber and Ottoman. Release from the rule of the Ottoman Turks, which extended from the border of Morocco to the Persian Gulf, was not completed until after World War I when by the peace treaty in 1920 the Ottoman Empire in Europe disappeared.

It is unfortunately the evil effects of such systems of rule that are now most prominent, especially the persistence in many countries of large estates owned by absentee landlords, so that the countryside may be said to be dominated by the towns. Such areas are often used inefficiently, and there is a rural proletariat only partly employed and living in poverty. Other features may be traced to the chaotic conditions prevailing after the decay of these strong governments, such as the excessive concentration of people in large centres for reasons of defence against piracy, a nuisance that persisted to the early nineteenth century. But probably worst of all is the vicious complex of soil erosion, impeded drainage and malaria. Only within the past decade has this debilitating disease been eradicated from a few areas after a scientific combat ; Cyprus and Sardinia are examples. Unfortunately science can never eliminate the earthquakes which so often have ruined settlements and aggravated the havoc of erosion by starting landslides among the hills. This is equally true of volcanic eruptions, which, however, are much more local in their effect.

Within the past century three new factors have appeared to alter geographical relationships in these southern lands : the opening of the Suez Canal in 1869, and in this century the discovery and exploitation of oilfields, and the rise of nationalism among the peoples of the Borderlands. The ship canal gave the Mediterranean a new significance for the rest of the world. In particular British trade and imperial relations were involved, as her possession of Gibraltar and Malta and her relations with Egypt acquired new importance on strategic grounds. For the Mediterranean powers, Spain, France and Italy, too, military considerations came to weigh in their policies of controlling the coasts opposite their homelands. The extraction of oil at an increasing rate has both provided an unexpected source of wealth to Iran and the new Arab states, and brought them abruptly into the field of current power politics ; while the nationalism of various governments of Islamic and some other countries reflects in part a realisation of their strategic importance due to their geographical position. The influence exerted by these states abroad is generally greater than their populations would imply on account of the United Nations constitution.

The Borderlands beyond the sea on south and east differ from southern Europe in certain outstanding respects. Large tracts are singularly uniform in altitude and relief, and these parts merge gradually into the desert while much of the habitable land is semi-arid. Then the vast majority of the inhabitants are Muslim, and their traditions and outlook are oriental. The variation in climate leads to a gradation in mode of life ; at the one end of the scale are the true nomads who, being dependent on the camel, have a great range of movement ; their more numerous brethren who are shepherds are less mobile. At the other end are the settled cultivators living permanently in villages. Between these there are many varieties, some living mainly in tents but resident during a period of tillage and harvest, others are villagers who practise transhumance with their flocks. In general the ancient tribal organisation holds where movement predominates, and the nomads remain little affected by the central governments. Where the latter are strong the villagers no longer have reason to keep on good terms with the nomads, but the two groups are still interdependent since each needs some of the other's produce.

Throughout the Borderlands villages and towns, whether Muslim or not, have preserved social features somewhat akin to those of their medieval counterparts in Europe. Outwardly this is most obvious in the towns, where there are many occupations ; in these a whole street may be composed of the workshops or booths of a single trade. Less easy to discover is the hereditary nature of these trades and occupations, a trait which is weakening, though slowly, in the large cities under Western influence. The peoples of the Borderlands have now all experienced some aspect of modern European and even American influence and they have reacted to it in varying degrees. But in no case do they seem likely soon to renounce their way of life. They are ready to welcome the technical improvements that lead to economic progress and better health, to make use of educational and military opportunities and, more hesitantly, to imitate European systems of government and administration ; but the fundamental social conditions remain generally as they have been for the past twelve centuries or much longer. In overwhelming measure the people are dependent on agriculture, which, in the case of most families, means bare subsistence. The benefits of rural improvements introduced from Europe or America are too often neutralised by rapid increase of population, which tends to outgrow the food supply. So we are brought back to the purely geographical questions of available water, the menace of soil erosion on slopes, and on the flats those of incrustation by salts, the diseases malaria, bilharzia and hookworm and of plagues of locusts.

CHAPTER 21

THE EASTERN BRIDGELANDS

THIS designation of the lands around the eastern basin in Africa and Asia, together with the Balkan Peninsula, describes an important historic function : it emphasises the long history of migration, traffic and the communication of knowledge that has mattered greatly to Europe. For mass migration into Europe the main corridor, no doubt, has been the Russian steppe, but this barbarian route will be referred to in a later chapter. As one of the consequences of their history the Bridgelands contain a complicated assemblage of racial and ethnic types which are easily recognised by the traveller although their proper classification may elude him. These lands abound in architectural monuments of many ages, which reveal not merely the historic continuity of art, but also the geographic spread of the styles along the old roads while reflecting the ethnic contacts and the traditions of the builders and the adaptation of form to the materials available. For example, the most distinctive features of Byzantine architecture seem to have originated in eastern Iran and spread westward, to be adopted throughout the early Christian world. Byzantine churches later were turned into mosques, and a new Mohammedan style evolved from them was propagated eastward to Iran and beyond, as well as westward to Spain. The visitor still gets a vivid impression of the commerce of older times from the animal caravans, from the vigorous coasting trade in small sailing craft, or from studying the oriental methods of merchants in the towns, so different from those of Western business.

The region under review comprises two very different kinds of land : in the south low plateaus and plains, largely desert or semi-arid with the exception of the Syrian hills ; and in the north a zone of mountains and high plateaus. The greater ranges have an annual fall of rain and snow equivalent to at least 10 inches of rain, and more than 20 inches in those that face the Mediterranean and Black Seas. This mountainous zone extends from the Danube almost to the Indus, although interrupted by the narrow Hellespont. In its general shape it follows the trends of the rocks folded in the Tertiary era, but its present height and most of its details depend upon broad warping accompanied by severe dislocation of the crust, which is still going on, and very few parts are immune from devastating earthquakes. The zone is composed of two sweeping curves. The western one bulges to the south, but the convexity has been broken by transverse fractures that led to the formation of the Aegean and Marmara Seas, with drowned rivers forming the Straits and completing the break. The eastern curve is convex to the north, apparently owing to thrust by the rigid slab of Arabia ; and here the bulge is marked by great elevation in eastern Anatolia and Armenia, which becomes less in Iran as the zone widens. As already mentioned the inner parts of Anatolia and Iran have smooth surfaces in which the bedrock is largely concealed by the waste eroded from the mountains ; but elsewhere the zone is marked by the abrupt and often rugged edges of the dislocated blocks set in more or less geometric patterns, and also by the gorges of rivers which have been eroding inwards as the general uplift proceeded. These form barriers more often than easy routes. In places, again, volcanic action has accompanied the fracturing, and it has altered notably the surface of the highest tract, enclosing the great lakes of Armenia and raising imposing cones like Ararat. Various sections of the zone, in Asia, have formed the cores of historic empires older than those of Rome and Byzantium, notably the Hittite, Armenian, Medic and Persian— named not in historical but geographical order from west to east. Each of them seems to have required territory comprising both high well-watered mountains and a tract of plateau. The character of Armenia, unique in height, relief and rigorous climate, seems to have appealed only to the Armenians, who have lived there probably for millenia and preserved their highly distinctive qualities of body and culture. After massacres by their southern neighbours, the Kurds, they were expelled from Turkey in 1919, but over two million Armenians still occupy the northern part of their land, now in the U.S.S.R.

The modern states among which the highland zone is now divided comprise four in the Balkan Peninsula, of which Yugoslavia and Bulgaria must be counted with the Danubian countries and so referred to again, thus leaving Albania, Greece and part of Turkey. The Asian part comprises the rest of Turkey, Iran and Transcaucasia, which forms a very distinctive section of the Soviet Union. Beyond Iran lie Afghanistan and Baluchistan, which may be omitted from discussion. Until very recent times all these countries have been untouched by Western industrialism, and their peoples are over-whelmingly concerned with agriculture and pastoral pursuits which may be generally regarded as ' Mediterranean ' in character. But there is consider-able summer rainfall in the northern Balkan Peninsula, and it is abundant around the eastern curve of the Black Sea and on the Iranian coast of the Caspian. Throughout the European and Anatolian parts cultivation of cereals and some other crops is possible wherever the soil is fit ; rainfall in good years suffices for this and temperatures as well, since grain is harvested on the Armenian mountains at some 7,000 feet. These conditions apply also on the northern and western fringes of Iran, but not in the large tracts of the inner basins. But such is the relief and so great is the loss of soil that only about one-fifth of Greece and of Turkey is actually agricultural land, and much less in Albania and Iran ; moreover, at least a third of the farmland throughout the zone is fallow. On the other hand irrigation is widely practised, and this extends cultivation farther from the mountains in Iran, and elsewhere increases the amount and the variety of the crops. But the proportion of the farmland so watered is small—under 1 per cent in Turkey—except in Greece, where modern engineering has reclaimed the larger marshy plains as part of the international aid in settling refugees from Turkey after 1923. Far greater than the farmland is that used for stock, which are still managed mainly in the ancient way. Thus from end to end of these mountains the flocks are on the move each spring and autumn between winter and summer pastures ; the dates vary with the climate, journeys differ in length and flocks in com-position. Nomadism increases eastward, and a spectacular example is the mass migration of the Bakhtiari twice a year through the Zagros mountains, following the valley of the Karun.

The old ways of these highland peoples are subject to change under the impetus of governments demanding greater output, notably in Greece and Turkey. But in the former, devotion to the commercial crops, currants and tobacco, has called for restriction in order to insure the supply of basic foods and reduce the risks due to uncertain markets ; this particularly after the immigration of the Anatolian Greeks, who had lived on the Mediterranean flanks of the Peninsula and were skilled growers of fruits and tobacco. In Turkey all food crops need to be increased, but there is much attention also to industrial plants such as cotton, sugar-beet and sunflower.

Some of the minerals of these lands have been renowned from very ancient times : gold from many sources, silver-lead from Attica where it is again worked, and copper gave the name to Cyprus, while the Hittites were probably the first makers of iron. The rocks of the northern and inner belts are the older and include igneous masses that have been intruded, while the later fractures have caused further mineralisation. So there are many and varied resources : copper, lead, zinc, antimony and molybdenum in Yugoslavia are of world importance, so are chromite and magnesite in Turkey, and the latter also in Greece, while Turkey alone possesses a coalfield of note, at Zonguldak on the Black Sea. Geologically the outer, southern flank of the zone is much more uniform with its sedimentary rocks, predominantly limestones, lying in longitudinal folds but overthrust in places. This banded structure is reflected in the relief for some 2,700 miles (4,300 km.) from the head of the Adriatic to the Indian Ocean, broken, however, by the sea west and east of Crete. Remnants of an independent fold system occur in Cyprus and Syria. The limestones in Dalmatia carry great reserves of bauxite, and near the other end in the folds of the southern Zagros lie some of the vast pools of petroleum that are related to those of the lowlands.

Caucasia may be considered as part of the Borderlands on account of the physical character in structure relief and climate as well as its older human affinities, but economically it is rapidly becoming welded into the Russian realm. Because the Caucasus mountains form a great natural barrier in all respects the southern glens are remarkably isolated, and although the range is separated from the Armenian highlands by a structural depression that contains low plains at both ends, the historic function of Georgia, nevertheless, has been that of a refuge rather than a route ; for it is mainly a high rough land that divides the rivers of the two seas. This is the Suram, or ' Little Caucasus ', which for long divided the Byzantine and Ottoman Empires on the west from the empires of Iran on the east ; it is now threaded and tunnelled by rail, road and pipe-line. Here, then, in Transcaucasia is a mosaic of peoples differing in appearance and language, some being Christian and others Muslim. The smaller and swampy plain of Colchis in the west, densely forested like the surrounding mountains, is contrasted with the much larger arid lowland drained by the Kura to the Caspian and comparable in many physical aspects with that of the Ebro in Spain. The western climate, vegetation and products—such as tea—are unique in the U.S.S.R., though matched in Iran facing the Caspian. The eastern plain now in the Soviet Republic, named after the Azerbaidzhani Turks formed the natural counterpart for nomadic movement to Iranian Azerbaidzhan on the plateau to the south. Development of the Baku oilfields followed now by irrigation of the plain for cotton growing, and the working of metallic ores have given Transcaucasia a new economy that links it with the north.

The physical unity of the lower Bridgelands to the south is perhaps less obvious since the significant element is rainfall. This is received in amount sufficient for cultivation throughout a curving strip of land that almost links together the irrigated flood plains of Egypt and Mesopotamia. Thus the rim of the plateaus in Iraq, Turkey and Syria that form the piedmont of the Zagros and the mountain ranges of eastern Anatolia, contains a chain of settled lands interrupted by stretches where limestone is too porous ; this piedmont, with its denser settlement on the two great rivers and the tributaries of the Euphrates, forms the northern arc in this girdle of the desert known as ' the fertile crescent '. Its southern limit lies near the line of the railway from Aleppo in the ' Syrian Saddle ' to Mosul on the Tigris. Thence the strip narrows southward to the River Diyala, Baghdad and the watered land of the Tigris. The Euphrates, too, is fringed by small river-bank settlements amid the pastoral plateau through which it flows to enter the deltaic plain only 100 miles (160 km.) west of Baghdad. Finally from this place the route of caravans strikes west for

Damascus along the fringe of the desert. Thus the head of the plain of ancient Babylonia has always been connected by trade with the Mediterranean at its extreme corner and, since the camel came into use, with the central coast of Syria as well. This east coast of the Mediterranean with the two parallel ranges of hills separated by the rift valley—the Bekaa and the Ghor—forms the western limb of the ' crescent '. Here, with strong relief and sea winds in the cool season, rains are much heavier and harvests more assured ; population is much greater and the area much more continuously settled. The high Lebanon is specially favoured and, moreover, in this central part irrigation of the plain of Damascus extends the peopled zone farther east. These Levantine lands must be counted along with those astride the Aegean and the Hellespont as of prime importance to Europe throughout a very long period of history. With their many trading ports they have been, as it were, the ' shop front ' of Asia as well as the producers of manufactures that were luxuries in Europe ; and the first exporters, the Phoenicians, are believed to have originated the alphabet. At three of their old ports oil from Iraq and Arabia is now pumped into tankers for many countries.

The history of these lands bordering the Mediterranean, and so also various facets of their geography, have been largely determined by the fact that Jerusalem contains the holy places of the three monotheistic religions of the west : the supreme case of a city owing its importance to spiritual assets, with partition as the grim result. The Crusades have left their most obvious mark in the noble castles built and rebuilt in dominant sites by Crusaders and Muslims alike. Signs of the insistent Western contacts during the period of Turkish dominion are to be seen in the seaports, as in those of the Aegean, the factories of the Genoese and Venetian merchants ; while the continued interest of several Western nations, particularly France, is evident in many ways among the merchants and, again, from the existence of the French mandate for Syria from 1920 until the Second World War. Because of their position and their long history of transit and conquest the population is an ethnic mosaic, but it is religious belief above all which divides them. Muslims, however, are greatly in the majority, with two exceptions. In the new state of the Lebanon the Christians are almost equal in number, occupying as they do a mountain refuge that is unique. In Israel the rapid increase in Jewish population has created a situation that affects the whole of the Bridgelands. The creation of the 'National Home for the Jews', now the state of Israel, was followed by immigration from many countries and from the most diverse economic and social backgrounds, thus filling the small state to the limit of its present capacity and causing the expulsion of Muslims long established there. This led to warfare and embittered relations between Arabs and Hebrews, and affected the foreign relations of all the Muslim countries.

The desert of Sinai begins near the southern frontier of Israel, and is the bridge between the great deserts of Arabia and Africa, but on its flanks are the gulfs of the Red Sea, the Suez Canal and the Nile valley, so Cairo, the successor of Memphis and Heliopolis, at the head of the delta and near the Isthmus is at a node of the highest order in the Borderlands, and since the foundation of Alexandria Egypt has been in direct contact with Europe by sea. This was certainly slight enough during most of the Turkish period, but it has been made anew in the past century, notably by the Suez Canal, the growing output of cotton for European markets and the development of aviation, while the strategic importance of the Isthmus has been emphasised in the two world wars. These economic changes, like the wars, originated in Europe, the canal being due to French effort, and the perennial irrigation that made cotton a leading product, while fostered by Mehmed Ali was ultimately effected by British engineers.

It is natural to compare the Nile valley in Egypt with the parts of Iraq and Iran that are deltaic plains, since life in both depends upon the rivers. Allusion has been made in Chapter 7 to the differing regimens of these rivers ; the greater irregularity of the Mesopotamian floods made their control in ancient times more difficult than that of the Nile. Yet in ancient Babylonia and again under the caliphs of Baghdad canals were made to water with regularity much greater areas than are now cultivated. Destruction by the Mongolian invaders and subsequent neglect caused the plain largely to revert to nature, and although the Ottoman government started to regenerate the system by construction of the Hindiyeh barrage in the Euphrates in 1913 the position is in great contrast with that of Egypt. Newer irrigation controlled by dams is limited to the lower Diyala fan and to an area near the lower Tigris below Kut, and none of this is perennial, but many pumps along the main rivers provide for this in a small way ; in Iran there are as yet no modern works. Thus vast tracts of the alluvial plain are still used as seasonal pasture land, while both the sparseness of population and the discontinuity of settlements provide striking contrasts with Egypt. Again, the great cultivation of the date palm along the lower reaches of all the rivers is the oldest characteristic of the Gulf plains : the youngest is the development of the oilfields. This began, as already mentioned, in the Zagros Mountains of Persia, in Khuzistan, with the oil piped to the Shatt al Arab at Abadan, where the great refinery was built ; this was followed by development in the foothills in Iraq near Kirkuk, with the oil led to the Mediterranean coast at Haifa and Tripoli by pipes that bifurcate in the Syrian desert. Then after the Second War various oil pools were tapped on the Arabian side of the Persian Gulf, in the Sheikhdom of Kuwait, next on the island of Bahrein, and finally in several fields on the mainland of Saudi Arabia west of it ; from these a large pipe-line was built by the American concessionaries across Arabia to the Syrian coast at Saida. The full effects of all this Western activity upon the governments, the national economies and the people of these lands of the Middle East can as yet scarcely be foreseen ; but they are likely to be revolutionary.

With the vast majority of the people dependent upon agriculture through-out the Eastern Bridgelands, except Israel, it may be said that the main prob-lems in all countries are those related to the use of the soil and the generally limited amounts of water ; and the solutions of many of them will be applicable in varying degrees to all parts of the Nearer East. They will include reforms of land tenures, and the education of peasants to induce improved methods of cultivation and stock rearing, while some material help to these ends will generally be needed. Demonstration farms well dispersed are likely to be more effective than theoretical instruction. All the governments have addressed themselves to these things in some measure, and it is generally recognised that much capital expenditure is needed to provide more water for irrigation and the proper drainage for irrigated land. This matter, therefore, depends upon the economic position of the various states which at present is entangled in political and military affairs. So we are brought back to the question of geo-graphical position. Egypt and Turkey have each an important international seaway situated within its territory, but near a land frontier ; and this is a dominant factor in the policies of both states, emphasised in the case of Turkey by the historic expansion of Russia toward the open seas. Similarly no Iranian government is likely to forget this latter fact, and in Greece a frontier with Bulgaria that is difficult to defend has the same kind of influence.

The location of the oilfields in Iran, Iraq and the Arabian states affects the policies of many countries, not only towards these but also Syria, Jordan and Israel, which transmit the oil to Europe and the west. Moreover, all this must be weighed along with the distribution of Islam and, within it, that of the Arabic language. In the present condition of the world, and in view of rising nationalism in these countries, it is not surprising then that military considerations are prominent ; and they encourage governments to arm and to create industries which may be uneconomic. On the other hand, all the Bridgelands would benefit from the growth of any manufacturing industries that are soundly based, as offering alternative employment and a means of improving trade balances and of raising capital for other national improve-ments. Meanwhile the increasing export of minerals, especially oil, helps the economy of some countries which otherwise have only agricultural produce to sell.

It is hard to assess the relative urgency of national improvements, but there are at least important distinctions to note in respect of pressure of population on cultivable land, and this is a leading factor. Egypt and Israel stand out as countries where this is very great, and Greece may perhaps be cited as well ; but there the likeness ends. Israel has been deliberately filled by immigrant Jews ; nearly four-fifths live in towns, yet the other fifth need to make the most of the agricultural possibilities. In Egypt the Nile water is now insufficient despite the raising of the Aswan barrage three times and the building of one at Jebel Auliya on the White Nile above Khartum, as well as of subsidiary works in Egypt itself ; the main reason for this is the phenomenal growth of population. Hence the Egyptian anxiety about control of both the White and the Blue Niles, involving costly projects in which Uganda, the Anglo-Egyptian Sudan and Ethiopia are all concerned. Greece offers a remarkable example of absorption of immigrants between the wars, amounting to a 14 per cent net increase of population. This was done by drainage and irrigation of the northern plains, and in the cities by development of industries. All the other Asian lands could support greater populations, given the improvements in agriculture that are possible, and this is especially true of Iraq, which needs an increase in population to make really large irrigation works worth while and successful.

It is tempting to try and envisage the consequences of the economic co-operation or even union that would be possible if the threat of war were removed from these and other lands. Natural and human resources might then be at wider disposal, limited not by frontiers but by economic bounds of movement for energy and products ; while rational migration might be promoted, as for example that of Egyptians to Iraq. Perhaps at least it is not too visionary to hope for co-operation between Turkey, Syria, Iran and Iraq in progressive regularisation of the Rivers Euphrates and Tigris, with reforestation of the Taurus-Zagros mountain arc and the eventual construction of storage reservoirs in some of the gorges within these mountains. Some of the minerals of eastern Turkey might perhaps be economically used in manufactures situated not too far from sources of electricity in this labyrinth of mountains. And more immediately, it may be asked whether some use might not be found for the natural gas that is now wasted in the oilfields— the ' eternal fires ' of the ancients. Whatever be the future developments in these parts, it would seem that the western, seaboard wing of the ' fertile crescent ' is almost bound to prosper from its position as the link with Europe, and in particular it may be hoped that the presence of a frontier will not prevent the district that contains Aleppo, Antioch and Adana with the port of Iskanderun (Alexandretta) from deriving the full benefit of its geographical nodality. Similarly, but on a much smaller scale, Aqaba at the eastern head of the Red Sea should not always be hampered by the three frontiers which meet the sea within its view. Between these areas lies the tract of the Jordan valley and the Dead Sea, unique in its climate and in the combination of fresh water for irrigation and power, and lake water so salt that it contains vast resources of potassium, magnesium and bromine, which are already being exploited in Israel; this is an obvious field which would seem to demand the fullest immediate co-operation of Lebanon, Israel and Jordan. Most of the Eastern Bridgelands have received material aid from the west, especially from America. This surely ought to be regarded as an attempt to repay the debt of all Western peoples to these lands for untold gifts, both spiritual and technical, from the distant past.

CHAPTER 22

THE WESTERN MEDITERRANEAN LANDS

IT is appropriate to consider together and compare the geography of the Iberian Peninsula, Italy and the Atlas lands despite many differences, of which the most obvious is their outline on the map. They lie around the western Mediterranean Sea, and the formation and the deepening of the several basins that compose it were due to the same forces that gave these lands their present shape and height; the southern boundary in respect of relief and geological structure, as of climate, lies beyond the Atlas ranges. Again there is no sharp division in racial characteristics between the peoples on the European and the African sides, for there have been migrations across the straits from very early times. The fact that the Arabs and Berbers speak languages very different from the Latin tongues, and that they are Muslims by religion certainly marks an important ethnic distinction, which is no less valid on account of the presence of French culture in their midst; but the economic status of the majority of indigenous North Africans differs little from that which prevails in the southern parts of Iberia or Italy. The climate which the three lands, including the islands, possess in common, coupled with the long history of intercourse, colonisation and rule from the opposite shores, have induced a similar basis of existence and a similar way of life. Moreover, these conditions of life in country and town extend to the Atlantic seaboard, and beyond this to the oceanic islands of Spain and Portugal. But there are certain real differences along the north-western shoulder of Iberia which shares in the climate of western Europe. Furthermore, the history of world-wide colonisation from the Iberian countries has many repercussions upon the human geography of present-day Portugal and Spain. Despite the undoubted western outlook of Italy the division of the Mediterranean adopted here may perhaps be criticised in detail on the ground that the Adriatic and northern Ionian Seas have in the past served as links rather than barriers. Thus, Roman and Venetian remains in Dalmatia and, throughout southern Italy and Sicily, towns of ancient Greek foundation and more or less modern colonies of Albanians certainly support this view. Moreover, if this division be admitted in the north there remains the question of Libya. In respect of relief, structure and climate this African territory belongs entirely to the east. But the two small coastal areas that are fit for permanent agriculture are widely separated by desert. Cyrenaica is marked by the colonial traces of Greece, Rome and modern Italy, while Tripoli from Carthaginian times has been contiguous with the settled fringe of the Atlas lands. The two are now united in the new Arab state of Libya, which has still to demonstrate its ability to survive. The fraction of France that is undoubtedly 'Mediterranean' in character will only be referred to incidentally in this section.

In recent times the interest of France and Spain in the African lands was a striking indication of the unity of the western Mediterranean. Similarly in the existing towns and villages there are many evidences of former influences from across the sea, but excepting that of Rome, which had lasting effects nearly everywhere, it is the southern part of the region which bears such traces in greatest variety. Thus in the Iberian Peninsula, those of the Phoenicians, Carthaginians and Moors ; in southern Italy, those emanating successively from Greece, Africa, Normandy and Catalonia ; in the Atlas lands, traces of occupation by Carthaginians, Romans, Byzantines, Arabs and Turks ; and, finally, the evidence of British sea power at the two straits operating athwart the modern penetration of Africa by the French accompanied by Italian and Spanish colonisation. This last is the most prominent because it is recent and strongly contrasted with a medieval Muslim culture and still older ways of life that persist. But while these historic currents have left their mark, guided by the all-pervading influences of land form and climate, the latter are directly responsible for the present general likeness of human life and economy throughout the entire region, and for most of the differences within it, as represented by the sharp variations in the density of population.

The western Mediterranean area forms a remarkable complex of high land and deep sea, and the distribution of the former can scarcely be understood without accepting the view that under the deep basins there lie old slabs of the earth's crust which by their movements first caused the folding of the more mobile zones between them, and then, by their collapse, produced the compensating uplift of the folded belts and those of the old blocks which did not founder. The most prominent of the old slabs are now the western part of the Iberian Peninsula and the two large plateaus enclosed by the Atlas ranges, that of Morocco, which is partially concealed, and the tableland east of the Middle Atlas that is wholly covered by younger sedimentary rocks. Sardinia, most of Corsica and small areas in Provence and Catalonia, are thought to be the remnants of a former mass in the north ; this one alone seems to have attained stability, making the area immune from earthquakes. In the Apulian 'heel' of Italy the unfolded strata evidently rest upon the block that underlies the Adriatic, while the Tyrrhenian Sea must cover another whose ancient rocks appear astride the Strait of Messina and in Tuscany. Finally, similar fragments on the northern coast of the Atlas lands seem to belong to a block now sunk in the parallel trough of the sea. There are seven other downwarped areas, not now submerged but covered by young strata.

The intervening zones conform to this pattern both in the trend of the folds, shown generally on the map, and they are now the high mountains owing to the last massive upheavals by warping or broad folding and dislocation. Beyond all these features, to the south, lies the long-rigid mass of Africa, but on its edge the pressures bent it downward on the east and upward in the extreme west, to form the high block named by its French explorer the Anti-Atlas. Because of this geological history the inland sea fills a rough triangle with Gibraltar, Genoa and Messina at its angles ; owing to their height the surrounding lands and the large islands may be visible from a large area of the sea. In this western basin there is no large expanse of shallow sea, and more important, only small areas of coastal lowland. The cause of this is the violence of the final episode that created these coasts. It is true that for the most part the great mountains and their rocks extend parallel to the coasts, the exception being the stretch from Genoa to Cape de la Nao in Spain ; yet the edges are nevertheless marked by great fractures or by evidences of steep warping, and in places by volcanic activity. The opposite sides of these mountains on the other hand show much less complexity of structure and relief : the Betic Mountains facing the Andalusian plain, the southern side of the Riff Mountains, the Saharan Atlas, and especially the outer flank of the Appennine system from Sicily in the south to Piedmont in the north. Thus while central Italy where drained to the Tyrrhenian Sea is a mosaic of hills and basins bounded by intersecting fractures together with a series of symmetrical cones of extinct volcanoes, the eastern slope has a simple structure although carved to strong relief by parallel rivers. The very abrupt slopes into the Ligurian Sea, again, are contrasted with the shelving shores of the Lion Gulf, which are backed by the exceptionally large lowland of Languedoc. South of this, however, both the Pyrenees and the Betic Mountains are truncated by the sea, and between these ranges the folds of Catalonia and the Iberian Mountains meet the coast obliquely in smooth steep slopes facing narrow coastal plains. East of the Balearic Islands, which are remnants of the Betic structures, Sardinia and Corsica, fragments of ancient masses, have been thrust up between the deepest troughs of this western sea and then greatly dissected by erosion.

Because they face the sea and are steep most of these coastal lands receive over 16 inches (40 mm.) of rainfall in the year, the amount that suffices for crops without irrigation in North Africa, but there are two notable exceptions : a strip of some 250 miles (400 km.) in western Algeria and Morocco, and most of the Spanish coast from the River Ebro to Malaga, where the index of aridity is between 5 and 10. But irrigation is so effective in this driest strip of the Iberian Peninsula that its agricultural productivity is unsurpassed. It is chiefly on account of the coastal climate that there is a high density of population ; certainly it is by no means even and many rocky promontories are deserted ; also where the small plains are irrigated and intensively worked the concentration is very great. But these coastal lands are more populous than the inland parts, except in central Italy where bad management and malaria were the causes, and there reclamation is now restoring the balance. Sardinia and Corsica are also relatively thinly peopled, but this is not owing to lack of rain or, in the former, of cultivable lowland, at least on the western side. Both islands throughout their history have been at the mercy of invaders and exploiters, yet culturally they have suffered from isolation, and their peoples have had scarcely any mutual relations. Neither of them has taken to the sea, and the fear of piracy and malaria has kept them to the hills. Sardinia, with considerable resources, offers a striking example of modern stagnation, but notable efforts have recently been made to improve its condition and provide for immigration from the mainland of Italy.

Italy, Spain and Portugal are confronted by the serious social and economic problem of ' the South ', which applies broadly to Italy south of Rome and to Iberia south of the Tagus but chiefly to land without irrigation. In North Africa similar conditions may be said to apply generally to agricultural land in the hands of the indigenous population, but for different reasons. The problem is how to make the land more productive of crops and how to ensure full employment and a reasonable standard of living for the majority of the people. Though it is to a very large extent a matter of climate, the condition of these southern lands is undoubtedly related to the prevalence of large estates held by owners who are well enough off to be uninterested in improvement, but in North Africa it must be recalled that despite French efforts the attitude of the Arab and Berber to the land is still affected by the long background of misuse that began with the invasions of nomadic tribes in the eleventh century.

In the two peninsulas the great estates are of old standing, in Italy from the beginning of the Era and in Iberia from the Christian Reconquest, but in parts probably from Moorish times. There is thus a general historical explanation of the low status of these lands and their tillers, but there are various degrees of injury to both, depending partly upon the land tenure of tenants. Where leases are long, peasants are encouraged to undertake improvements by their own efforts, as for example by planting fruit trees or digging wells. But the problem as a whole is largely that of restoring fertility to soil that has become exhausted by unsuitable cropping as well as by erosion ; for this two methods seem to deserve greater practice than is common : the introduction of leguminous fodder crops and the extension of xerophytic fruit trees, especially the olive and the carob. In addition of course there is extended irrigation, which generally involves action by the State. The problem of ' the South ' then cannot be solved merely by enactment providing the landless peasants with holdings taken from the large estates, and this is now realised by the governments, each of which is now attempting to tackle the problem scientifically. So far, however, the scale of the reforms has been rather small, since they involve not merely agriculture and associated engineering but also education and, unfortunately, politics as well.

In French North Africa about one-quarter of the cultivated land is held by Europeans and while much of this land was originally in small farms, the number of large ones has steadily increased, especially with the use of motor power. The remainder is cultivated by traditional and usually much less efficient methods. The chief problem has been that of improving the output of these native farms and to encourage semi-nomads to become sedentary husbandmen, and although gravely retarded by World War II, the process has met with considerable success and various co-operative systems have been established in all three territories.

Beyond the inner ring the three main parts of the region differ so much in form that they must now be reviewed separately.

THE IBERIAN PENINSULA

The most obvious qualities of the Iberian Peninsula as seen on the map are its simple shape—a relatively short coastline containing a large area—and its great average height ; seen from the ground it is the monotonous smoothness of the the tableland that is most impressive. The warped or fractured margins have been roughened by rapid erosion since the general uplift, but only the great rivers have had much effect upon the interior. The chief exception to the smoothness is in the Central Sierras, that rise to mark a zone where the old mass yielded to the pressure that built the Betic Mountains in the south. Similar warping produced the Cantabrian and the Morena ranges. The buckling of the crust and a westward tilt probably determined the main river basins, but the depression occupied by the Ebro is associated with the earlier rising of the Pyrenees. This river system has since been excavating the weak sediments that had filled the hollow so that it is now a hilly lowland. By contrast the two marginal lowlands of Portugal and Andalusia include real plains that are partly covered by young deposits. The Peninsula in all these characteristics resembles Africa beyond the Atlas ; moreover, in its effect upon the atmosphere it acts like a miniature continent with wide seasonal range of temperature on the plateau, diversion of depressions during the winter and great evaporation in summer, and in all respects differing from the marginal lowlands. Much of the tableland then is semi-arid, its soils where derived from old sediments are poor in lime, and the natural woodland is now represented by heath of various kinds after a long history of pastoralism and of prehistoric shifting agriculture. For the most part the dryland farming provides for bare subsistence and the population in general is sparse. Yet this bleak poor region in virtue of its position dominates the Peninsula, and has hitherto assured the unity of Spain : Toledo, a Roman city, was Gothic and the Moorish capital, while Madrid was created to replace it nearer to the Central Sierra. The medieval kingdom of Castile established upon the plateau by the principal adversaries of the Moors was named appropriately from the numerous fortresses of the advancing frontier ; and so Castilian is the literary language of Spain and of Hispanic America.

The northern margin from the Pyrenees to the Douro presents a very different picture : high relief, rainfall copious and coming at all seasons, broadleaved forests persisting except in the west, a long growing season, perennial and rapid rivers, many harbours and plenty of fish, to say nothing of minerals still to be mentioned. With these advantages the strip from the Basque provinces to the Douro holds 20 per cent of the Iberian population, 18 per cent of that of Spain, and 27 per cent in Portugal ; and its share in the cattle of the Peninsula is still higher. As in its climate so in the settlements, and in the traditional modes of life this is an outlier of north-western Europe ; if the Portuguese in the north irrigate as much of their land to supplement rainfall as do the Valencians in default of it, this is because of the great numbers to be fed. Yet in Portugal there is a gradual transition to pure Mediterranean climate, and this whole strip is in all its relations bound to the Peninsula. Indeed, it contains the very cores of the two nations (Fig. 45). It was the least Romanised part, and to judge from the place-names it had most of the Germanic colonists of Gothic times, and in the remote fastnesses, unconquered by the Moors, the Christian resistance was organised. The Peninsula is divided linguistically into three longitudinal zones because of the course taken in the Crusades that began while the Romance languages were developing, and which continued intermittently from the eighth to the end of the fifteenth centuries. In this period the several Christian kingdoms were extended southwards : from Galicia and the County of Portugal in the west ; from the Catalan Counties in the eastern Pyrenees ; and, between these, from nuclei in the Cantabrian Mountains and the western Pyrenees—a group ultimately dominated by Castile. Linguistic divisions contain the seeds of separation, but only in Portugal have these been allowed to bear fruit. Equally potent is the latitudinal division of the Peninsula into zones corresponding to the degree of Moorish influence and to phases in the history of the advancing frontier (Fig. 45). These factors explain, for example, the contrasts in land tenure north and south of the Central Sierras, and in Portugal north and south of the Tagus ; or again, the abundant relics of prolonged Muslim occupation and civilisation in Murcia, Andalusia and Algarve. Moreover, Arabic place-names become steadily more numerous from north to south. With all this the importance of the Pyrenees in restricting contacts with Europe must be appreciated. At every stage the Peninsular peoples have evolved their own variety of western civilisation, and during seven centuries a unique form known in relation to art, as Hispano-Moresque. A prominent effect of the isolation is the very special and lavish ornamentation in stone and ironwork in the late Gothic and Renaissance churches, while the Moorish influence appears in the domestic buildings of the south, and in Portugal the embellishment of walls, including the newest, with blue tiles of varied design is widespread. The magnificent churches are one of the evidences of the wealth acquired in the ' Indies ' after 1500, and this bears upon the fact that Spain and Portugal have been ' backward ' countries since they embarked upon overseas conquests. There are many and complex explanations of this ; among them are inflation due to vast imports of silver and gold, the expulsion of the Moors and loss of their skill in agriculture, and then of the Jews and the descendants of Spaniards who had accepted Islam, loss of man-power, which in Portugal was remedied by bringing in African slaves. Whatever the cause, decadence set in, and only in this century have the governments grappled seriously with the results.

The mineral wealth of the Peninsula, and especially of Spain, formed the principal attraction to the Phoenicians and all their followers, and it is sympto-matic of the modern Spanish economy that the minerals are still extracted largely with capital from northern Europe. There can be few parts of the world where as many hillsides are scored with old workings, and no country whose ores have been sought so consistently by foreigners from the repre-sentatives of King Hiram of Tyre through the Fugger family of Augsburg to the British Rio Tinto Copper Company, and many others ; and indirectly most of these contributed as much as they took away. Structural stresses and tensions have favoured the deposit of metallic ores mainly in three zones ; thus, to mention only those of present importance : in the Betic Mountains iron, lead and copper ; in the Sierra Morena sulphides of copper and iron, lead and mercury ; and in the Cantabrian Mountains iron and zinc—as well as the only great coalfield. Two other mineral localities are northern Portugal for tungsten and inner Catalonia for potash. Although mining employs only a small proportion of the people the products amount to about one-tenth of the value of the exports of Spain. Among these minerals the most recent discovery is the potash, and this alone is directly related to the much-needed regeneration of Spanish agriculture. Towards this end the government has ambitious plans for controlling the rivers of the Meseta by methods already employed on the Ebro system and—with foreign capital—the rivers of Catalonia, giving irrigation and power for manufactures. These schemes will affect the Douro near the frontier—to benefit both countries—the upper basin of the Tagus and the middle basin of the Guadiana. The areas to be irrigated, however, while important, are small compared with the vast tracts of dry-land cultivation for which other remedies must be sought, and these touch upon the serious social problems of Spain. Related to these is the political disunity that ravaged the country in the Civil War 1936–9, in which it was significantly the inhabitants of two of the densely occupied margins who resisted the action that brought the Falangist government to power. These were the Cantabrian coastlands with their farmers, fishermen and miners, and Catalonia, the chief industrial region and the one with the most pronounced nationalism, along with the peasantry of the Levant coast, whose language is Catalan and whose life is one of organised co-operation for watering their land.

ITALY

Italy covers the same latitudes as Iberia, but about a third of its area lies farther north and embedded in the continent ; again, owing to its narrowness no part of this peninsula has a climate like that of the Meseta, or is so dry in summer as south-eastern Spain. Atmospheric depressions haunt the seas west of Corsica and east of Sardinia, so the abrupt coasts of Liguria, Calabria and Sicily have high rainfalls, while Apulia receives the least amounts. The map invites comparison between the basin of the Ebro and that of the Po, but in regard to both relief and climate they differ profoundly, and especially because in place of the high hills of Catalonia is the Gulf of Venetia, from which moist air penetrates the northern plain and the surrounding mountains help to induce precipitation in summer. This valuable plain owes its existence mainly to the denudation of the Alps ; Alpine rivers build it, water it and give power for its industries ; and this is true of the Pyrenees and the lowland of Aragon only in small degree. Without the Alps and the plain Italy could not have gained the position it holds among the powers of Europe ; but the life-giving rivers have to be restrained, and this has required great initiative and organisation. The productivity of northern Italy in agriculture as a result and the concentration of modern industry there have been referred to in earlier chapters ; and despite the importance to the country of the Italian share in the Alps, these mountains will be treated as a unit and a part of central Europe.

In peninsular Italy and the islands there is much lowland favoured by Mediterranean climate of a benign type ; but unfortunately most of this, and much of the higher Appennines also, consists of rocks, such as marls, clays and soft shales, that are subject to rapid erosion.   Thus the effect of prolonged deforestation is more serious than in Iberia with so much hard rock ; so good land is lost above and drainage is impeded at low levels by deposition of the waste—a condition favouring malaria.   Landslips and mud-flows, too, make buildings unsafe in many parts.   Moreover, southern Italy suffers from frequent earthquakes which have serious results in closely built villages and towns.   These were severe, for example, in the years 1905 to 1908, and, as a consequence, emigration from several provinces—which was then possible for large numbers—was greatly increased.   These natural curses, to which the risk of crop failures must be added, have contributed to the misery of southern Italy ; furthermore, for nearly 2,000 years it has suffered from misrule of one kind or another.

Because it is relatively narrow and so has the rain more evenly distributed, Italy has a much greater agricultural population than Iberia, and the eastern slope, which is notably uniform in structure and form, shows very even and high densities, the sole exception being the Gargano and the dry plain behind it. West of the Appennines two areas of high density are outstanding—the plain of Campania behind Naples and the plain of the lower Arno.   A more extensive area of high density mainly rural, lies northwestward of Venice. The greatest area of high population density, however, is in western Lombardy, which is the region of Italy's greatest development both in agriculture and industry.

Among the cities between the south end of the transalpine routes and the river Po, Milan, site of a Roman *castrum* and a later imperial and ecclesiastical centre, had a nodality that enabled it to take the lead under the *signoria*. Here the transalpine routes joined the east-west route to Venice and the Dinaric lands and the route that crossed the Po to follow the Via Emilia along the Appennine piedmont to Bologna and the south.   Monastic skill and Milanese capital together converted the western Lombard plain into rich agricultural land.   With the growth of modern industry and its gravitation from the small ore deposits and primitive water-power of the Alpine valleys and hillfoot to the axis of the plain, Milan continued to be its focus.   Meantime the organisational and military strength of Piedmont had enabled it to take the lead in the movement for the unification of Italy.

Rome, where north and south meet and the imperial and ecclesiastical traditions both make their most powerful appeal, became the capital of unified Italy.   But, though the population of Rome has swollen with the functions of the central government in the twentieth century, the western Po plain had an economic impetus enabling it to extend its dominance over the industrial and commercial life of the country. In the mid-twentieth century about a third of all Italian industry was concentrated in Lombardy alone, and a half in Lombardy, Piedmont and Liguria together. Genova, with its smaller neighbour Savona, was the passageway for about a quarter of Italy's movement of goods by sea.

Italy's central position in the Mediterranean and its long tradition of skilled craftsmanship and commerce were in themselves no longer enough to keep it in the front rank after the industrial revolution. Coal and raw materials for heavy industry had to be imported. Its disadvantage in energy supplies has, however, been gradually lessened by the exploitation of the hydro-electric potentials of its mountains, especially in the Alpine valleys, and, notably since World War II, of its hydrocarburants.

The need to export was accentuated by the greater difficulties that, after World War I, beset overseas emigration, which for long not only took off, permanently or seasonally, much of the surplus population, but, through remittances from abroad, helped the country to balance its payments. Italy was second only to the British Isles as a source of emigrants. Italian migrant manpower still plays an important part in the economy, not only of Italy but of several other European countries. Neither the comprehensive schemes of land reclamation nor the agrarian reforms within the country can do more than touch the fringe of this population problem. The South presents some aspects of the problem in extreme form.

Italy has throughout its history been a political crossroads. Its transalpine links have recurrently shown their strength. But the peninsula is also well placed in mid-Mediterranean between Europe's southern gateway toward the Atlantic on the one hand and the way to and through the eastern bridgelands on the other. The large overseas populations of Italian origin and the important mercantile marine are both aspects of the seaward interest. The large tourist traffic is the more material facet of Italy's great legacy, due to its location and history, of European traditions in the visual arts.

THE ATLAS LANDS

The similarities in physical structure and climate between the Atlas lands and those on the opposite shores have encouraged movement of peoples around the western Mediterranean since prehistoric times. But the Atlas lands are also stepping-stones between the eastern bridgelands and Europe and between Europe and Africa. In particular Islam swept to its far west in Morocco along this corridor between the Mediterranean and the Sahara, cutting directly across the north-south lines of cultural movement. The eventual disruption of the old ties with the rest of the western Mediterranean lasted until the nineteenth century, when the north-south tie was again strengthened through the colonial and strategic interests of France, Spain and Italy. Phoenicians, Romans and Arabs have thus been followed by French, Spanish and Italian settlers. The evolution of the resulting contacts has given distinctive regional quality to the modern political units of the Atlas lands.

The areas of coastal lowland are small but their steep background has helped them to get sufficient rainfall. The Tellian Atlas, too, was accessible and early attracted settlers. In contrast the Riffian Atlas has favoured resistance groups rather than development, while the secluded bays in the steep coast, here and farther east toward Algiers, were long the haunt of the Barbary pirates. Between the littoral ridge and the Tellian Atlas the long furrow drained westward by the Chelif and eastward by the Sahel provided an easy route for the greater part of the Algerian section, between Oran and Bône, of the east-west trunk railway. Eight centuries before, nomadic invaders bringing a way of life very different from that introduced by the Arab conquest of the eighth century, entering from the gateway of Biskra, had passed along this depression and thence westward to the Muluya valley and through the defile of Taza between the Rif and the Middle Atlas into the rich oasis of Fez. The two extensive high plains—the meseta of western Morocco, between the Rif, the Middle Atlas and High Atlas, open to the Atlantic, and the long high plain of Oran and Algiers, enclosed by the Atlas ranges in Algeria—are on the whole less favoured by precipitation. But, where water is available in summer both from occasional rain on the higher and more exposed slopes and from late-melted snow, irrigation was carried out long before European influence was felt. In the Hauz of Marrakesh the springs have long been tapped by a remarkable system of underground aqueducts and along the piedmont zone from the Hauz to Fez, where the immensely thick detrital deposits carry much water, there is a zone of orchard villages. As sources of water the rivers of the Atlas lands are mainly of local importance but, especially on the Atlantic slopes of the Moroccan Atlas, which possess the largest potential water resources, development was accelerated after 1938, both for irrigation and for energy supplies. The digging of deep artesian wells, too, was left to Europeans who achieved early success in this in the Hodna basin in Algeria and along the so-called Wed Rirh to the south of the Shott Melghir, to the great enrichment of date-palm owners.

The agriculture of the Tell (meaning good cropland), where precipitation is adequate for grain and other annual crops and for vineyards and orchards, is by far the most important. The Romans had colonised the grainlands but after their departure there was a relapse into pastoral nomadism, which the Arab conquest only served on the whole to intensify. Here barley, the principal food grain in North Africa as a whole, is supplemented by wheat. Before World War II all three countries of French North Africa had an export surplus of wheat but, though production has increased in all three, this subsequently disappeared except in Tunisia. In barley the Atlas lands together remained among the larger exporters.

Dry farming has long been known to Berber and Arab husbandmen, but its large-scale application to the grainlands of the semi-arid Moroccan meseta and Algerian high plains was left to the French settlers, who bought up the rights to large areas and introduced mechanisation. With large-scale application of modern dry-farming methods, grain production can be pushed further into the semi-arid areas formerly inhabited only by a semi-nomadic population.

In value, however, the leading agricultural export of the Atlas lands, both before and after World War II, was wine exported for diluting the domestic wines of France, the great bulk of it from Algeria, of whose exports it accounted for half. Following the wine and barley the most valuable agricultural export was olive oil, mainly from the great monoculture of the Tunisian Sahel behind Sfax and Sousse. In all these exports the risks of unstable markets must be added to those of fluctuating yields.

The Atlas lands have long been known as a source of minerals. The Carthaginians worked both lead and copper ores and Phoenician traders procured lead nearly as far west as Mogador. The Romans were more systematic miners and extracted iron in addition. The Arabs, though they continued mining and metallurgy, did not get all they needed at home ; the real exploitation of mineral wealth was left to the French. The two most important minerals are phosphates and iron. The reserves of phosphate of lime are very great. The phosphatic rock of North Africa outcrops from the Atlantic to the Red Sea but the greatest masses are in the Atlas lands, where the production, mainly in Morocco and Tunisia, is the greatest outside the United States. The iron ores occur in a belt running through the entire Tellian Atlas. They are of high iron content, generally free of phosphorus and often contain manganese.

Native industries, in which a high degree of skill is reached, have existed from time immemorial but they are of but little importance to the outside world. Modern industry is but little developed and the economies of the three countries are based on the great primary exports : wine (Algeria) and phosphates (Morocco and Tunisia) and to a less extent, alfa, or esparto (Tunisia), olive oil (Tunisia), barley (Morocco) and iron ore (Algeria). With the rapid growth of population and increased mechanisation of agriculture but little industrial employment, the growing surplus of agricultural population has been a severe problem.

The very rapid growth of the population as a whole in recent decades is critical in all three countries but their different relationships to France affected the way in which its economic and political consequences unfolded. Algeria has had the longest association with France, having been occupied by French forces in 1830 and annexed in 1847, and a hundred years later officially declared to be part of France. In the years after World War II, of the 1½ million European settlers, one million were in Algeria, half of them in the four larger towns and most of the others in the three coastal departments. The movement, however, was far from one-way, especially when all Algerians were granted French citizenship. France became the market not only for Algerian wine but for its surplus labour.

While Algeria became for France a colony of settlement, Tunisia, with a larger indigenous middle-class and already, when it became a protectorate in 1881, a more urbanised society, developed closer cultural relations with France and was also more accessible to Italian influences.

Morocco, a protectorate only in 1912 and under complete control only in 1934, became the most highly planned of the Atlas territories, the transformation of its landscape in twentieth-century style contrasting with the nineteenth-century Europeanisation of much of Algeria.

French initiative and capital provided the stimulus to North African economic development, built railways and roads, opened up mineral resources and raised agricultural production both through extensive mechanised farms and through modern irrigation systems. Economically the north-south link is primarily one of dependence of the Atlas lands on France. But these countries also lie between Europe and possible developments south of the Atlas lands. The political problem that arose more acutely after World War II derived from the crossing of this north-south axis by an east-west axis of awakening national movements that stretches from Morocco as far as south-east Asia.

CHAPTER 23

THE DANUBIAN LANDS

THE choice of a watershed bounding the basin of a river to delimit a region seems to be justified in this case, if the upper part of the basin is eliminated. Its lowlands have a distinctive climate that is transitional in type between those of the Mediterranean and of the plain beyond the Carpathians. The region, again, has always been one where peoples of different origin have mingled and been subject to the impact of alien incursions and cultures ; it is the focus of routes from Asia on both sides of the Black Sea and of others from Peninsular Europe. While the Alps and southern Germany are clearly parts of central Europe in the narrower sense, Bohemia, although drained by the Elbe, is in many ways a Danubian land ; on the other hand the Balkan Peninsula has already been discussed as forming a section of the Bridgelands, and its Danubian aspects remain to be treated.

The drainage basin of the Danube east of the Alps includes nearly all the Carpathian mountain system and the widest part of the Balkan Peninsula ; the two great lowlands, the Pannonian and the Romanian, occupy about the same area as these highlands, the former being much the larger. The plan of this combination of mountains and plains is due broadly to the subsidence of the crustal blocks to form sea or lake basins that have been gradually filled by sediments, and, as in the case of the Mediterranean, the existence of these buried masses doubtless determined the original folding of the rocks in the mountains ; so also their sinking has been balanced by the re-elevation of the mountains to their present height, after denudation. The Danube and its tributaries provide the drainage and the alluvial top-dressing of the plains ; but they did not make the basins. These vertical movements were once violent enough to produce a whole series of volcanoes within the Carpathian arc, and there is evidence that they have not ceased. The Danube inherited also the depression north of the Alps which marks its upper course to Vienna, and thus is the essential link of a large part of Europe ; although it flows in defiles at each of the barriers, its course forms a great natural route and its plains have been a notable arena for the fusion of cultures and the contest of languages, religions and, latterly, of nations. Because of the simplicity of their plan, the Danubian lands have lent themselves to the conquest and organisation, in large part, by empires centred successively in Rome, Budapest, Istanbul and Vienna. Indeed it is partly—perhaps mainly—owing to the character of

Turkish and Austro-Hungarian rule that these lands have lagged in social and economic progress. But this backwardness derives also from the poverty of their resources in fuel and from the presence of great industries in Germany ; it has had serious effects, too, on account of the high birthrates of the Danubian peoples. On the other hand, these lands have great advantages for agriculture and stock-keeping ; many parts of the plains were tilled in Neolithic times, and they are among the great granaries of the continent. The climate allows of a large range of crops, including maize, for which this is the typical area, but because of the political conditions just mentioned these advantages have not as yet been fully exploited, and the surplus produce which formerly was sent up the Danube now goes to the east.

The division since 1919 into states corresponding generally to the several ethnic groups tends to mask the physical unity of the Danubian basin ; but each of the peoples occupies one or more of the principal sub-regions except the Pannonian plain, which is parted by highly artificial frontiers.

The varying width and height of the surrounding mountains has been, and is, of great importance in history and human geography. In the north-west the two structural corridors followed by the Danube and the (northern) Morava converge upon the basin of Vienna, where German meets Czech ; evidently a key position. In two other places the mountains are narrow and low ; these are situated at the ends of the longest axis of the Pannonian low-land, which coincides with the structural fracture extending from near the head of the Adriatic for over 400 miles and dividing higher from lower land. In the south-west the plateau of the Julian karst between the Alps and the Dinaric mountains has allowed civilisation to pass into the basin, and here Italian meets Slovene. In the past the Julian saddle has played a part in various imperial strategies : it formed the chief access to the Danubian provinces of Rome ; Napoleon's short-lived Illyrian Provinces with the capital at Ljubljana (Laibach) were created to control it ; Trieste was the principal port of Austria, and the district has been the subject of contention for Italy and Yugoslavia after both world wars. At the opposite end of the lowland the Carpathians offer only a slight barrier because all but the outer or sand-stone zone of the mountains has been engulfed ; so the Dukla and other passes there have many times seen the irruption of invaders. Most of this narrow tract of the mountains and the near part of the plain are peopled by Ruthenians, so in 1919 this territory, previously in Hungary, was tacked on to the new state of Czechoslovakia ; now it is part of the Ukrainian S.S.R. and undoubtedly an area of importance in Soviet strategy. The remainder of the northern Carpathians forms the homeland of the Slovaks, while the much larger area of the southern Carpathians—or Transylvania—is occupied, with an important exception, by the Romanians. Essentially a people of these wooded mountains, the Romanians have spread out upon the plains when it was safe to do so, but although subject for many centuries to Magyar and Turkish rule they have retained their own culture and notably their, mainly, Romance language while adhering in majority to the Greek Church. Transylvania, in fact, has proved to be a natural fastness. Nevertheless, because of its position in relation to the eastern plains, it had to be defended, and this fact led to the ethnic exception mentioned above. The Magyars who were the last of the Danubian peoples to arrive, c. 900 A.D., having conquered the Pannonian plain, installed colonies of their Szekler kinsmen within the sharp bend of the Carpathians, to defend the passes, and then, in the twelfth century, other colonies of Germans who established the towns and developed a vigorous commerce. The descendants of both remain as compact adjoining groups, numbering (about 1939) some 600,000 and 200,000 respectively, and as the Szekler territory is now declared autonomous and lies in the middle of Romania it is perhaps unlikely again to be a strategic area of importance. But these lands of the Szekler and German minorities form a notable example of pronounced geographical individuality that is due to deliberate colonisation and has persisted for eight centuries ; in the upper basins of the Rivers Mures and Olt within the Carpathian salient the aspect of the towns, villages and farms is plainly exotic, and so are the languages, religions and customs of these peoples who were privileged under Magyar rule.

It will be recalled that, in regard to the Balkan Peninsula and Anatolia, a distinction was drawn between the relief of the inner and outer zones, the former nearer the Black Sea consisting of block-mountains and basins, the latter of almost continuous ranges of mountains. Thus in the Danubian part of the Peninsula the Dinaric system is the most serious barrier and the least hospitable tract, on account of the climate and the prevalence of porous limestone ; it culminates in the karstic plateau of Montenegro (Crna Gora), and then recedes from the Adriatic and bends south in Albania. On the opposite side there is the Balkan arc, not exceeding 40 miles (65 km.) in width, and the massive highlands of Rhodope and the two large lowlands without very high barriers from the Black Sea. Between the western and eastern mountains is a maze-like area of fractured blocks and basins occupying the 300 miles (480 km.) from the Danube to the Aegean Sea, and through this the direct southward route from the Pannonian plain. It rises at the watershed between the Morava and Vardar rivers to little over 1,000 feet (300 m.), and here about these headwaters the first Serbian state arose in the twelfth century. From the middle Morava valley a comparable route branches at Nish, the Roman Naissus, leading to Istanbul ; it passes through Sofiya near its summit, but the medieval heart of Bulgaria lay north of the Balkan and near the sea. Thus the southern Slavs have had different histories in the west and east of the Peninsula, intermingling with different earlier peoples—Illyrians and Thracians—subject in different degrees to the successive influences of the Byzantines and Turks according to their position in relation to the Straits and to the routes. In the west, again, there is the still noticeable difference in the social character of the Slovenes and Croats on the one hand and of the Serbs on the other, despite the unity of the Serbo-Croat language. This is the result of the prolonged inclusion of the Slovenes and Croats in the Austro-Hungarian Empire, and of their adherence to the Roman Church. The religious schism is of a long standing while the eastern boundary of Bosnia and Herzegovina until 1919, although not then coinciding with the ecclesiastical division, was of great antiquity, since it corresponded to a provincial partition of the Roman Empire made in the third century A.D. But more important than these divisions of the southern Slavs is their long adaptation to the physical environment as herdsmen and small farmers, among forests which they have gradually cleared from the basins, and to which they retreated—at least in the west—from Ottoman rule. The civilisation of the great majority came from Byzantium, but later many accepted Islam, and Muslim groups still exist in parts of both Bulgaria and Yugoslavia.

The Pannonian basin has been since the tenth century principally the land of the Magyars ; they dominated the kingdom of Hungary, which was limited in north and east by the Carpathians and in the west by the several subalpine Marches, a frontier that has virtually persisted. Like the Normans in England, the original Magyars were not numerous, but their language was adopted by the Slavs and others in whom they merged and whose agriculture they learned. The Danube from its entry delimits the upland part of the basin to south and then west of the river. This was the Roman Pannonia, but from the point of view of the Magyars, out of the east, it is Trans-Danubia. The relief is dominated by the Bakony Hills, which are bounded by the fracture mentioned earlier in the chapter, and this and lower faulted blocks separate the Great from the Little Plain (or Alföld), the latter being a western forecourt of the former and guarded by the much-contested city of Bratislava (Pozsony or Pressburg).

The human settlements of this basin and those of the lowlands beyond the southern Carpathians and in the Balkan Peninsula owe their character in large measure to the effects of the Turkish occupation and of recolonisation after the Ottoman withdrawal, from the seventeenth to the nineteenth centuries. The rural economy is now partly in transition towards collective farming on the Russian model, but progress in this is uneven, so that most of the plains on the left bank of the middle and lower Danube must still bear the stamp of the conversion from large estates to small farms which was rapidly completed after the Second War. Within the Balkan Peninsula, Transylvania and western Hungary these changes are less obvious since the relief makes areas of continuous farmland less common and, except in Transylvania, the land already belonged mainly to peasants. Furthermore, it was chiefly this history of deliberate colonisation of unoccupied land which produced the remarkable ethnic mosaic, notably in the southern part of the Great Alföld now in Yugoslavia and Romania. There were not enough Magyars to occupy this plan fully even on a mainly pastoral basis, so that the predominant populations in the south came to be southern Slavs and Germans, Romanians in the east and Slovaks in the north. Because of this history the plain is marked by very large villages and rural towns, closely built for defence in case of those which survived the Turkish occupation, while the colonies of the eighteenth century are largely open agglomerations of cottages with a grid plan. Many of these have now declined in favour of dispersed farms, with greater agricultural efficiency, but collective farming will doubtless again lead to more concentration. In 1919 Hungary was enormously reduced in area, and, owing to the difficulty of finding satisfactory ethnic boundaries over a quarter of the Magyars were left as minorities in the neighbouring states.

On Fig. 45 (p. 256) it is seen that the nuclei of the modern states are not necessarily the same as those of the medieval kingdoms, but in all the cases now under consideration they are areas that were relatively immune from Turkish attention: the wooded hills of Transylvania and north-western Hungary; the oak forests of Serbia athwart the lower Morava. These three, along with the Peloponnesus in Greece, are the only centres from which native insurrections led to liberation. But the foothills of the Carpathians and the northern valleys of the Balkan are also shown as the districts in which national feeling and the spirit of resistance were maintained by Romanians and Bulgarians respectively, pending liberation from Turkey by the Great Powers, especially Russia. In and about these cores the several national characteristics may still be studied in purest form.

Slovakia, coincident mainly with the northern Carpathians, was never subjected to Turkish rule, but for a far longer period than this episode it was under the Hungarian crown. The Slovaks, then, who were so long repressed remained a backward people even after a generation as citizens of Czechoslovakia; it is significant, too, that the capital, Bratislava, is close to the frontiers of three countries, away from the main body of Slovaks. The plain here with many Magyar inhabitants merges in that of the Morava (or March), peopled by Czechs, which was an Imperial Mark and, together with Bohemia, was under Austrian rule for four centuries. Thus the end of the Carpathians coincides with a cultural divide which the Republic has not yet obliterated. The Bohemian-Moravian plateau lies physically and culturally in central Europe, yet its form made it for long a bastion against the Germans, and so it remains a western outpost of the Slavs. Its mineral wealth, however, includes coal and iron, and its people have developed many skills. Therefore, under the Habsburgs, and especially in the past century, this became the leading industrial province of the dual Empire. The industries of Slovakia, by contrast, were only moderately developed under Hungarian administration, although the Ore Mountains are rich in the metals that were mined by the Germans from the Middle Ages. Under the Republic, also, Slovakian industry has remained behind that of the Czech lands.

This discussion of the Danubian lands has so far emphasised mainly the contrasts which they present, and it is time to revert to their inherent potential unity. When the Habsburg Empire crumbled in defeat it was often described as 'rickety' or 'ramshackle', and so it was, but the reasons were historical and political. The Empire embraced the greater part of these lands and some beyond their limits, while World War I began with an attempt to push farther into the Dinaric part of them. It is a reasonable view that the Empire as a unit was politically infirm but in the main geographically sound, and further, that the partition was a misfortune because the constituent parts, that are naturally so interdependent, were subsequently administered in an ultra-national spirit. Certainly there is no other part of Europe where the need of some bond of economic association is more clamant. Nevertheless, whatever the political and social bases of actions by governments, there is much evidence of recent works of construction apparently so planned that they should lead to a widespread economic benefit.

The most obvious natural links are the Danube and its tributaries. The importance of the waterway has long been recognised internationally, so also has the need to cope with the danger of flooding, but hitherto without great effect. There remain the questions of harnessing the rivers for power and irrigation, and these require international co-operation to attain the best results; all these aspects of hydrography are closely interrelated.

In the Pannonian basin the physical forces—like the ethnic—are delicately balanced. The waters from all directions meet here; their deposits have accumulated to great depth as the bottom sank; while deepening of the canyon outlet by erosion has drained the Pannonian lake, the rivers need all the help man can give to keep them in their beds. The Tisza is the most serious menace since it occupies the lowest part of the basin, first following the long-axis mentioned earlier, and then flowing southward to the Danube. On this winding course for some 700 miles (1,100 km.) its average fall is about 1 foot in 5 miles (1 m. in 27 km.), and in the last 150 miles (240 km.) 1 foot in 10 miles (1 m. in 54 km.). Moreover, it gathers in most of the Carpathian rivers, and is thus a very poor conduit for their flow in the spring, more especially because the Danube, swollen by the thaw in the Alps, then acts like a dam at the confluence. From 1845 onwards much land was protected by shortening and embanking these rivers, canals made and marsh reclaimed, the whole river system being then in Hungary and unified control of the upper courses feasible. Now the rivers come from three other countries, and the Tisza's lowest and most sluggish part is in Yugoslavia. Renewed technical progress is now reported on this river: the first of three barrages has been built, at Tiszalök near Tokay. It is said to be 9 metres (30 ft.) high, so must make a large reservoir above it, and provides much electricity as well as water for irrigation. The other two dams are planned for Tiszabö and Szeged. It seems unlikely that these works would have been undertaken without assurance of control beyond the frontiers.

There are many indications of a great effort in the Danubian countries to create manufacturing industries, and so eventually bring about a change in their economic structure after the pattern of the U.S.S.R., and to reduce the extreme pressure of population upon the agricultural land. Moreover, the policy appears to be to avoid concentration of industries, and indeed in the absence of any great coalfield other than that of Silesia there is no necessity for this, provided electricity is available and transport facilities adequate.

CHAPTER 24

CENTRAL EUROPE

UNDER Rome the south-western part of central Europe lay within the Empire, but the historic events that still dominate the region are the subsequent movements of the ' barbarians ', for these determined the present distribution of the German language between the North Sea and the Alps. The firm establishment of Germanic tribes in the central and eastern Alps and their acquisition of the whole valley of the Rhine has given this people a substantial and varied block of Europe for its evolution, and one situated in a key position. The plain east of the Saale and Elbe bears traces of the medieval history of German eastward expansion, with Slavonic place-names abundant, with visible remnants of Wendish settlements and even an ' island ' of Wendish speech about the upper Spree. Along the Baltic the evidences of German rule or influence extend beyond the present frontier of the U.S.S.R., but inland they are less evident beyond the Oder. The basin of the Vistula then is definitely Polish, the heart of the historic kingdom and the modern republic alike. Poland will be regarded here as part of central rather than of eastern Europe. The Czech nation was able to develop within the lowlands of Bohemia, defended by high and wooded plateaus and ridges, and there it was reborn in 1918. Culturally this part of Czechoslovakia belongs to central Europe, but as already noted it is otherwise inseparable from the Danubian lands. In the west the importance of the Rhine valley as a route and the attraction of its rich lands have influenced the course of history sometimes to the disadvantage of the German states, without, however, bringing the distribution of the French language to the Rhine, except partially in Alsace. On the other hand, the Dutch nation with its language akin to the neighbouring Low German speech has developed its own very distinctive culture in and adjoining the delta ; and beyond this the two geographic and ethnic units, Flanders with virtually the same language as the Dutch, and French-speaking Wallonia with its core on the Roman approach to Köln, are united in the modern Belgium. These two ' Low Countries ' must be considered in some ways as in central Europe, but at least equally as western nations ; Luxembourg, too, although German by language, certainly shares in the economy and culture of her western neighbours. The survival of the Friesian language in the northern part of the Netherlands and in Slesvig is an interesting case of association during 2,000 years of a people with a special habitat of sea-marsh and islands.

Switzerland is the unique state with four official languages ; it traces its political origin to the union of the Three Forest Cantons with the neighbouring district of Luzern, which together control access to the passes leading directly from central Europe to Italy. By progressive adherence to this federation of cantons, in majority German, followed by those of French, Italian and Romansh speech and culture, Switzerland only in 1815 reached its present extent and obtained full value from its position between the Juras and the ' Italian ' Lakes. In the south-east Austria is more restricted to the Alps than Switzerland is; it remains a German bastion that is greatly concerned with the Danube, its main artery, and would be greatly hampered if circumstances restricted its relations with the plains to the east. The leading fact about central Europe is that some 75 millions of its inhabitants have German as their mother tongue, and that they form a solid block. This is flanked on the west and east by territory that must be considered at least partly within the region, inhabited by some 52 millions speaking other languages. Central Europe, therefore, derives its unity from the course of history which made it substantially German, but this in turn was deeply influenced by the natural relations of the plain with the system of plateaus, ridges and basins to the south and of these again with the Alps. In particular the arteries of the region have always been formed by the valleys of the combined systems of the Rhine and Weser and those leading from the former to the upper Danube.

The diverse relief between the plain and the Alps is due to erosion working upon most varied geological structures. These are simplest in the south within the triangle bounded by the Alps, the Bohemian and Thüringian Forests, and, on the west less clearly by a line from the latter ridge to the Black Forest and the Jura. The part of this area south of the Danube is the plateau known as the Alpine Foreland, extending from the Lake of Geneva to Upper Austria ; the chief roughness of its surface is due to the litter of moraines left by former Alpine glaciers. North of the river are the scarplands of Swabia and Franconia, which resemble those of England in origin and trend. The whole triangle which is drained by the Danube, Neckar and Main is occupied by sedimentary rocks that are without valuable minerals, so the inhabitants have depended very largely upon agriculture and stock-keeping. Most of the territory came to be absorbed by the two largest German kingdoms, Bavaria and Würtemberg, and the Swiss cantons ; but the small Hohenzollern state astride the upper Danube and Neckar is of historical significance.

Enclosing this triangular tract and extending from Germany into France, Belgium and Czechoslovakia are the remnants of the ' Hercynian Mountains ', of late Carboniferous times : nothing but the worn stumps of this system, but nevertheless consisting of hard and crumpled rocks. These remnants form the highlands from the Vosges and the Belgian Ardennes in the west to the

Jesenik which overlook the Moravian Gate (Czechoslovakia) in the east, so they occupy all of central Germany. The entire area might be termed the mosaic of mid-Europe, the pieces being the hills of the strong rocks and the basins and vales in which younger and weaker strata are preserved. The joints of the mosaic like the young valleys that are deeply etched in the plateaus tend to follow three directions : WSW.-ENE., NW.-SE., and NNE.-SSW. As a result of this complex pattern, which is largely due to dislocations that have guided the erosion, there are few direct and easy routes, and the Rhine is the only river which crosses the whole belt. Moreover, since none of the basins is large, this middle zone lacks a natural core for human development ; hence throughout history there have been many tribal areas succeeded by a medley of small states presenting a mosaic much more intricate than that of the relief.

Several basins, however, are of special importance : the rift valley of the middle Rhine and the inner basin of Bohemia as well as those that are open to the plain; the embayments of Köln and Westphalia and that of Saxony and Thüringia. All these are largely floored by rich soil, much of it on loess, and all have mineral resources. It happens that the disturbed geological history of the Hercynian system led to the deposition of metallic ores in what are now the heights near the plain. Thus mining, which is recorded since the tenth century and which had its effect in spreading the German civilisation far beyond these hills, also contributed to the wealth of the hill-foot belt of the plain. Some of these mines survive, but not now as leading world sources of silver, lead, zinc, copper, tin or iron, although Jachymov—formerly Joach-imsthal—seems to have this status in respect of its pitchblende for uranium. On the other hand, the structures buried under the basins mentioned above contain the leading coalfields and the salt and potash fields of Germany, while large amounts of lignite lie almost at the surface. The French source of potash is in Alsace and the hill-foot zone in Poland contains the coalfield and the zinc and lead of Silesia. So the southern margin of the plain, and especially the embayments, has seen the rise of great modern industries that are often located where medieval crafts had their origins, and where the crossing of trade routes had long favoured the foundation of towns.

As already suggested there are some good reasons for including in a discussion of central Europe the great plain from the Franco-Belgian frontier in the west to the Russo-Polish frontier in the east ; even though the nations involved differ greatly from the Germans in many respects, and these flanking territories are certainly transitional in character. The eastern political limit that has been selected coincides generally with the isthmus of Europe between the Gulf of Danzig and the mouth of the Danube in its northern half ; and it will be recalled that about this line there is a more abrupt transition in climatic and dependent phenomena than farther east. The area of the plain in Poland is now about twice as large as that in Germany ; but about half of Poland—the west and north—was held by Germany throughout the nineteenth century, and parts of it for much longer. Moreover, in contrast to the present affiliation, the historic relations of Poland were with the west.

The plain except near its southern rim is virtually without economic minerals other than sand and clay, so its products are those of mixed agriculture and forestry. But varied industries have been created at the ports and inland cities connected with them. The natural factors affecting the agriculture are first, the decrease in the length of the growing season eastwards and, secondly, the variation in fertility of the soils which is clearly related to the deposits laid down during the Ice Ages. The natural zones then from that of the loess in the south to the boulder clay on the Baltic coast within the latest end-moraines are recognisable in the present use of the land, since this has been determined under scientific guidance for a long enough period, save perhaps in eastern Poland. Forest, therefore, prevails chiefly on the poorest sand-spread and the stonier moraines, pasture in the moister flood plains and former melt-water valleys ; the rest is cultivated land. In the Low Countries and Germany to the Elbe the naturally rich land, the loam in the south and the reclaimed marsh of the coast, is separated by the much wider sandy *geest*, with peat bog in places which is partly reclaimed. East of the Elbe there is more variety, but a similar zoning occurs. The coast almost throughout is low and the river mouths are estuaries, those on the North Sea being strongly tidal. All have their ports at which trade was fostered by the Hansa merchants, and their establishments can often still be recognised as the nuclei of vast modern installations in the greater ports.

Germany

Germany although dominant in central Europe is the youngest state, and the new empire of 1871 resulted from the hegemony of Prussia, which had expanded from its core in Brandenburg east of the Elbe. Throughout the Prussian kingdom Slavonic place-names—Wendish and Polish—were as common as German, since this was colonial territory. Thus Berlin itself, bearing a Slavonic name, and sited at a crossing between lakes, was scarcely the ideal capital for a nation whose roots lay west of the Elbe and whose culture originated along the Rhine and in the hills. The Hohenzollerns as guardians of the Mittelmark, the vulnerable passage from the east, had to be well armed, and so militarism was rooted in this German outpost east of the Elbe. While Prussia was growing in strength, Germany south of the plain was a mosaic of small states, and on a political map of the period there is little to suggest the inherent importance of cities such as Köln, Frankfurt a/Main, Leipzig or Nürnberg.

Among the more spectacular developments on the plain during the decades after 1871 were the rationalising of agriculture with extension of potatoes and roots including sugar-beet, the exploitation of the potash salts and their use in agriculture along with phosphates from the steel works, the multiplication of pigs, reclamation of peat bogs. With the improvement of seaports there was also great development of fisheries. Without all this the vast increase of coal-mining and manufacture and the creation of fleets for peace and war could not have taken place. The formation of the 'Wilhelmian' Empire, under the hegemony of Prussia, accounted for the mushroom growth of Berlin. Today Berlin is but 50 miles (80 km.) from the frontier, and the nearest port Szczecin (Stettin) is in Poland. Germany has lost the lands that had surplus agricultural produce. After World War II, the Soviet occupation zone extended beyond the line of greatest Slavonic expansion at the time of Charlemagne, notably where it embraced the whole of the Saxon and Thüringian embayment and the Altmark. By this it included much of the richest farmland, most of the potash and lignite deposits and many great industries. A reunited Germany, even with the serious truncation in the east, would remain a remarkably well-balanced geographical and economic unit with a great variety of resources, and there is surely a strong case for the selection of a new capital city placed nearer the heart of the old German civilisation.

The Low Countries

The pattern in northern Germany of population density, of towns and of high farming is seen to be repeated on a smaller scale in the Low Countries. Belgium, another young state created in 1839, amalgamates two ancient and rich lands different in language and culture : the one, the hill-foot zone bordering the Rivers Meuse and Sambre and the Roman road from Gaul to the lower Rhine, the other, Flanders with its estuaries including that of the Schelde. These are not far apart, and the poorer land between was made highly pro-ductive in the Middle Ages. Farther east a very narrow strip of the Nether-lands, the Province of Limburg, reaches the hill-foot and its coalfield. But the great majority of the Dutch live on the rich coastal and deltaic marsh reclaimed by themselves and extending from Zeeland through Holland to Friesland and Groningen. And this is backed, as in Germany, by the sandy *geest* and the peat bogs which once formed the nearly empty frontier belt towards the Germans. But the most distinctive trait of these two kingdoms is their dominance of important routes, from France and England to the Rhineland and beyond, and, in the case of the Netherlands, astride the mouths of the Rhine and the Schelde. Modern Belgium has made the most of her position by developing railways and waterways and the port of Antwerp. The

Dutch have flourished at sea, and by the exploitation of tropical agriculture and minerals in the colonies—most of which are now lost to them. While constantly reclaiming and defending their land against sea and rivers they have ensured access to the seaports ; but the Netherlands is greatly dependent upon the prosperity of German industries along the Rhine. Both countries have large interests overseas, in trade, finance, transport and work. As a result of these facts the population densities are the highest in Europe and, as with Britain, both nations must import much of their food as well as many of the materials for their manufactures. For these they pay with goods, services and foreign investments. The two countries have recently suffered from German aggression—twice in the case of Belgium despite the treaty guaranteeing her neutrality ; and this has given them further encouragement to look to the west, at least politically. The effort to create a single economic union for Belgium, Netherlands and Luxembourg (Benelux) has been protracted because some Belgian and Dutch goods, especially farm produce, are in competition in foreign markets. Again the Dutch suffered more heavily from the war than the Belgians, and economic differences resulted from this. Finally the Belgian desire to be linked directly to the Rhine by a new canal has met with Dutch caution.

Poland

Poland is about five times the size of the Low Countries, but its population is only one-third larger. To be comparable with them economically and culturally Poland needs time, since, despite the long history of the old kingdom as the outpost of western Christendom, this is virtually a new country, reborn after devastation in two wars ; indeed, this is a second rebirth and with revised frontiers. It is difficult for a British citizen to appreciate the effects upon a nation of such large territorial changes as have taken place in this part of the plain. Those of the eighteenth century led to complete suppression, that of 1919 remade Poland, but with some very awkward boundaries in the interest of the Germans of the Baltic lands and in Silesia. By the latest changes these have been eliminated and accompanied by mass movements of population. Both frontiers on the plain have been shifted westward, that with Russia by some 100 miles (160 km.), while the German has been placed—at least provisionally—on the Oder and the Neisse to the northernmost point of Czechoslovakia. This means a large reduction of area, but undoubted gains in other ways. By the acquisition of German Silesia, the Neumark, Danzig and most of Pommern and East Prussia, Poland fell heir to highly productive farmland, the German part of the Upper Silesian coalfield with its heavy industry, the coal of Lower Silesia and two important seaports. Whatever justification may be urged for these changes based upon the history of the last

200, or even 40, years, the Germans cannot acquiesce easily, if only because their ancestors conquered the lost territories at various dates from the tenth to the fifteenth centuries.

There can be no doubt that Poland has become economically a well-balanced state, capable of great production. It consists mostly of plain, but in the south, with low scarplands and the stumps of Hercynian folds rising gently in the Łysogóry that are thrust forward from the Carpathians and are embraced by the upper Vistula. The hill-foot zone has the same character as in Germany save that only a few towns like Kraków, once the capital, have a long history built into them ; also, the top of the hills bears the frontier with Czechoslovakia. In the middle of the zone is the great coalfield lying just outside the Moravian Gate, for the existence of both has a single geological explanation. Most of the field is in Poland, and it forms a notable focus first of industries and secondly of railways which serve them as well as the distribution of coal throughout and beyond the country. Poland is changing rapidly from a mainly agrarian state to one with a balance more typical of central Europe, and less than half of the workers are now engaged in agriculture. The process has been accompanied by adoption of the economic and social organisation of the Soviet Union. The fact that the Polish and Czech languages meet in Upper Silesia and that the two nations share in the resources of coal makes economic co-operation most desirable, and it is already being accomplished. As already noted, the Moravian Gate provides the natural access from the Baltic to the Danube, and it seems likely that the two states will soon make this a reality for shipping by building a canal southwards from the Oder.

The Western Fringe

The ethnic transition on the western fringe of central Europe was evident in the division of Belgium and in dual affinities of Luxembourg. It is seen further in the history of Lorraine and Alsace. The iron field of Lorraine, which is almost entirely in France, is of great importance to Belgian and German industry. Similarly the territory of the Saar, containing a coalfield adjoining the iron, has been a source of dispute between France and Germany since 1919. This whole belt of plateaus west of the Rhine has indeed had a chequered history ever since the partition of the Carolingian Empire by the treaty of Verdun in A.D. 843. Perhaps it is a happy augury that the Council of Europe selected Strasbourg as its seat and, in a smaller way, that a university has been founded in the Saar Territory with an equal number of French and German professors. France, Germany and Switzerland meet at the Gap of Burgundy, one of the nodal points of Europe ; beyond this two of these countries share the Rhine and two the Jura Mountains, the outwork of the Alps, as their frontiers.

The Alps

The Alps provide a key to the understanding of geographical relations of lands on all their sides, and four of the major regions adopted in this book meet among these mountains. For convenience, therefore, and because of their unity, the Alps must be considered as a whole at this point. The system owes its origin to folding of the rocks, prolonged throughout most of the Tertiary Era by pressures generally from the 'Italian' or inner side, and this involved the thrusting of great overturned and recumbent folds one upon the other. The Alps derive their shape in plan (Fig. 46) from the position of older crustal blocks of 'Hercynian' Europe against which the pressure was exerted. East of Lake Constance the resistant mass is concealed, but its edge presumed to lie along the foot of the Alps seems to have the 'Hercynian' trend (ENE.-WSW.) that is common farther north. Adjoining this are the visible blocks of the Black Forest and the Vosges; then after a gap in which there has been room for the milder outer ripples, the folds of the Jura, comes the Central Massif of France, and finally, in the south-west, the mass of Provence. The outer or 'Prealps' reach farthest west in the group round Die (Provence) (D on the map), where the folds begin to trend from east to west affected by this block of Provence.

The Alps owe their height to a posthumous upwarping of the whole system, after enormous denudation of the original crumpled structures had been effected. To this elevation are due first the very deep dissection by rivers, and secondly, the heavy glaciations which followed and altered the form of mountain and valley in many details. It is probable that rivers in many cases acquired their present courses owing to unevenness in the general elevation.

There is a fundamental difference between the western and eastern halves of the mountains. The former, which is strongly curved in plan, is the higher and the narrower half, and it has a very steep inner slope. The division follows a line from Lake Constance to Lake Como, which has the same trend as the Rhine rift between the Vosges and Black Forest, and it is followed by important valleys. The very deep carving of the Alps by rivers and former glaciers makes the mountains less of a barrier than their average height would suggest. In the first place the over-deepened troughs of the lower valleys are spacious and low enough to support a large agricultural population who grow the same crops as those of the neighbouring plains. And again, far above these troughs, many of the passes are surprisingly low in relation to the peaks, while beneath some of them the railway tunnels are not inordinately long because glacial erosion has steepened the slopes on both sides. Most of the glens are like stairways with gentle and steep stretches in succession, and if this is a nuisance to the road builder, the steep falls offer abundant sites for power stations.

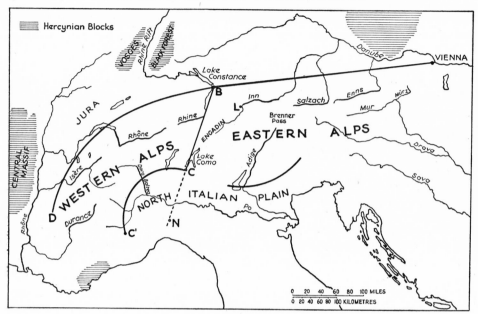

Fig. 46
Sketch map of the Alps

The structural division between the west and the east, Bregenz (B) to Como (C) if prolonged reaches the junction of the Ligurian Alps and the Appennines south of Novi (N). The outer margin of the Alps is straight from the Danube to the Rhine (B) ; from this valley to the Diois group (D) it is an arc of some 300 miles (480 kilometres) radius, and equal in length to the straight edge to the east (312 miles, or 500 kilometres). The inner edge of the western Alps is also an arc, with radius of 68 miles (110 kilometres),extending from Como (C) to Cuneo (C¹). One radius of both arcs is followed in part by the deep transverse glens of the Rhône and the Dora Baltea, and since this line, like the structural division BC prolonged, meets the abrupt end of the Appennines it may well be of structural significance. In the Eastern Alps the southern edge is an arc convex to the south and centred at Landeck (L) on the Inn ; this southward bulge is crossed by parallel transverse glens similar in trend to the BC line, that of the Adige giving access to the Brenner Pass.

From end to end the outer part of the system is marked by the Alpine Furrow, the feature which most consistently coincides with structural lines ; it is followed, in order from west to east, by parts of these rivers : Durance, Isère, Rhône, Rhine, Inn, Salzach and Enns, each of which turns out through a deep transverse glen. The inner margin of the system has nothing to compare with this, but in the south-east the rivers Mur and Mürz, Drava and Gail and the Sava occupy a series of diverging valleys that conform to the structural elements. Finally the unique long oblique furrow of the upper Inn—the Engadin—leads from the Alpine Furrow at Landeck over to Lake Como.

The Alps have been so thoroughly exploited by a tireless peasantry that every patch of gentler slope is used for cultivation or pasture, and most of the torrents serve for irrigation. The mountains have their own climates, and although these have been referred to in earlier chapters precipitation may be mentioned again. The wetter parts, receiving the equivalent of over 60 inches (1,500 mm.) of rain, extend across the central Alps from the Bernese Oberland to the Italian Lakes and thence on the ranges near to both the plains, the wettest being those to north-east of the Adriatic Sea. In contrast some of the inner valleys have less than 25 inches (640 mm.). The western Prealps in their northern part are fairly well watered, but very much drier in the south where the Mediterranean climate has its effect. On the whole, it may be said that penetration of the Alps is easier for man than it is for rain. Because of the rainfall the remaining forests are chiefly on the wet outer ranges on both sides of the eastern Alps ; and the effect of precipitation is seen also in the distribution of animals, the proportion of cattle to sheep declining toward the south-west.

The rain- and snow-fall of the Alps is of inestimable value to Europe since it feeds the Rhine, Danube, Rhône and Po and many of their tributaries, provides water for irrigation along their courses and permits navigation and, in places, the generation of power in the lowlands. Electricity raised within the mountains is also an export ; but this is more profitably used near its source, especially where raw materials are local as in the wood and paper industries of Austria. Besides these exports—water, electricity and a wide range of manufactures, there are the cattle which go out to replenish the herds of the plains, and by no means least in importance, people—those who desert the less accessible villages, together with seasonal or temporary emigrants. On the other hand, the mountains now serve an ever widening circle of Europe as a resort for the leisure of townspeople. Switzerland has shown the way to welcome this annual flood of visitors, and the other countries are learning quickly how to profit from their scenery and climate in this way.

Political control of the Alps, like other human relations, has been closely bound up with communications. The Swiss example has been mentioned ; but long before the union of the Forest Cantons the Romans were concerned with keeping the routes over the Alps safe and fit for troops and trade in luxuries. Thus the following are cases where the modern roads have evolved more or less from Roman bridle and cart tracks : Turin to Valence by the Mont Genèvre ; Ivrea to Lyon by the Little St Bernard ; Milan to Bregenz by the Splügen ; Verona to Augsburg by the Brenner and Udine to the Pustertal by the Carnico Pass. During the Middle Ages the Brenner route was the most important in the trade of the Holy Roman Empire. Monasteries in high places throughout the Alps serve to recall the interest of the Church in transalpine travel. Command of the western passes enabled the House of Savoy to maintain its rule across the Alps for nine centuries ; similarly the interest of Austria in Tirol and later on the plain of Italy led to the building of proper roads over the Semmering, the Brenner and other passes ; but the other principal carriage roads belong to the Napoleonic period, since they were essential to the strategy of the time. Motor traffic has caused the revival of road engineering, and a road tunnel through Mont Blanc has been projected by France and Italy. From 1850 railways diverted attention from the roads, and the tunnels came to be of great economic advantage to the various states, notably to Italy and there, above all, to the city of Milan. The Mont Cenis and the Simplon tunnels were driven under frontiers, and therefore were international by intent, but in the south-east there were two, formerly Austrian, that became international by the creation of Yugoslavia—that of Triglav on the former Italian frontier and the Karawanken tunnel on the Austrian boundary.

It is not easy to assess the relative importance of these mountains to the countries which share them. Whatever the political division the rivers would flow as they do, but the sites for hydro-electric power are real national assets. Among other assets not so far reviewed are the minerals, which, however, are not present in great amounts despite the geological variety of the Alps. They are found now chiefly in the east, where Yugoslavia has good sources of zinc and mercury, and Italy zinc, while Austria possesses really large quantities of salt and iron. The former comes from the Triassic rocks of the Prealps, where there are many ' salt ' place-names, of which one, Hall on the Inn, is the chief mining centre ; the iron, again, which has long been worked, gives the name to the range, the Eisenerzalpen. In France deposits of anthracite and iron ore near Grenoble are comparatively unimportant. Of the forests the greatest are those in Austria, while those of the Venetian Alps are specially important to Italy. The most widespread industries are the textiles, which are highly developed in certain valleys in each country, and each again has its quota of the newer chemical and metallurgical factories near the sources of power. There can be no question that the Alps mean much more to the Swiss and the Austrian nations than to the Italian or even the French. It should be noted that the people of Germany, although very little of the mountains is within their territory, are very conscious of this share, and consider that Bavarians and Austrians differ chiefly in name. The Alps certainly have induced a way of life among the inhabitants, of whatever ancestry or language, and the modern changes in the economy that are due to technical developments seem to have had similar effects throughout the mountains, the chief variable being the degree of industrialisation. There have been, however, certain causes of disharmony between the Alpine states due to the treatment of ethnic minorities. By far the most serious within the mountains was the case of the 300,000 Austrians who became Italian subjects when South Tirol passed to Italy in 1919. After World War II Alto Adige became one of the autonomous regions under the new Italian constitution.

Switzerland

Switzerland is distinguished among the states of Europe for several reasons : first from the ethnic variety of the cantons composing the Federation, secondly from the national policy of perpetual neutrality—a distinction shared with Austria after the Treaty signed in 1955—and thirdly on account of the economic relations of the Swiss with many countries. The geographical bearings of these distinctions are plain. In view of the physical character of the country the population of about 5 million represents a high mean density, and apart from farm produce there are few resources derived from local materials. But a very large proportion of the water power is harnessed, and there are varied manufactures located chiefly on the plateau, using imported materials, and this without the advantage of a seaport. Efficiency at home and good understanding with neighbouring countries are therefore essential. So just as the Swiss were formerly valued mercenary soldiers in foreign armies, so they now sell their skill and services in the crafts and professions to a wide foreign market and place investments abroad. The enormous growth of the tourist industry both provides national income and helps to ensure that foreigners are favourably disposed to trade. With these normal relations established, it has paid the great powers to respect the Swiss desire for the last four centuries to keep out of their wars. This policy, however, might have failed in the two world wars but for the known efficiency of the Swiss army and its powerful fixed defences ; by the Second War the Swiss Alps were converted into the ' national redoubt ', probably impregnable and certainly a very costly military objective for an invader ; in the event of its fall the Swiss would destroy the transalpine routes, including the tunnels. The policy of perpetual neutrality is a consequence of the country's position as the small neighbour of great powers, in control of indispensable routes between them. In justification of this policy Switzerland has accepted great international responsibility in many spheres, most notably perhaps in relation to the Red Cross.

Central Europe : Contrasts

The constituent parts of central Europe present the greatest possible contrasts in relief and in rock structure. Because of the relief there is sharp local variation in climate, and together with this a gradual climatic change from south-west—as along the middle Rhine to north-east, in eastern Poland. The loamy soils of the inner vales and the hill-foot have been cultivated since Neolithic times, and these are still the most populous parts. The coastal marshes again, inhabited very early for their pastures, have seen a change but only in degree, being now the scene of perfected dairying and high farming. Throughout the greater part west of the Elbe and south to the Alps the land is worked in small family farms, largely by the owners ; but while this ensures care and inherited skill, full efficiency is impossible from the scattering of strips making a farm. Consolidation, however, proceeds steadily, and the population problem in western Germany will hasten it there. In most of the region except the lower Rhinelands and the mountains farmers live in villages, and these belong to several well-marked types whose origin is bound up with history, while the styles of the houses can be linked to the early distribution of the various Germanic and other peoples. The general effect is that of an old-established rural life and landscape in the west, from coast to Alps ; but this is less characteristic of the eastern lowland with its history of German colonisation, reform under great landlords, and, more recently, reorganisation under Russian influence. There is comparable transition in appearance and function of the towns, and in Chapter 11 the date of origin was stressed as bearing upon these aspects of urban life. The fact of Roman foundation is seldom apparent, although sometimes this affected the medieval plan, but the geographical reasons for these early locations are illuminating in detail. The effects of the progressive establishment of urban life may be traced eastwards, and three elements are to be seen singly or combined in any old town of importance ; those due respectively to the Church, to the princes where not clerical, and to the merchants and their gilds. The architectural styles are distributed, of course, in accordance with the period and with the materials available ; but the degree of elaboration reflects the local prosperity at the time. Of the churches, the older are predominantly Romanesque, but in the towns Gothic churches are probably more numerous. It is rather the Baroque architecture, however, that typifies the region, first in the later Roman Catholic churches, and secondly in the houses of the aristocracy, and especially of those of the numerous rulers who spent freely on the setting of their petty courts.

The eastward gradient in the standard of living and general culture has for long been accentuated by the fact that the whole region except Switzerland has been the theatre of many wars. Most of them were dynastic and need not concern us here, but since 1871 a united Germany with allies has twice made ' total war ' in a way that was possible only because of the productive capacity of central Europe in mine, farm and factory, and of the ability to obtain additional supplies of food and fodder and minerals from the Danubian lands, iron ore from Sweden and fish from the adjoining seas. The wars emphasised the technical efficiency and economic integration that was attained.

CHAPTER 25

THE EASTERN PLAIN

OWING to the decision to adopt in this book the old conventional eastern limit of Europe discussion of the eastern plain must be incomplete ; the Ural has never been a substantial barrier or carried a major political boundary, and the action of the Soviet government, aimed at even greater integration of the whole Union makes the separation highly unrealistic in many ways. It may be noted, however, that Russian geographers for convenience of description and cartography have included the Urals, the Caucasus and Armenia in the ' European ' part of the Union. The Caucasian and Armenian areas, however, have already been included in the southern Borderlands because of the great physical and ethnic differences from Russia, by which they were conquered only in the nineteenth century. It may well be thought even less reasonable to include Karelia, Kola and even Finland with Scandinavia, especially since the boundary is virtually along a main waterway of Russia ; the justification here is almost purely physical. These two outlying regions are essential to the political integrity of the U.S.S.R., and their products now being developed in great variety are indispensable to its economy. Moreover, Josef Stalin was a Georgian.

Europeans of the west have difficulty in appreciating the vastness of the eastern plain and its monotony as compared with their homelands. Yet the history and the character of the Russians have been affected by this vastness and uniformity, and by a third geographic fact, accessibility from Asia. Thus, there has so far been no lack of room, although all round the margins of the plain this had to be found amid alien peoples, or taken from them. The Russians again have thought little of considerable migrations, since these did not usually involve great change of environment. And as for past relations with Asia, it is enough to recall two historical facts : that Russia was more or less under Tatar rule for two centuries (*c.* 1240–1440), and that Russian adventurers reached the Pacific coast some sixty years before Peter the Great had opened his ' window on the Baltic ' and founded Petrograd (1703).

There are no sharp natural boundaries except the rivers, and these have formed the chief network of settlement and intercourse. The elements of climate are all marked by gradual increase in their intensity across the huge territory ; so the various types of soil and natural vegetation are distributed in zones which merge into their neighbours, and the same is true of the various farm crops. Hence, since the inhabitants until this century have lived mainly by agriculture, stock-keeping and wood-cutting, the distribution of rural population has tended to conform to these natural zones; while the towns have been situated on the rivers which flow partly along, but mainly across, the zones. Thus the wedge-shaped area of dense population described (p. 236) as penetrating Russia from the south-west with its axis from the upper Prut to the central Ural represents adaptation to the most favourable climate and soil. But this was not always so. It is true that Kiev, 'the mother of towns', is still near the axis just mentioned, but for long it marked the southernmost settlement of the Scandinavian (i.e. Swedish) or 'Rus' adventurers trading on the Dnepr as the route to Byzantium; Novgorod-the-Great, at the outlet of Lake Ilmen, was the northernmost. Thus the land of the early Russian state extended from north to south across the glacial deposits, the main watershed and the zone of mixed forest, the northern river arteries from the Baltic to the Dnepr being the Neva-Volkhov-Lovat through Novgorod and the Daugava (W. Dvina) from the Gulf of Riga. The later eastward extension of this national core is shown on Fig. 45, from Novgorod to all the mesopotamia of the upper Volga and the Oka, as this was the heart of the Muscovite state, that of the Great Russians. Within this triangle are the oldest Russian towns with their forts and Byzantine churches and monasteries, where such have survived the Second World War. The western part is now the relatively backward and unproductive Republic of White Russia (Byelorussia), which has recently benefited from its westward extension by some 150 miles (240 km.) at the expense of Poland. In the Great Russian part there have been contrasts in the fortunes of the old towns, as in the case of the two Novgorods, which are about equidistant from Moscow. Novgorod-the-Great has long been overshadowed by Petrograd (Leningrad) and has languished. Nizhni Novgorod, now Gorki, from the thirteenth century was like the other city a great commercial centre, but with Asia as its hinterland, and so a northern counterpart of the ancient Antioch. Its location at the confluence of the Volga and Oka has insured its continued trading functions, but in addition Gorki has now become a leading industrial city. Apart, however, from the recent urban growth of which this is typical, the zone of greatest population density has coincided with the tracts where the soil is mostly black earth, somewhat altered by leaching, and where woodland was formerly mingled with tall grass and other herbs. This was the first country to be settled in the Russian advance southward as the Tatar danger receded; it is the historic Ukraine or march, a land of mixed farming and orchards. Most of the area is today in the Ukraine Republic and occupied by the Little Russians, but similar country is included on both sides of the upper Don marking the early Muscovite progress. Many towns throughout the zone were founded in the sixteenth and seventeenth centuries. Contrasted with this is the zone to the south that formerly was treeless prairie, and was first colonised and cultivated in the eighteenth and nineteenth centuries. The black soil prevails but yields to chestnut earth near the coast, rainfall decreases and becomes less regular southwards, while erosion by torrents and wind has to be countered, but irrigation from the lower Dnepr has transformed the agriculture over a limited area, and this will soon happen along the lower Don as well. The former prairie zone is some 100 miles (160 km.) wide in the west, but broadens toward the east so that it embraces the Donets coalfield and the other mineral and industrial districts of the south.

Physical Conditions

In recognising physical influences upon life in Russia the main emphasis must be upon climate and soil, both being uniform over great distances, and upon the rivers which will be further discussed below. The question of relief however, must not be forgotten, as may be the case if the term 'plain' be interpreted too literally. Certainly it is the virtually flat land that is dominant; visible slopes are exceptional and found mostly on the banks of rivers or along their valleys. The plain, in fact, is a dissected plateau; gradual withdrawal of Quaternary marginal seas as well as upwarping of the earth's crust caused the rivers to dig themselves in. The broad differences of altitude have little relation to the underlying rock structures, so the plateau technically is a peneplain, a surface of prolonged erosion which has bevelled the rocks of many ages previously more or less deformed by earlier earth movements. Historically the relief of the river banks, however slight, affected the siting of forts and settlements—most of all on the great southern rivers which have high and often steep right banks. The irregular relief of the moraines in northern Russia influences the land-use and the placing of innumerable dwellings. Throughout most of the plain the bedrock is concealed by superficial deposits except where rivers have exposed it. At some places very hard rock in a channel has always been important, as causing rapids; the leading example is at the granite defile in the bend of the lower Dnepr, where boats had to be landed and hauled past the obstruction. These rapids were replaced by the great dam with a canal and the power station of Dneproges, which, restored after the war, has attracted numerous industries and provided pumped water for irrigation; so a natural menace has been turned to great advantage. Still greater water power will be harnessed at two stations on the big kink and defile of the Volga about Kuibishev. This feature results from a different geological cause, an east-west upfold and fracture of the ancient rocks.

River Systems

The striking fact about the river system is the absence of high divides between the sources of opposing rivers, especially on the main European watershed, where the glaciers or melt-waters of the Ice Age probably were most effective agents in causing such gaps. So portages for boats were established in early times, and then under the Tsars many of them were replaced by well-used canals and for the period a well-integrated system of water transport existed under the old régime, one which included provision of safe harbours for river craft during winter. It is not surprising, therefore, that in Soviet Russia new plans involved the fullest possible development of the waterways in such a manner as to combine this with harnessing water power and providing for irrigation where needed. There could be no more spectacular evidence of the natural unity of European Russia than the scheme to link together the five seas with the metropolitan district communicating with each. Moscow is already specially favoured by the old canals, and by its own new direct link with the Volga ; moreover, the capital is the hub of the railway system, and it is in the same latitude as the Trans-Siberian Railway, which is reached by lines across the Urals with but little deviation. The five seas plan calls for engineering works such as are possible under a totalitarian régime when they are regarded as essential to economic revolution. Space permits reference only to certain elements, enough to indicate the bold changes to be made in the physical geography of Russia. Apart from the winter freezing, the chief defects of the rivers are their variable seasonal volume, their lateral erosion and the silting of their beds. The ordinary measures of maintaining banks and beds need not be discussed ; but they represent vast expenditures owing to the great length of the rivers ; moreover, they are generally simplified by the more prominent feats of dam building which give head for power stations while regulating the flow of water. The first example of this, on the Dnepr, has been mentioned. In two notable cases advantage has been derived from the presence of low, almost flat land near main watersheds for the construction of great reservoirs. The first, north of Rybinsk on the upper Volga, helps to regulate flow and gives access by canal to the Great Lakes and the Baltic, while yielding much power below the main dam ; the lake would be large enough to submerge most of the central lowland of Scotland. The other, which would cover most of England south of the Thames and Bristol Channel, lies in the north-east and connects the head-streams of the Pechora, the Northern Dvina and the Kama ; yet its main purpose relates to the Caspian Sea and the lower Volga. Dams on this river, including those mentioned near Kuibishev, will provide storage and much power to be used partly in raising water to irrigate the arid, and higher, land on the left bank. This irrigation would soon accelerate the shrinking of the Caspian Sea, of which the surface has sunk by several feet in recent years, so the headwaters of two Arctic rivers over 1,000 miles (1,600 km.) away are to be used in compensation. Finally, here in the south-east the narrow but formidable plateau dividing the elbows of Don and Volga has been surmounted by a new canal, and the largest river of Europe is for the first time connected with a branch of the ocean. In addition to these specific works most of the old canals are to be made fit for the large ships of modern inland waterways.

Agricultural Progress

The efforts of Russian scientists to improve agricultural production by means of plant-breeding and mechanisation have been mentioned in Chapter 16 (pp. 192-3). This generally amounts to getting more out of a given climatic zone than was possible before, and by these and other means various crops are extended northwards to their cold limit or south-eastwards to their dry limit. More spectacular is the attempt to extend the growing of trees towards the southern coasts; the purpose is to mitigate the effect of wind, direct and indirect, and the plantations are planned as four continuous windbreaks.

If successful this will represent a triumph of botany and forestry. A change is being slowly brought about also among the moraines of the north by the removal of peat. This has, of course, always had its uses for the peasants, as for litter; but it is now cut at a much greater rate to be used as raw material for chemicals and as fuel for at least three large electric power stations.

Mineral Development

The Soviet policy of industrialisation has led to an intensive search for minerals and so to great increase in geological knowledge as well as expansion in the mining industry. While all this applies specially to Asia it is true to say that the rock structures underlying the European plain have acquired new practical importance. Thus the mining region of the Urals is now flanked on the western piedmont by others newly located at intervals from the Arctic to the Caspian: coalfields on the Pechora, the Taimyr Peninsula and Novaya Zemlya; salt, potash and oil near the upper Kama; phosphates on both sides of the lower Volga; and oil in the Caspian lowland. The immense body of iron ore in the Kursk region between the upper Don and the Desna has been studied but probably remains unworked; on the other hand, the bauxite of Tikhvin east of Leningrad has formed the chief material, albeit of low grade, for Russian aluminium. The metal is made at the Volkhov hydro-electric station only fifty miles from the ore. This proximity is rare in Russia and the industrial planners usually have to allow for long haulage of bulky loads; the interchange of iron ore and coal between the central Ural and the widely separated coalfields, the Donbas and the Kuzbas (cf. p. 200), is typical of the bold planning demanded in this huge realm.

The economic interdependence of the various natural zones and administrative territories has never been greater, and it will certainly increase with improvement in means of transport. Thus there is surely need for more railways if only from the slowness of water transport and its seasonal interruption. Apparently railway building at present is chiefly confined to Asia, but it would appear that the government intend to remedy the serious lack of good motor roads in European Russia.

The Ethnic Pattern

Attention has been given above to the western part of the plain because it included the formative area of the Russian people and state. Progress from Novgorod or Moscow throughout the northern forest involved conquest of indigenous Finnish tribes, while the grasslands of the south had to be cleared chiefly of Turkish-speaking nomads ; and remnants of both these peoples are to be found in the eastern part of the plain. Thus beyond the original Muscovy between the Volga and Oka, a linguistic map of 1939 shows the area of Russian speech as lying in a net of valleys separating ' islands ' of Uralic and Altaic languages, a pattern that reflects Russian colonisation from the sixteenth century onwards.

This composite tract broadens eastward to reach the Arctic and the Caspian shores, and a good deal of it falls within the chain of Autonomous Soviet Republics bearing the tribal names, together with the Kazakh Republic— of a higher political order like the Ukraine—penetrating from Asia nearly to the lower Volga. These republics while retaining the ethnic identity of their majorities must not be regarded as resembling native reserves in the Union of South Africa ; they are all involved in the economic system and developments of the U.S.S.R., even if progress may be relatively slow in some cases. During and since World War II there has been much migration within the U.S.S.R., and doubtless the peoples are much more mingled than in 1939.

The ethnic divisions along the Baltic were formerly sharper than those in the east : Russians with the Estonians, Letts and Lithuanians. For these three peoples the beginning of their short period of independence between the wars meant release of nations, composed chiefly of peasants, both from hated Russian rule and from subjection to landlords descended from the Teutonic Knights. The medieval conquest by this Order, which is still recalled by the imposing castles of the Knights, resulted in the acceptance of Christianity under Rome, but subsequently rejected in favour of the reformed religion except in Lithuania. In the northern half of the territory a period of Swedish rule came in the seventeenth century between that of the Order and that of Russia. These facts, together with the commerce, of the ports account for real cultural differences from Russia, and these are recognised, at least outwardly, by the status of the nations as separate Union Republics. That of Lithuania was extended to Kalinin, formerly Königsberg, thus marking a constant aim of Russian policy, in the west as in the Far East, to acquire coasts with warmer and more open seas. Commercially these Baltic ports Tallinn, Riga and Kalinin must be related to Leningrad, second city of the Union ; perhaps comparison with the association of Southampton and London is appropriate.

From the River Neman (Nemunas) in Lithuania to the Carpathians the plain has been marked by the mingling of peoples, especially Lithuanians and Poles, whose nations were united from the fourteenth to the eighteenth centuries. But these peoples had mixed also with the White Russians and still more with the Ukrainians south of the Pripet marshes. Furthermore, this whole tract included the greatest assemblage of the Jews in Europe, living in towns of all sizes (cf. Fig. 21), and there are still some 2 million Jews in the U.S.S.R. As in the case of Byelorussia the frontier has been moved westward to the River Bug and encloses most of the debatable lands on the plain, and, as already noted, a highly important section of the Carpathians. By the reconquest of Bessarabia, between the Rivers Dnestr and Prut, now the Moldavian S.S.R., a similar region of mixed population was absorbed since, while the majority previously were Romanians, there were colonies of Ukrainians, Bulgars and Germans as well. Thus the western frontier of the U.S.S.R. is established almost directly across the easternmost isthmus of Europe, with one salient over the mountains to the plain of the Tisza ; throughout most of its length it takes in tracts that were not peopled wholly by Russians in 1939. With the exception of Romanian Moldavia the entire Eastern Plain is now included in the Union.

Despite the great area of Soviet Asia the European part of the U.S.S.R. continues to dominate its life and economy. Settlement and industrialisation certainly proceed apace in many regions beyond the Urals and the Caspian, but in 1939 less than 15 per cent of the population lived in Asia, and there is no evidence that this proportion is greater today ; the population added by territorial expansion in Europe, 1940–45, was roughly equal to that of the Asian part in 1939. It may be assumed that relative productivity of the two parts can be measured generally by their population, so in default of statistical evidence it may be accepted that the economy of the Union is still overwhelmingly dependent on the work of its European citizens. Nevertheless many of the indispensable materials are produced mainly in Asia— cotton, gold and some other minerals, for example—and the proportion of goods manufactured in the Asiatic part of the U.S.S.R. may be expected to increase rapidly.

The U.S.S.R. owes its high place as a world power to various factors, of which the following are perhaps the most important : the extent and geographical position of its territory which, like that of the U.S.A., reaches across a continent ; its population, and the fecundity thereof ; the endowment in agricultural land with its capacity for feeding the present population ; its great resources of coal, oil, water power and minerals ; the speed with which these natural resources have been developed and manufactured—suggesting comparison with the U.S.A. ; finally, the record of this people in war and also in peace when organised almost as in war, and notably their resilience on the Eastern Plain of Europe.

CHAPTER 26

THE NORTHERN LANDS

THESE are taken to embrace Denmark, Norway, Sweden and Finland, as well as the Soviet territory west of the White Sea, which is included mainly because it is physically inseparable from Finland. But the real emphasis is upon the culture of the Scandinavian peoples and their Finnish neighbours, who have a western background and outlook. The total population is about twenty millions, assuming that in the Soviet Union—Finno-Karelians, Russians and Lapps—number some 1·5 millions ; because of their different history and situation the following considerations do not apply to these Soviet citizens. Finland has enjoyed independence only for a generation, but prolonged Swedish rule and influence have had great effect ; the other three are remarkable for their long history as nations, although their territorial importance has waxed and waned. These are not great nations by their numbers—respectively over 4, 3, 7 and 4 millions—but the parts played in history by Denmark, Norway and Sweden have been disproportionately great. The vast majority of the peoples belong to the Protestant Lutheran Church ; the Scandinavian written languages are mutually understood, while in Finland Swedish is an official language and is still the speech of 8 per cent of the population. The 30,000 Lapps are mostly in Norway but extend eastward to the Murmansk district. It is perhaps reasonable to select one social characteristic for mention because it is easily measured—dependence upon the telephone. In 1950 the numbers of persons per telephone were : in Denmark, 6 + ; Norway, 7 + ; Sweden, 5 − ; and Finland, 13 − (cf. U.K., 23). This is a good indication of progressiveness in educated nations, of which, about 1900, less than 1 per cent were illiterate ; the use of the telephone is also related to the wide scattering of the population from geographical causes.

The climate which makes human settlement so successful in such high latitudes derives its quality mainly from the western seas that are so abnormally warm ; but the Baltic Sea, with lesser climatic influence, has enabled the Swedes and the Finns to maintain the western contact and outlook. The principal trend of the outer coast, from south-west to north-east, is vital since it allows the Atlantic Drift with its moderating effect and its countless fishes to follow the entire seaboard. This trend is due first to a geological event in the distant past, the Caledonian crustal folds and overthrusts against the Archaean massif or shield of Fennoscandia, but more directly to the formation or the deepening of the Norwegian Sea and, presumably in the same late-Tertiary times, the posthumous upheaval of this outer zone of Scandinavia. This led to increased precipitation and so, in the cold periods of the Pleistocene, to the formation of the great ice-sheets. From the glaciations and their sequel the whole region derives its detailed land-forms, the character of its rivers and lakes, and the presence or absence of detritus and so of soil fit to cultivate. Fennoscandia has been denuded of vast amounts of mantle rock that now lies upon the European Plain and under the western seas. Denmark, a projection of the plains, has benefited and consists of the deposits behind and before the end moraine that forms the axis of Jutland (Jylland). In the glens of Norway and the adjacent part of Sweden moraines and outwash terraces form the more habitable land, while farther east, to the Baltic and White Sea, settlement and routes have been guided by the similar deposits of the ice-sheet and the sinuous gravel ridges, the eskers or åser that mark former subglacial river courses. Furthermore, a fortunate sequel to withdrawal of the ice was sub-mergence of the lower land, and then gradual but partial recovery, by crustal bending, ever since the ice-load was removed. Hence the precious veneer of marine or lake silts that yield good soil. The upward movement continues, by about a metre (three ft.) per century around the Sea of Bothnia where it is greatest, and has its effect upon the rivers on both sides, and especially upon the intricate lake shores in Finland ; while certain of the old harbours have had to be moved as the Baltic shore receded.

The relief of Fennoscandia and various aspects of its human geography have been greatly affected by shattering of the rocks in the past. No doubt most of the metallic ores have formed in fractures of the originally deep-seated Archean rocks which predominate ; but much more obvious is the influence of such dislocations upon the relief and drainage system of Scandinavia. It need not concern us whether this has acted directly or indirectly by promoting erosion on certain lines of weakness ; but the latter may doubtless be traced in the grid-like pattern of Norway's relief and, owing to submergence, its extremely indented western coast. In Sweden again, the central lowland, the axis of which is prolonged by the Skagerrak and the Gulf of Finland, is an area of structural weakness shattered into angular slabs by intersecting faults. Many of the higher blocks of ancient crystalline and ice-scoured rock have long been the scene of metal mining, whereas the lower slabs are covered by lakes or by the best soils in the country, thus providing two reasons for the concentration of nearly half of the population here.

The natural endowments of these lands are their water power, forests, metallic ores, fisheries and soil. Denmark shares only in the last two of these, and the others are unequally distributed. The first exploitation of the resources, except the power, is prehistoric and so also is the seamanship of the Scandinavians, which has enabled them to exert their influence throughout Europe and the world. Most of the areas now most densely peopled were the earliest to be occupied by Neolithic cultivators, and, whatever the effect of changes in climate during the long intervening period, by the third century A.D. the good land was largely settled by tribes who used runic writing of a Germanic language. Many of the names of districts and settlements date from this period and various towns stand on the sites of ancient tribal centres. Although Uppsala and Trondheim, the ancient national sanctuaries of the Swedes and the Norwegians, yielded political dominance to cities with greater commercial advantages, they still play leading parts in the life of the nations. On the other hand their Danish counterparts, Ringsted in Zealand, Ribe and Viborg in Jutland, have faded into comparative obscurity ; Lund, however, in Sweden has since the seventeenth century, remained the capital of Skåne. Thus the three nations have grown from centres established by the Danes and the kings of Svea, conquerors of the Goths, long before Christianity was accepted, while Trondheim grew in fame later, indeed as the sanctuary of the King Olaf who converted the Norwegians. Bergen, Oslo, Stockholm and especially Copenhagen (Köbenhavn = merchants' harbour), are strategically placed as commercial ports, and their growth as such recalls the geographical advantages of Scandinavia for maritime adventure and trade that have been utilised from about 800 A.D. to the present day. The first three centuries marked the Viking Period during which the Danes and Norwegians established their colonies and outposts on Atlantic and Mediterranean coasts, and the Swedes (Varangians or Rus) founded Novgorod and Kiev and so the Russian State. There is a family likeness, now chiefly architectural, about the old quarters of many seaports around the North Baltic seas that bears witness to close intercourse from the Middle Ages onwards, fostered by the German Hansards until the fifteenth century and then by the Dutch. For this reason the entire Baltic coasts might perhaps be regarded as within the Northern lands ; but modern history has broken this Baltic unity.

Since cultivable land in the ice-scoured lands is sparse and irregularly distributed increasing effort has been needed to feed a population that is more and more devoted to industry. The cultivated area of Norway amounts to 3 per cent, of Sweden 9 per cent, and of Finland 10 per cent ; but in each case natural or semi-natural grazing land must be added. The proportion of the population dependent on agriculture is about 25 per cent in Norway and Sweden and 40 per cent in Finland, but these figures are less precise because for many Norwegians farming is combined with fishing, and for Swedes and Finns with forestry ; in Finland 60 per cent of the forest belongs to farmers. In all the countries the emphasis is on livestock, and hay is the principal crop, followed by oats ; but the bread-grains, potatoes and turnips are still speading northwards in varieties suited to the climate and favoured by the long summer day, and with winter or spring wheat tending to replace rye or barley wherever possible. Nevertheless only Sweden can do without much import of cereals, and all four must import fertilisers.

In several respects Denmark differs from the others : 77 per cent of the land is cultivated, yet here, too, only a quarter of the people live by agriculture despite its first importance in the national commerce ; much grain for man and beast and large amounts of manure must be imported in order to maintain the chief exports, animal produce. Although traditional methods and simple tools prevail in many areas, notably western Norway, scientific agriculture is well understood in all four countries, so also is co-operation, in which Denmark was the pioneer. The farms generally are small, the average for Denmark being highest, and the vast majority are worked by the owners, the only real exception being a quarter of Swedish farmland that is held by tenants.

The northern forest covers roughly a quarter of Norway, over half of Sweden and nearly two-thirds of Finland : from the Norwegian Eastland to the Baltic and then to the White Sea it is never out of sight. But while agriculture has led to clearance of large patches, trees elsewhere have been felled at a rapidly increasing rate as new uses and markets have developed and new sources of power have been discovered. For long they were needed for building houses and boats, to make pitch and charcoal for smelting and to provide firewood. Additional uses call for pine for sawing, spruce for grinding to make cellulose, birch for plywood and furniture, aspen for matches. So the Northern lands have now to husband their resources and ensure that production is continuous. Thus, comparing the yield in 1937, when the rates of felling and growth were on the whole balanced, with those of 1950, there was a reduction in ' round wood ' of 31 per cent ; production of sawn timber fell by 29 per cent, but that of wood pulp by only 11 per cent, and that of newsprint remained the same. The aim, then, is to manufacture more wood and sell more valuable products. In further comparison, the wood-pulp total of over 6 million tons, half of it from Sweden, was about 1 million less than that of Canada in 1950. The output of newsprint, half of it from Finland, was about equal to that of the U.S.A. or one-fifth of Canada's product.

CHAPTER 27

FRANCE

The Greek geographer Strabo early in the first century A.D. wrote in his description of Celtica (or Kraul) : ' The whole of this country is watered by rivers ; some of them flow down from the Alps, the others from the Cemmenus (Cevennes) and the Pyrenees. . . . The river beds are by nature so well situated with reference to one another that there is transportation from either sea into the other ; for the cargoes are transported only a short distance by land. . . . But it is above all worth while to note again a characteristic of this region . . . the harmonious arrangement of the country with reference not only to the rivers, but also to the sea . . . one might believe that there is confirmatory evidence for the workings of Providence (προνοίας), since the regions are laid out, not in a fortuitous way, but as though in accordance with some calculated plan.' [1]

This ' harmonious arrangement ' of the isthmus of western Europe has much to do with the evolution of the French nation and its function in the continent. But it will be well first to examine briefly the ' calculated plan '.

France occupies a compact territory, roughly hexagonal in shape, bounded on three sides by sea, on two by the high mountain ranges of the Alps and Pyrenees and only on the northeast by a less well-defined frontier. Remnants of the Hercynian mountain system form the plateaux of the Central Massif, Armorica, the Vosges and the Ardennes, of which a fringe lies within French territory.

Perhaps the most important features in the history of man in France, in so far as determined by geography, depend upon the circumstance that France is the westernmost land of the continent easily accessible both by land from the northeast and by sea from the southeast and further that the continent here narrows to a much greater degree than anywhere else—to 500 miles (800 kilometres) along an easy route from the Channel to the Mediterranean and to about 225 miles (360 km.) along a still easier route from the Garonne estuary to the Mediterranean. Hence not only did France present the shortest routes of early commerce and culture between the Mediterranean and the oceanic fringe, including Britain, but she has been open to influences, climatic

---

[1] *Geography*, Book IV (1) 2 and 14, in The Geography of Strabo, Vol. II, pp. 167 and 209. Trans. H. L. Jones 1923

and human, of the Mediterranean, of the continent and of the ocean. The broad central plateau, all over 650 feet (200 metres) save for a few valleys and much of it over 3,000 feet (900 metres) separates but does not isolate regions where cultures of north and south have been at work for ages. The Alpine crustal wave approaches the Central Plateau near Montélimar ; thence the deep furrow of the Rhône and Saône, an ancient arm of the sea, gives easy access into the heart of France from the Mediterranean, the Levant and Africa. An easy passageway at low altitude, marked by the medieval stronghold of Carcassonne, leads from the Aude to the Garonne at Toulouse and the basin of Aquitaine. The broad gateway of Poitou, between the Central Plateau and Armorica connects Aquitaine and the Atlantic with the Paris basin. The still broader passage from that basin over the low plateau of Artois leads to the North European Plain, while the no less important Gate of Burgundy, leading to the Rhine, is also separated from the basin only by the low plateaus between the Central Plateau and the Vosges. Belfort commands this passage between the Vosges and the Jura.

The regional diversity offered by the Mediterranean, Atlantic, north-eastern and high-mountain or upland facets of France, together with the ease of movement favoured by the structural pattern, contributed increasingly to the enrichment of the whole as national unity was gradually focused on the Paris basin. The centrality of Paris is a persistent theme in the evolution of France. Already the Romans had remarked on community of interest among the Gaulish tribes. Strengthened by the Roman traditions that permeated the country, and especially by the language that became the expression of national unity, the monarchy, which had confirmed the status of Paris, made this pre-Roman bridge-point of the Ile de France and focus of Seine tributaries the core of Europe's first nation-state. Contrasts between north and south and regional changes of allegiance due to the wars of the Middle Ages were eventually overcome and Paris became the hub not only of France but of western Europe. This long continuity of predominance received a further powerful impetus from the Revolution and from more deliberate Napoleonic planning. When the industrial revolution came the road and railway net already centred on Paris attracted to the capital both the new industries and the population.

France has still over a third of its occupied population in agriculture. While about two-thirds of its area is agricultural, the character of the land and that of the agriculture vary as much as the scenery. Since the eighteenth century arable has been losing ground to pasture and pasture to forest, the last now covering a fifth of the area. The development of industry has been relatively slow in France. Its mineral raw materials are mainly peripheral in location and their character offered certain other disadvantages. The prolongation of the main European coal-bearing zone into France on the northern slopes of the Artois anticline is marked by thin and faulted seams and lack of coking qualities ; the iron ore of the Jurassic limestone in Lorraine, though offering the greatest reserves in Europe, was not considered of any importance in the earlier stage of industrialisation because of its high phosphoric content ; the significance of the bauxite, the chief mineral resource of the south, was not recognised until much later, with the growing demand for aluminium.

The northern coalfield, benefiting too from nearness to the Channel ports for import of raw materials, has retained its lead in heavy industry, chemicals and textiles, while Lorraine has remained predominantly a smelting centre. Along this northeastern periphery, then, especially in the two northern departments, which are responsible for two-thirds of the coal, half of the textiles and a fifth of the metallurgical production, but extending also into Lorraine, is the greatest concentration of population, and in particular of industrial workers, outside Paris. In the capital itself the great concentration of industries in consumer goods has been supplemented by the development of the lighter engineering industries and most notably by that of the automobile industry. Industrialisation elsewhere has not been on the massive scale but scattered, some in smaller centres, especially along the eastern edge of the Central Plateau, and maintaining old traditions of specialised skill, others at the seaports.

Agriculture, too, reaches its highest development in the north, between Flanders and the southern limit of the Paris basin, where the two greatest concentrations of population and of industrial technique have encouraged modern large-scale farming on France's most extensive area of good soils, where, on open fields and large wheat and beet farms, two-thirds of the country's arable land is responsible for about three-quarters of its agricultural production. The poor soils of the uplands and mountains are used for pasture and the *bocage* of the wetter west combines polyculture with stockrearing. Yields are low in the centre, west and south, for both physical and social reasons, except where specialisation is favoured by unusually good production or marketing conditions.

The wealth of France, both industrial and agricultural, is thus mainly in the basin or scarp lands of the northeast. The rural population, however, is spread at a rather low density but remarkably evenly over the country, save for the high mountain borders and the limestone or chalk plateaus. The flow of population from the rural areas and the smaller towns has been to Paris rather than to other cities. None of the score of cities of over 100,000

population approaches the capital in order of magnitude.   The unrivalled
centrality of Paris would appear to have had even more than the usual attractions of convenience and amenity offered by other capital cities.   Its administrative, political, intellectual and artistic life absorbs an unusually high
proportion of the country's human resources of energy and ability.   The
demographic drain toward Paris and the absorption of much of the foreign
immigration in the industrial north are reflections not only of administrative
and intellectual centralism but of the distribution of the country's material
resources.   The economic and social effects of this gravitation of the most
active population are accentuated, however, by the low birthrate that has
been a notable demographic feature of France for many decades.   In 1800
France, with 28 million inhabitants, had the largest population in Europe
(excluding Russia) ; by 1850 it was exceeded by Germany, by 1890 by the
United Kingdom and by 1930 by Italy.

Though the agricultural population was declining in the sixty years before
World War II, there is still a relatively high proportion of the occupied
population in agriculture—36 per cent, rising to 60 in the west.   This is partly
responsible for the low average income per caput in France, particularly since
by far the greater part of French agriculture is subject to low yields, due to
occupation of marginal land, to unsuitable though highly protected crops,
and in many areas to the need for better techniques and more enterprising
management.   Industry too has been relatively conservative.   While the
numbers employed in the older industries, coal and textiles, have contracted,
expansion of the newer branches in engineering, chemicals and electronics has
been slow in comparison with other countries of similar size.   Here, too,
enterprise, capital and labour have been less mobile than would appear
necessary.   Again, this inflexibility has been blamed on the demographic
structure, the insufficiency of labour in the more active and mobile age-groups
and the discouragingly small internal market.   The traditional sentiment for
protection of the peasant and the small artisan has been amply seconded by the
political pressure exerted by these large social classes.   On the other hand,
after World War II plans were made for modernisation of industry both in its
general direction and in its equipment, while some notable steps were taken
for the wider exploitation of the waterpower that is a large potential of the
mountain borders and Central Plateau, in order to make up for the serious
deficit in coal production.

Modern industry was relatively late in development in France and met
with unfavourable demographic trends that hindered the further structural
evolution both of production and of exports.   The national economy had
acquired, but still needed to widen, a resource base different from that of a

mainly agrarian age. New problems of balancing an enhanced diversity of regional interests also arose as industry grew in the more favoured regions. The centrality of Paris that had in the past enabled it to weld France's rich regional diversity into one of the most unified nation-states in history and to make France for long not only the military and diplomatic leader but the cultural centre of the western world was put to new tests of adaptability. Overseas, France, which had rivalled Britain in its power to build up successive empires—in America from the sixteenth to the eighteenth centuries and in Africa and Asia from the latter nineteenth century—was faced with a rising challenge to its political and cultural ideals.

BRITISH ISLES AND NORTHERN ISLES

THE only excuse for considering together these outliers of Europe is their common insularity ; they are very widely dispersed, and their inhabitants have more to do with the continent than with the other islands. Two of the large islands, Great Britain and Novaya Zemlya, are separated from the mainland by narrow straits and are alike in their northward extent ; but the latitude of the Kara Strait is 20° higher than that of Dover and, being beyond the reach of the North Atlantic drift, is only kept clear of ice with difficulty for a few weeks in summer. The Spitsbergen Archipelago, although still further north, is touched on the west by warmer sea and is more regularly free of pack ice. Since its complex structures include workable coal this factor of access by sea may be vital. The Polar ice regularly clings to the north coast of Iceland, which is situated almost entirely south of the Arctic Circle. Unless Novaya Zemlya contains valuable minerals in its ancient folded rocks the U.S.S.R. would appear to have been better without this large island to prevent warmer currents of the Barents Sea from reaching the mouths of the Ob and Yenesey. In Iceland, despite the threat of pack ice and forbidding climate, the settlements have been maintained since the ninth century. But prosperity based on Icelandic participation in fisheries and political autonomy date only from the twentieth. There are no natural resources to compare with fish ; the island is built up of young volcanic rocks and is without valuable minerals. Volcanism has brought serious disasters but also some permanent advantage in sources of natural steam. The Icelanders suffered in the past subordination to the Hanse and to Denmark, and from isolation to which nevertheless are due the language, culture and individuality of this small nation. Geographical position has proved invaluable in confirming their regeneration by providing a first-class air station on the northern transatlantic route. Thus in respect of fisheries and of air transport over the Arctic Ocean special functions may yet emerge for the islands surrounding the Norwegian and Barents Seas.

The Faeroes and the Shetlands on either side of the important channel by which the main Atlantic current passes northward mark convenient stages on the voyage between Norway and Iceland, and together with the Orkneys they had a Norse culture in common which has left its marks on the two nearer groups, after four centuries of Scottish nationality. While the three archipelagos differ completely in their rocks, all are ice-scoured, and per-petually wind- and wave-beaten remnants. But they have agreeable tempera-tures and long summer light. Along with Iceland the three groups provide an interesting section across the broad oceanic fringe where human existence has been difficult and stock-keeping and fishing more reliable than corn-growing. In existing conditions the prosperity of the communities depends increasingly upon communications, and perhaps the most surprising fact about them is the growth and vigour of the Faeroese people.

The great physical variety of Europe has been described in Chapter 1 as due to geological causes. For their size the British Isles perhaps offer the supreme example of this. The rocks are of every geological period, with the oldest (Archean) in the north-west and the youngest (Pliocene) in the south-east. The older strata display the foldings of both Caledonian and Hercynian paroxysms, and the two trends converge in Wales and in Ireland ; while the Alpine movements probably account for volcanic features of the north-west as well as the splintering of all the toughened rocks of the west and north to form geometric patterns of valleys and coasts eroded on lines thus weakened. Submergence has given the islands their present shores, and glaciation the final trimming to most of the land. The fact that the English lowland lies nearest the continent, and has the best climate for farming has been vital throughout history. Its present aspect reflects its agricultural evolution to a stage of great production with the minimum of workers. But it is the interpenetration of the rural landscape by the urban which is the key to the economy of Britain. The riches of coal, iron and salt lie around the rim of the lowland and underlie it in part. Industries are found not only there but near the ports in the estuaries, along the main railways and above all near the capital, and depending more and more upon the close net of over-worked roads. Precious food-growing land must yield place to works and workers' homes. Nowhere in Europe is the urban pull quite so insistent as in Britain, and the most significant aspect is the rapid spread of London's tentacles, and beyond their obvious limits the distribution over all the home counties of people who are more or less concerned with affairs in the capital. Several new towns complete with industries are growing up as the result of planned limitation upon the further growth of London. Happily the rural charm of the English lowland persists where the stages of historic development may be traced—here and there— from Neolithic settlement onwards, and some cathedral cities and many market towns have avoided the worse excesses of thoughtless modern building.

It is not surprising that history took a different course in the north and that the Scottish nation grew separately from the English until 1707. The length of Britain and the presence of a considerable Mid-Lowland screened from England by hills, coupled with a different ethnic assemblage are fundamental. The relief of Wales made it a natural refuge in which the Welsh have kept their language more successfully than the other Celtic peoples ; but it proved a hindrance to unity that is still evident and thereby hastened the conquest of the Principality.

The highlands of Ireland are much less compact than those of Wales or Scotland ; they embrace many vales, and there is a central plain ; this is comparable with East Anglia in area, but as much of it consists of peat bogs and lakes, it does not constitute a populous heartland as might be expected. Apart from the neighbourhood of Dublin and Belfast, the greater densities occur among the hills with the wetter and milder climate, in short, the most ' Atlantic ' habitat. Ireland is quite unlike Britain in its recent demography. By 1845, with expanding agriculture, the population numbered over 8 millions, a total reached through inordinate dependence upon the potato as food. With the famine that followed the failures of this crop Ireland lost one-fifth of its population by 1851 by death and emigration, and half in the hundred years. In Eire the decline continues on account of emigration ; in Northern Ireland the trend is marked by slight increase. These facts indicate the striking differences between Great Britain and Ireland, which are attributable chiefly to historical causes, but underlying these are the geographical facts of isolation and the virtual absence of coal and other minerals and formerly also water power upon which the Industrial Revolution was based.

The main developments in Great Britain and Ireland, however, can be little understood save in the world setting. Once relatively stable government had been attained in Britain, its peoples had greater freedom behind their protective barrier of sea to direct their resources to mercantile ventures. Britain's position at Europe's northern ocean gateway helped it to take full advantage of the wider possibilities of overseas trading in the age of trans-oceanic discovery. So capital was available to exploit the outburst of technical innovation that made Britain the pioneer in the Industrial Revolution. A new pattern emerged in the landscape as population clustered on the coal-seams near the junction of the lowland with the Hercynian and Caledonian high-lands yet never far from the advantages of sea transport. Here, too, heavy industry developed and in Northern England and the Scottish Mid-Lowland the textile industries were strengthened. Cotton textiles superseded woollens as the leading export and Lancashire dominated the world textile market. The squalor of the urbanisation that resulted in Britain from the Industrial Revolution contrasted with the verdant hedgerows with which the Agricultural Revolution had transformed the rural landscape.

The growth of overseas investment in the latter half of the nineteenth century was accompanied, to the advantage of both sides in the transaction, in the mid-latitude lands by British emigration, largely from the Hercynian and Caledonian highlands, and in the tropical lands by British administration. These overseas investments were reflected in the growth of British exports of heavy capital equipment, a returning flow of raw materials and, aided by the repeal of the Corn Laws, of food. By 1880 the rural landscape was changing more rapidly, as former corn lands went down to grass in face of massive grain imports from the new lands opened up overseas by British rails and steamships. Rising urban standards were reflected in the larger population of fat stock and dairy cattle. Ireland became part of the livestock producing zone for this British market and, despite political differences, has remained linked with the larger island through this as in some other aspects of its economy. Three-quarters of its total exports are to Britain and most of the rest is to Northern Ireland.

By World War II only a twentieth of the occupied population in Britain was engaged in agriculture, the lowest proportion of any country in Europe or elsewhere, and only a quarter of the country's food was grown at home. Above all, the tendency to a downward trend on the world market of agricultural prices relative to those of manufactures as new lands were opened up and better methods introduced, directly favoured the highly industrialised countries like Britain, though there were also repercussions on sales of manufactured goods. Under the system of multilateral trade that grew up from 1870, Britain thrived not only as an exporter of manufactures and importer of food and raw materials but as the greatest supplier of shipping and other mercantile services, the leading overseas investor and the world's financial centre. The system had reached its zenith shortly before World War I. The changes that were to break it up were only accelerated by the two World Wars and were largely set in motion by Britain's own pioneer efforts.

Like those that had preceded, some of the new changes in the economy were gradually making themselves evident in the pattern of the British landscape. Foreign competition in the heavy industries had increased since the seventies and much of Britain's own exports of machinery had gone to equip its rivals in textiles, particularly in cotton and jute. New industries, stimulated by new technical developments in chemistry and electricity or by increasingly varied possibilities in consumer goods rather than capital equipment, were becoming more important both at home and abroad. Many of these had no strong link with the coalfields and ports and the industrial balance was tilting from the highland edge toward the English lowland and especially to London and the Midlands. An axis of high though not continuous population density was now forming between Lancashire and the West Riding in the northwest and the London area in the southeast and along this belt, on less than a fifth of Britain's area, is now found well over half its population. In the older industries too the effort to meet competition was largely by a shift of emphasis toward the finishing stages and to goods in which skill and experience play a greater part. It was this trend, as well as the growing emphasis on tertiary activities in the economy as a whole, that were responsible for the interwar urban and suburban spread, especially in the English lowland.

The way of life of Britain's dense population depends on the productivity of its highly industrialised economy. It must supplement its own resources with large imports, roughly half of them food and raw materials not available in Britain for climatic or geological reasons, another third more economically bought from abroad and the remainder part of the international exchange of specialised manufactures. In other terms, two-fifths of the imports are food, two-fifths raw materials and one-fifth manufactures. Since the middle of the nineteenth century Britain has not met all its import requirements with exports of merchandise but to a great extent with services, mainly connected with finance and shipping. But World War II rapidly reduced Britain's remaining overseas assets and its place among the shipowning nations is now second to that of the United States. With imported food and raw materials costing relatively more in terms of manufactured exports, the menace of deficit in the balance of payments was much more serious. A surplus was needed to rebuild the capital assets abroad that might eventually bring in a net income again ; debts incurred through the war effort had also to be repaid and reserves of gold and dollars restored. These tasks were not easy in the postwar world. Britain's high degree of dependence on overseas trade made its economy peculiarly sensitive to economic conditions in other parts of the world and to international political relations.

A striking effort to reduce imports was, of course, the campaign for increased food production in World War II, when the pre-war proportion of three acres of permanent grass to every two acres of arable was reversed and self-sufficiency in food was raised on a wartime dietary from one-quarter to two-fifths. But while half of the total land in Britain is, according to the Land Utilisation Survey, possible arable, only a quarter is good arable land and the attainment of higher proportions has meant heavy subsidisation and unfavourable repercussions on other sectors of the economy. In the mining sector the export of coal that played such a significant part in British trade and shipping has been replaced by imports, production having declined since 1913 and postwar efforts having been hampered by shortage of miners. The hydro-electric potential of the highland zone, though more rapidly developed after World War II, is small. Britain's main hope in the field of energy production lies in nuclear energy. Not only energy production but transport and steel are among the basic industries that require priority in re-equipment in order to maintain Britain's productive capacity, while export industries have to be kept flexible enough to meet changes in the technique of production and in demand.

Before and after World War II Britain was responsible for about a tenth of world trade (excluding the U.S.S.R. and China) and a fifth of world exports of manufactures. The metal and engineering industries account for half the total exports and, as we have seen, machinery and electrical goods and road vehicles have taken the lead over textiles in the export trade. The Commonwealth countries and the U.S.A. continued after the war to be the leading individual destinations of British exports and sources of British imports but Europe as a whole still, with one-third of the total, far exceeded any one of these countries. In economic as in political relationships Britain thus looks both to Europe and to the world overseas; a tradition that links her with the rich diversity of European culture has to be reconciled with that of a pioneer in contacts with civilisations outside Europe and in opening up the newer lands overseas. On the one hand Britain owes much to the different temperaments and aptitudes of its component nations as well as to its cultural links with the European mainland; on the other, its political and economic empiricism has enabled the British Commonwealth to evolve into an association of states whose past history has given them more intimate understanding of each other's problems.

INDEX

Printed in Great Britain by
Thomas Nelson and Sons Ltd, Edinburgh